TROUBLESHOOTING ELECTRONIC ASSEMBLY

Wisdom from the BoardTalk Crypt

by

Phil Zarrow and Jim Hall

Phil Zarrow
email: phil_zarrow@itmconsulting.com
ITM Consulting
3624 Legacy Dr.
Springfield, TN 37172

Jim Hall
email: jim_hall@itmconsulting.com
ITM Consulting
22 Shore Drive
Waltham, MA 02451

First Edition - Spring 2020

Programs written, recorded and transcribed by Phil Zarrow and Jim Hall

Hear these programs at http://www.circuitinsight.com/channels/board_talk.html

A Pragma Media Project.

ISBN 978-1-7322836-8-8

Copyright © 2020 Pragma Design, Inc.

Pragma Media publishes direct technical content by and for professionals, researchers and STEM educators, including the "SOIC and Friends" picture book series introducing children to electronics and technology.   http://pragma.media

PML3TA

To my late wife Golda and my persevering wife Alix
for putting up with our antics and ongoing love and support.

- Phil Zarrow

Contents

Reflow and Reuse 85

Finishes and Fluxes 111

BGAs, J-Leads and Squeegees 129

Handling paste, 'Uncommonly Harsh' and Humidity 213

Solder Icicles, Selective Soldering, and the Grape Effect 237

Afterword 261

Index 265

About the Authors 271

Foreword

Many excellent papers relating to the challenges of electronic assembly are published at conferences like SMTI and APEX. However, there has been no repository of advice for the myriad of problems that daily face a process engineer. The Assembly brothers, Pick and Place, (aka Phil Zarrow and Jim Hall) have stepped in to fill this need. Their audio podcast, "Board Talk," has addressed the type of practical problems that plague the process engineer. Their format has always been witty and to the point. For quite a few years now, Board Talk has been an oasis in the desert of lack of practical electronic assembly knowledge.

It is a blessing to us all then, that a compilation of all of this useful information is now in a book form.

Ron Lasky, PhD. PE

Senior Technologist, Indium Corporation

Professor of Engineering, Dartmouth College

Hanover, NH November 2019

Preface

This book is intended to provide a highly indexed reference for the process engineer or assembly technician who is encountering a particular problem or would like to learn about how others have dealt with myriad SMT assembly issues.

Since each SMT assembly problem and topic comprises multiple different issues, each episode could be categorized in multiple topics. Instead they are organized here roughly in chronological order with added highlight headings and keywords. The reader is encouraged to utilize the book either as a process first-aid reference in emergency, or to leisurely absorb the entire book, section by section, on vacation, by the pool or during those long periods of smooth, problem-free manufacturing so common to modern surface mount operations.

Ed.

Introduction

Welcome to BoardTalk with Phil Zarrow and Jim Hall – the Assembly Brothers ("Pick and Place") whose day jobs are as mild-mannered principal consultants with ITM Consulting.

We've both been in this industry for a very long time – since the mid-70s. We've known each other since the early 80's from the early SMT seminar tours (or "Rubber Chicken Circuit"). One would expect that it would seem like an eternity but it really hasn't – because this field is both challenging, ever-changing and fun. Let's face it, we could all be making a lot more moolah in IT, real estate or lawyering. But electronic assembly is a far more noble cause than scoring the big bucks (though, it would be nice).

After all these years and hundreds (maybe thousands) of assembly facilities, lines and processes, we've seen a lot of "stuff" – good, bad and indifferent. That's what BoardTalk and this book are all about.

Obviously, we were (and remain) big fans of Ray and (the late) Tom Magliozzi ("Click" and "Clack", the "Tappet Brothers") and Car Talk. We both have listened to them since their early days. When Phil first moved to New Hampshire in the mid-80's, the first place Jim took him was to Harvard Square to look up to the revered offices of "Dewey, Cheatham & Howe". (Years later Phil had the opportunity to have lunch with Tom and Ray which was very inspiring, to say the least).

BoardTalk had its humble beginnings as a session at an SMTAI conference where, for a donation to the Charles Hutchins Scholarship fund, you could ask us technical questions as well as hear us rant on our latest soapbox. It was more like "Stump the Chumps" but was fairly well-received. However, our good friend Jeff Ferry, founder and publisher of Circuitnet and later Circuit Insight, had a vision. He wanted to make BoardTalk more accessible to the (huddled and befuddled) masses of our industry. His concept was to produce a podcast where people would send in their technical questions and we would attempt to answer them in approximately 5 minute broadcasts. In addition, listeners and readers could post comments to our commentaries sometimes agreeing, sometimes disagreeing, and sometimes castigating us for not mentioning some additional pertinent point. (Hey, it's difficult trying to explain the meaning of life in just 5 minutes!) We say listeners and readers because we have observed that if you're under 35, you likely listen to BoardTalk whereas if you're somewhat older, you read the BoardTalk. transcripts. Doesn't matter – it's the same opinionated information.

Ten years and over 200 episodes later, BoardTalk with Phil and Jim, the "Assembly Brothers – Pick and Place" prevail. Thanks to www.CircuitInsight.com BoardTalk is heard all over the world ("Keep on Troubleshooting in the Free World"). Looking back, we found that the advice we gave was still relevant and surprisingly applicable. With the strong encouragement of our good friend and colleague, Dr. Ron Lasky and others, we decided to embark on putting the collected decade of "wisdom" in this book you have in your hands. At the time of publishing we believe it is the only book on troubleshooting electronic assembly processes, equipment and materials.

For each episode, we read and discuss the questions and our take on the problem off the air, but once we are recording it is unscripted, verbatim and recorded on one take (except for the time when Laika the dog decided to bark while we were recording and we had to do a second take – she was likely taking issue with our advice). Of course, Jeff has someone clean up the recordings for broadcast (taking out the "uhs", "ehs", and "duhs") but never editing or censoring the content. We occasionally disagree with each other but usually come to terms by episode end (and without incurring any violence). We don't make this stuff up, either. (Really !) It's all based upon our experiences and those of our wide network of friends and colleagues whom contribute an enormous wealth of experience and information. Thus, we are learning something new every week – and hopefully so are you.

We appreciate all of our readers and listeners that make this work possible.

And thank you for acquiring this book. We hope it serves you well.

Beyond that, keep the kids away from the flux pot and whatever you do –

Don't solder like my brother!

Phil Zarrow and Jim Hall

Acknowledgments

As SMT and electronic assembly continues to evolve, we learn something new almost every day. We are fortunate to have had a wonderful circle of associates, friends, and colleagues who have contributed to our collective knowledge (and opinions) and therefore the ideas expressed through BoardTalk.

We'd like to thank:

Our ITM Brothers: Bob Klenke, Ron Lasky, Joe Belmonte and the late, great Ron Daniels.

Our Publisher, Jeff Ferry who believed in the BoardTalk concept and made it happen. Ray and (the late) Tom Magliozzi (Car Talk) – the inspiration behind the BoardTalk concept. And to our print publisher, Pragma Media and Jeff Dunnihoo who helped us condense the years of verbiage into these pages you now hold.

Special thanks to the late, amazing Rich Freiberger (Phil's mentor), the late Harold Hyman (Jim's mentor), the late, insightful Charles Hutchins, and the late, venerable Jim Raby.

Our spiritual guide, the late Jean Shepherd.

And of course: Mark McMeen, Terry Munson, Mike Bixenman, Rob Rowland, Tom Dory, Bob Willis, Mike Conrad, Dave Heller, Dave Hillman, Mike Buetow, Debra Dresser, Gary Ferrari, Leo Lambert, Jean-Paul Clech, Kim Hyland, Chrys Shea, Dave Raby, Chris Fussner, JoAnn Stromberg, Mike Buseman, Andy Mackie, Mitch Holzman, Rick Short, Rich Heimsch, Andy Rector, Bob Wetterman, and Vern Solberg.

Solderability Issues and Stencils

Problems with Reflow Oven Profiles

(reflow, soldering, thermocouples, profiling,)

Jim ›› We've got a reflow problem from J.R..

Phil ›› Okay, and let's see what old J.R. has to say. "Our company is a low-volume, high-mix EMS." There are a lot of those out there. "I'm a good doobie. I profile every individual board."

I use at least three TC's on every board and more on complex ones." So far so good. "I've heard you guys talking about attaching TC's with epoxy or a high-temp solder. Well, I use Kapton tape and I get good results."

Jim ›› You say the TC's stay attached. How do you know, J.R.? Do you ride the boards through the oven?

Do you have webcams in your reflow section? Kapton is a great material, that's not the problem. The problem is the adhesives. The adhesive that holds that Kapton layer on are temperature sensitive. They can soften at high temperature and if it softens, contact between the thermocouple and what you're trying to measure can be reduced and it doesn't take much to give you an inaccurate reading.

Phil ›› You could be reading the joint temperature, but you could be reading the temperature of the air, the tape...

Jim ›› Remember, the greatest risk is when the temperature's the highest. That's at peak reflow temperature, and that's probably the most critical point, particularly if you're doing lead-free and you're working with a really tight process window.

What's confusing is as you go through cooling, the adhesive re-hardens and it looks fine when it comes out. So, the bottom line is, the Kapton tape works most of the time, but you can never be sure on any given profile on any given thermocouple.

Phil ›› The whole purpose of profiling is that attain as accurate as possible temperature measurement as possible.

The best procedure we have found, and believe me, we've tried lots of things over the years. The first thing is once you pick your point, the joint where you're going to be attaching your thermocouple, you want to remove as much of the existing solder that's there first. Get it off there. And this is what's going to save you lots of headaches because otherwise if you leave the old solder it's going to undermine the connection.

And unless you want to be doing this over and over and over again. You want to do this right. (Let's face it, profiling a PCBA is one of the most boring things you can be doing out on the manufacturing floor.) Use some solder wick. Get as much of that old solder off and then you want to use a very small amount of solder, high temp solder or a conductive epoxy.

The reason we emphasize using a small amount is that you don't want to have too big a mass at that interconnection that may give you inaccurate readings. You know all that Kapton tape you bought, use it for strain relief.

So again, this is the most time-tested method, either high-temp solder or the conductive epoxy. As Jim said, we've tried everything. Did I ever tell you about the time I tried using RTV? It was one of those things that seemed like a good idea at the time, but well, we won't go there.

Can a Wave Solder Air Knife Cause Defects?

(wave-solder, through-hole, flux, hole-fill, contamination, wetting, solderability, bridging)

Phil ›› We're in the soldering lab today because we have a wave solder question from J.S. : "We use a hot air knife in our SMT wave soldering process. We're seeing what appear to be deformed, unwetted solder joints as the board is moved past the air knife. Can anyone tell me what's causing this? We've adjusted the air pressure up and down, but we can't seem to find a setting that keeps this from happening."

Well, this is an interesting one.

Jim ›› I think we have to step back and describe what an air knife is because I don't think a lot of people have seen one and some people may not even know that they exist. An air knife is a tool that's an option that's added to the end of a wave soldering machine below the conveyor right after the final laminar wave. It directs a focused stream of hot air or hot nitrogen on the board to remove bridges.

They can be very effective tools, but they are somewhat controversial and they're not a panacea for removing the most difficult bridges.

Phil ›› This is an interesting case because every once in a while we encounter situations where a tool or a methodology is masking a defect. In this case, it's actually working to reveal a defect- the root cause problem.

Jim ›› That's right. The basic principle of the air knife process is that it can blow off a bridge hanging between the joints that's only held by the cohesive forces within the molten solder.

It cannot under virtually any circumstances remove the solder that is properly wetted to the leads and the pads around the through holes. Those are the adhesive forces bonding the inner metallic formation and that's very strong and you can't strip those off.

So, if you were seeing truly unwetted solder joints after you've gone through the air knife, there's not a problem with the air knife, the problem is that you do not have good wetting in your basic wave process.

Phil ›› Let's throw out a few ideas in terms of what may be affecting the wetting. Of course, there's some of the common problems, for example, you're not getting good hole fill and that could be caused by a number of things originating in the wave solder settings, conveyor height, and wave height. Or it can be the result of the inadequate plating and the finish inside the holes. We've even seen black pad effect on hole fill on some ENIG finished boards.

Jim ›› It could be any of the basic processes for your wave. Do you have enough flux? Is the flux activated or is it preheated too little or too much and burned off?

Regarding a design of experiment, a DOE. Remember, wave soldering is a very sophisticated process. There's a lot going on. We're adding flux. We're adding heat in two or three different stages. We're adding solder and then we have to remove bridges. All the factors, times, temperatures, and materials have to play together so it's not a trivial process.

Don't forget the possibility of lead contamination. Even with the best process, if you get some dirty materials going in, the solder isn't going to "stick" and the air knife is going to blow the solder away.

Phil ›› Put your hands up and step away from that air knife! Do not touch that air knife.

Go back and check out your process. Maybe turn the air knife off and run some sample boards, check the soldering on all the leads. When that's optimized, then go back and attempt to optimize the air knife pressure to remove the bridges and give you the correct shaped fillets.

Solder Paste - Type 3 or Type 4?

(solder paste, powder, 01005, stencil, aperture, 5-ball rule, fine-pitch, oxidation, printing)

Phil ›› We have a question from R.W. wondering, "What are the determining factors in switching from a Type 3 solder paste to a Type 4 solder paste for the printing operation?" Well, R.W., that's a good one. There's some real drivers there and perhaps you're seeing finer pitch components and some of the smaller passives and therefore, some of your apertures are getting smaller.

Jim ›› That's exactly correct, Phil. The only reason to move to a Type 4 paste - and what that means is that it has a Type 4 powder. That solder powder within the paste has smaller particle size. Type 4 paste particles are smaller than Type 3. Another one of those wonderful inverse scales that we have to deal with, such as wire gauge and golf scores.

With smaller particles, it's simply easier physically for the paste to flow into and out of the smaller apertures. And the rule of thumb that we typically use is called the five-ball rule.

The largest particle in a Type 3 paste is 1.7 mils. The five-ball rule says that the smallest aperture I should use with that paste is at least as big as five times the diameter of the largest particle, which means for a Type 3 paste, that would be an 8.5 mil aperture. Anything smaller than that, five of the largest particles would not span across that aperture and that's an indicator of the ability of the paste to easily flow in and out of the aperture. Type 4 has a smaller particle size. Its largest particle is 1.5 mils, so it can go down to an aperture of 7.5 mils.

In practical sense for leaded components, this transition is usually seen between 20 mil pitch (.5 millimeter), and 16 mil pitch (.4 millimeter). In other words, most people feel no problem doing 20 mil pitch with a Type 3 paste but if you get down to 16 mil pitch, that's when you usually run into these limits of this 8.5 mil aperture.

Phil ›› That isn't to say you can't use a Type 3 paste for going down to a 12 mil pitch. We've done it but it gets pretty tricky. You start fooling around with not only your aperture reduction but also the shape of the apertures. So, you get to the point, why make life difficult for yourself? (Or do you feel lucky? Well, do you?)

And, of course, we're also talking about what we call ultra-miniature passives these days, 0201's, and 01005's with very small apertures.

Jim ›› These are driving a lot more people to look at the application of a Type 4 paste.

Phil ›› And driving a lot more people insane.

Jim ›› In fact, for 01005's, people are actually looking, at least in theoretical laboratory experiments, at Type 5 powders to print these very small apertures for these small chip components.

Phil ›› We'll talk about some of the limitations in the future, but there are some limitations using Type 4. But you can use a Type 4 across the board, even with large apertures although there's a few reasons why you wouldn't want to and the first one is that it costs more. One thing that should be noted is that more and more people, because of the mitigating factors we mentioned earlier, are starting to use Type 4 and so the cost is going down as demand increases.

And there are some other problems of using Type 4 because we're talking about more particles and therefore, more aggregate surface area. The solder paste companies, with increased demand, have been working on trying to reduce these effects.

Jim ›› Let's review. With smaller particles, you still have the same volume or weight of metal in your joint, but it's divided up into smaller particles which inherently have more surface area, therefore more potential oxide or more potential oxidation during the process. So, concerns include increased solder balling, poor wetting, and perhaps a greater probability to have to use nitrogen or another inert atmosphere during your soldering to prevent oxidation.

Phil ›› Another addition to process cost.

Jim ›› The other thing is that in addition to smaller particles, a Type 4 has a narrower range of particle size, so they tend to pack together more tightly. This can give you increased viscosity, which has been seen to make printing more difficult. And because the particles are packed tighter together, it's possible to get more entrapment of the flux gasses, resulting in higher levels of voiding.

These are all known factors that have been around and with the greater increased interest and use of Type 4 paste, the solder paste manufacturers have been working very hard to overcome and mitigate these concerns. We would say to you what we say with any new material or new piece of equipment, check it out. Do a proper solder paste evaluation of your Type 4 powder in your process with your stencils to make sure that it gives you the right combination of improved printing versus solder defects.

Phil ›› Remember, all solder paste manufacturers are not created equal and neither are their products.

Stencil Printing: Stepped Stencil Review

(stencil, printing, solder paste, intrusive reflow, pin-in-paste, reflow of through-hole, aperture, squeegee, PCB)

Phil ›› Today's question comes to us from G.M. who asks, "I've heard you guys advocate the use of step stencils as a means of getting the proper volume of solder paste down when you have a wide range of quoted lead densities. So, can you use a metal squeegee with step stencils or am I stuck using a rubber squeegee?"

Jim ›› The idea that you need to use a rubber squeegee so that it can deflect down into the step is just not correct. The squeegee is not pushing the solder paste into the aperture.

Phil

The squeegee is causing the solder paste to roll on the stencil, which reduces its viscosity because it's a thixotropic or sheer sensitive material and that allows the paste at the lower viscosity to flow down into the step and adequately fill the apertures within the step, even though that squeegee material never comes down to the top surface of the bottom of the step.

We're killing two myths at one time. The idea that you have to use a rubber squeegee, and that the squeegee pushes the solder paste in the apertures. The real question here and the answer is, yes, you must be using or should be using a metal squeegee. In fact, we don't see polyurethane squeegees used much for except maybe adhesives.

Jim ›› Very few people are using the urethane squeegees to print solder paste.

Phil ›› Basically the two real questions here are how far down can you step and when you do step down, how close can you have adjacent apertures with a step in between?

Jim ›› Most people who are using step stencils feel comfortable with a 1-mil step. They feel that that gives them good results and some people will go to a mil and a half. Above that, you get into varying opinions. I've seen people stepping down 2 mils.

One of the leading stencil fabricators claim that they step as far as 3 mils. Now that's a lot.

Of course, they would have a lot of benefits for a very complex assembly, but I honestly have never seen an application using that big a step and certainly the degree of difficulty would be increased in terms of getting consistent fill and release and getting your whole process balanced. Certainly, if you're starting at 1 mil, you'll probably have a higher success rate even starting out.

But what about the spacing, Phil, how close can I get my apertures to the edge of the step?

Phil ›› The bottom line being how much space do I have to allow my board, because in many applications, space is money and I want to put the components as close together as I can.

We've heard all kinds of numbers thrown out. Some people claim that 125 thousandths is as close as you can get.

Jim ›› That's a nice conservative number. You'll have no problems at that.

Phil ›› Generally, you shouldn't.

Jim ›› But what do some of the experts say?

Phil ›› A good friend of ours from a squeegee manufacturer (and who has a heavy duty background in printing) has determined 0.062" as a proximity. It's about 1/16th of an inch, for you guys who have rulers.

Jim ›› That's half the space of 0.125, so you picked up a lot there. Again, the aforementioned stencil fabricator uses a formula that's based upon how tall the step is, and they say they want 35 mils of spacing for every 1 mil of step height. So, they're saying if you have a 1-mil step, you could put the apertures as close as 35 mils to that step. Now that's pretty aggressive.

But I would consider that the range: 125 mils would be very conservative, 35 mils per mil of step very aggressive.

Phil ›› That's in line because if you're doing a 2 mil step, which is generally what I like to do, it's about 70 mils and that's pretty close to the 0.062. So, we're in the ballpark.

Jim ›› Remember, this is not an exact science. Many people have differing opinions of what the limit should be and what works best for them. You have to make the step parameters work with your paste, your printer, and all the other parameters for your stencil printing operation. Obviously if you're more conservative, take shorter steps with more spacing, you'll probably have less problems and less difficulty optimizing your process.

Phil ›› You definitely need to do a design of experiment (DOE) and bear this out with your application and your boards, your stencil source, your printer and your solder paste.

What is the Ideal Stencil Thickness?

(solder paste, printing, stencil, aperture, step-stencil, area ratio, fine pitch)

Phil ›› Today's question is from V.F. who writes "I have several PC boards with mixed density components. In other words, I have some of what you guys call coarse pitch, 50 mil big capacitors and the like, but I also have some difficult fine pitch, including some .5 millimeter pitch CSP's. If I use a 6-mil stencil, I have problems with my CSP's and if I go down to a 4 or 3 mil stencil, how do I get sufficient volume for the big boys? So, what do I do? I'm all mixed up. Help me!"

Jim ›› Before we get started, let me talk about the rampant use of the term "mixed".

Phil ›› Soapbox Alert!

Jim ›› This questioner is using the term "mixed densities" to describe having different sized components on the same board with different pitch or size leads.

Think of the other times mixed has been used. I defined "mixed technology" 30 years ago as printed circuit boards that have both surface bound components and through hole components on the same board.

Phil ›› Yes, you did, Jim – I remember your proclamation as if it was just yesterday

Jim ›› But more recently, we've talked about mixed assembly being backward and forward compatibility with lead-free assemblies, in particular backwards compatibility with lead-free components being introduced unknowingly or inadvertently into a tin lead assembly.

So be careful when somebody says mixed. It's a very common word. I would have to say most boards assembled in the world today fall into this category where you have some 50-mil pitch IC's and some big capacitors which require a relatively large volume of solder. If we consider the solder fillet on the side of the leads, to get a good solder joint, you need a relatively large volume relative to the size of the pad.

On the other hand, for fine pitch 20-mil pitch IC's or in this case, 0.5 mm pitch CSP's, they're very small balls on the bottom of the CSP's. They need a relatively small volume of solder and solder paste to be applied in order to get the appropriate joint.

What are some of our options here, Phil?

Phil ›› The obvious is we could do a reduced aperture and that would to a certain degree help out the little guys.

Jim ›› That's where we'd stay with the thicker, in this case the 6-mil, stencil. Normal apertures for the big components, reduced apertures for the small components.

Phil ›› But the liability here is what we like to call "too tall and narrow" apertures.

Jim ›› For a thick stencil, as we start making the aperture smaller and smaller, we reach a point where the aperture becomes so tall and narrow that it's difficult to get repeatable flow of solder paste in and out of the aperture. So therefore, when we go to print, we don't get consistent results because the solder paste just won't fill and release repeatedly from this tall, narrow aperture which can be quantified by calculating the Area Ratio..

What other options might we have?

Phil ›› Well, of course we can go to the other extreme. We can go down and reduce the thickness of our stencil. Let's go down to say a 4-mil stencil and that would certainly help out those little CSP interconnections.

Jim ›› Right, but then what do we do about the big guys?

Phil ›› That's right. Yeah, what do you do? If you go into an overprint, you're going to risk things like bridging and of course the ever present, ever ominous solder balls, so that may or may not work.

And finally, another solution, and it goes under that category of everything old is new again, the good ol' step stencil. You want to explain what a step stencil is?

Jim ›› A step stencil is really the most robust solution for this problem. It's where you actually create different thicknesses in the stencil in different areas.

The most common technique would be start with a thicker, in this case, 6-mil stencil, and then in the areas where you have my fine pitched parts reduce the area, usually by milling or etching the thickness of the stencil to what's required for the fine pitched part. You don't have to do any aperture reduction. You can get good fill and release and get the proper volume for the parts.

Unfortunately, when you go to a step stencil, you open a whole bunch of other potential problems for design, process variables, limitations, and so forth. I think that's as much as we can say now. We're going to have to come back on another session and talk about the details and trade-offs for step stencils.

Phil ›› You essentially have, three options: thick stencil aperture reduction, thin stencil overprint, or a step stencil.

Are Gloves Required for PCB Handling?

(soldering, printing, PCB handling, contamination, conformal coating, Best Practices, wetting)

Jim ›› We've got a question about printed circuit board handling from B.W.: "At present, our operators and technicians do not wear gloves when handling PCBA's. Now I heard that this is not a good practice and we will get in trouble. How do you guys weigh in on this issue?"

Phil ›› Weigh in on this issue? Okay, here we go.

Jim ›› Soapbox Alert!

Phil ›› We consider a Best Practices, (in other words something that should be employed om a world class manufacturing process), that anyone coming in contact with a board assembly, prior to final soldering, should be wearing gloves or finger cots. Period. No exceptions.

Jim ›› That means even the quality assurance supervisor who comes over to look at a board, don't just pick it up off the rework table. Put on gloves or finger cots.

Phil ›› In fact, if the PCBAs are going to be conformally coated, keep those gloves on. The reason for this is because your fingers have oil and dirt, what we commonly call contaminants, and these can be transferred to the board and the result can be poor adhesion of your conformal coating as well as poor wetting, weaker solder joints, voids, and a host of other fun things.

Jim ›› Remember they're contaminants, and fluxes in your wave soldering machines do not reliably remove contaminants. If you get contaminants on those soldering surfaces, you're asking for possible problems.

Phil ›› You would think this would be common sense, yet per our process audits the manufacturers who are actually doing this are in the minority. Most manufacturers really can't seem to be bothered. I don't know if it's bother or what else do you think, Jim, possibly "cheapo"?

Jim ›› "Cheapo" and they're not tracking their defects. The same thing we talk about all the time. That was no joke about a quality control manager coming over after the first side of double-sided reflow and picking up a board to inspect it to show us something with her fingers touching the bottom side of the board which was then going to be flipped over and stencil printed and reflowed.

Phil ›› We see this kind of nonsense in CEM's and OEM's, alike, but probably one of the most important pieces of industry lore comes from our good buddy, Terry Munson at Foresight.

In a previous life, when we got to know Terry way back in the days of yore, he had established himself as the contamination and cleanliness expert at a very humongous automotive electronics company.

Terry conducted a very interesting test when he was at this company. What he did was he made various cleanliness and contamination tests on circuit boards built on certain lines. He conducted a run of cleanliness tests on the boards produced on the morning shift.

Then, using the same line, same boards, same materials, same application, and same operators, he tested using the same cleanliness examination test on boards built after lunch.

This is something that came to be called the Lunch Hour Effect because what Terry observed was that the levels of contamination on boards built after lunch went up by several magnitudes and again, for the obvious reasons. During lunch, workers come in contact with food and do things like brush their hair, maybe apply lotions, go to the bathroom. And remember, many people don't always have the best hygiene practices. Probably this is the same reason you shouldn't eat peanuts in a bar (please don't visualize that) but in the case of assembling PCBAs, it's a variety of contaminants that are being transferred to your boards.

The number of people that are actually using gloves and finger cots are far and in-between. This is a practice everybody should be doing, but people reason, "Well, I'm getting adequate results."

But again, the question is, are you getting zero defects? We believe that over time, as Jim mentioned, if you're actually tracking your defects and you employ this practice, you will see an improvement. I can guarantee it and, of course, Terry's data backs that up, too.

Now, of course, if you are wearing gloves and finger cots, wear them properly.

Jim ›› We've seen some seemingly unbelievable things, particularly in rework areas, where people wearing their gloves have cut out the fingers where their fingers touch the board in order to get better feel and control over handling the boards, defeating the exact purpose that they're wearing gloves for in the first place.

This doesn't speak much to the training integrity of that kind of facility because people are wearing gloves, but they obviously have no perception of why they're wearing them.

Phil ›› Which underscores another important idea is that you should not only tell people what to do, you should tell them why they're doing it. Knowledge is wonderful and knowledge is power.

Solderability Problems at Low Humidity

(solder paste, printing, flux, humidity, slump, solder balls, ESD)

Phil ›› Today's question is from S.D. who has a humidity question. S.W. writes that "some experts say that a circuit assembly production facility's temperature should ideally be set between 70 and 78 degrees Fahrenheit and the humidity of 40 to 70 percent when working with electronic assemblies.

The facility I work in has a current temperature of 76 degrees and the humidity level of only 16 percent. Will that humidity level affect the solderability of our assemblies?"

Jim ›› Where do you get humidity down to 16 percent? That is incredibly dry. I think we can assume that S.W. lives in a desert region.

Phil ›› Or in a "Snow Belt" region. If he's writing this in the middle of winter and they've got the heat cranked up the relative humidity goes down and dryness prevails. You can strike a match on anything. But in any event, to answer Scott's question...

Jim ›› No, S.W., you should not have problems with solderability at that low a humidity level and that moderate a temperature. You should have no problems. Also, regarding your MSD components, you can have significantly improved increased out-of-the-bag exposure times. Looking at the tables from moisture sensitive devices in IPC JEDEC Standard O33, if you have a Level 2A, your exposure time goes from 28 days up to 124 days and a Level 3 goes from 7 days up to 10 days.

So those are nice advantages. But we have some other concerns that we think are very significant. One is ESD.

Phil ›› Yeah, absolutely. As we say, that dried air, oh, boy, sparks must be flying.

Jim ›› Don't you see sparks flying all over the place whenever you're touching non-conductive materials? I would think this would be painfully obvious as a highly hazardous situation for all of your sensitive ICs.

Another issue is your solder paste, its work life on the stencil and on the board in terms of tack and workability, particularly if you're using an OA water soluble paste. OA's tend to dry out.

At that low a humidity level, you could be seeing problems. Perhaps Scott is observing soldering problems that he's attributing to solderability and they're really resulting from the fact that his solder paste is drying out.

Certainly, the solderability of materials is not affected by low humidity, but the working life of your solder paste could be a significant issue. That could give you some of the same kind of problems.

I think if you go to your solder paste spec, most of them are going to tell you that you should not be operating at 16 percent relative humidity.

Phil ›› Most solder paste wants to see the same ambient conditions in terms of temperature and RH that humans like to work in. However, once again, read and understand the solder paste's manufacturer's data sheet. If you still have a question, call their Technical Support department.

Do Vacuum Packed PCBs Need Baking?

(PCB storage, PCB handling, humidity, moisture, IPC-1601, moisture barrier bag, baking, soldering, dry cabinet)

Phil ›› Our question today is from G.K. The question is, "I understand from some EMS industry sources that PCB baking is not necessary if the PCB is vacuum packed by the PCB supplier. Is this true or do we still need to consider baking for our process?"

Jim ›› This is a really interesting and pertinent question, isn't it? The concept of moisture sensitivity of printed circuit boards is really getting a lot of attention.

In fact, the SMTA, which has had a Moisture Sensitivity Device Council for several years is now focusing most of its attention not on components, as has been the tradition, but on printed circuit boards.

We also see that the IPC has, at long last, established a specification: IPC 1601 - Guidance Document for Storage and Handling Issues for PWB's and Assemblies.

Go to the website and download it - what you'll see is the same kind of handling procedures both for suppliers, in this case PCB fab suppliers, and for assemblers in how you have to handle this.

Phil ›› This is long overdue because what we see a lot in the field is a lot of unnecessary baking and other times when baking should take place and isn't.

Jim ›› Well, what happens if you don't bake the board? What would cause a person to bake a board?

Phil ›› It's going to be that moisture gets trapped in the board and that moisture may cause delamination.

Moisture can also dilute your solder and fluxes, and so you're going to see incidents of bad soldering, possibly as radical as dewetting and solder balls (Those pesky old solder balls are everywhere.) The other side of the coin is we always advise not to do any unnecessary baking if you don't have to.

Severity of solderability issues can be affected depending on what the surface finish is, as well.

Jim ›› You can bake in nitrogen but that's another expense and so forth.

Phil ›› Exactly, so this is good that finally we're being led away from the seat of pants approach on PCB storage and handling.

Jim ›› An out-take from 1601 is that printed circuit boards should be treated as an MSL Level 4 classification and not left open to the floor for more than 72 hours. But most PWB suppliers guarantee a shelf life for six months for an unopened package.

So, going back to the original question, if you keep them sealed in their vacuum bags, they're good as long as you don't expose them on the floor for more than 72 hours. Now that's a very general statement.

It was also determined that different laminates that are going to be more sensitive such as newer high Tg laminates that are being used in lead-free assemblies. They may tend to absorb moisture faster and they would get an MSL rating that would be higher. If you can guarantee that your boards aren't exposed more than 72 hours before their final reflow, you'll probably be in good shape.

Phil ›› So you want to obtain and understand IPC 1601.

Maximum Time Between Printing and Reflow

(solder paste, printing, reflow, tac time, humidity)

Jim ›› Today's question is from R.W.: "What is the maximum allowable time for a PCB after it leaves the screen printer but before reflow? We're using water soluble lead-free paste; PCB is densely populated with over 10,000 apertures, and it's 90 mils thick."

Phil ›› What you're asking about is something called Tack Time. It's really dependent on two things: one is the chemistry of the solder paste and basically this is inherent with the particular manufacturer.

The other factor is the relative humidity and temperature in your facility. Temperature is particularly critical with water soluble because typically the solvent mechanism is isopropyl alcohol based so they tend to evaporate a little bit quicker. The actual tack time you should be able to find in the specifications from the solder paste company.

There is an easy test to determine this. This is one of the tests we do at ITM, when we do our solder paste evaluation testing. Our test procedure for tack test goes as follows: what we do is we'll take a board, and it doesn't even have to be a live board because we're very economical when it comes to testing. What you do is you take a real stencil and print it on a board with the solder paste in question.

What you're going to do next is to populate it with approximately 100 relatively low-mass components - passives and discretes Maybe an SOIC-8 (if you're feeling care-free).

Use your pick and place machine to populate it with the proper procedures, including getting the right depth of the component in the solder. This is real life, so you should do it in the production environment with the typical relative humidity and ambient temperature.

Now, you've taken the board, printed it and populated it, as we described, and now at T-0, time zero - immediately after populating it, you take the board, turn it 90 degrees so that it is perpendicular to your work surface, and, holding it about an inch above the work surface, release it so it kind of taps the board, Now hold the board upside down, parallel to the work surface. Next you count how many components fall off!

Now your immediate reaction is: Well that's easy, they're all going to fall off. But the reality of it is that there's pretty good tack. In most cases the components probably won't fall off.

Now that's at T-0, and you repeat the test at one-hour intervals. So, after one-hour has passed, you do the same thing, hold the board 90 degrees an inch above the work surface, and let it drop to create a tap.

Hold it upside down; count how many components fall off. Go out as many hours as you feel necessary. Usually we don't do it beyond four hours; although, in the early days of solder paste testing we've gone out as much as 24 hours. I can tell you that we've tested pastes, both no-clean and OAs that even after 24 hours have not had components fall off.

Jim ›› Yeah, the solder paste manufacturers are aware of this and they certainly try to give you a good tack time when they formulate it, but it depends on the other properties, some pastes have better tack times than others.

Phil ›› So try this test at home, R.W., and everybody else out there. It's a good way to benchmark the paste you're using now, and it should be an essential test when you do any solder paste evaluations.

What are the Proper Storage Conditions For PCBs?

(storage, PCB handling, humidity, moisture, IPC-1601, moisture barrier bag, baking, soldering, dry cabinet)

Phil ›› Today's question is from a T.S.: "Is there a specification for proper conditions for the storage of PCBs?"

Well the answer to your question is YES. Thank you for listening to Board Talk. We'll be back - actually, let's elaborate on this a bit, right Jim?

Jim ›› This is the second question we've had on this subject recently. The last one was on baking, but the answer is basically the same. The proper way to store your raw boards is in a moisture barrier bag that's vacuum packed and sealed. Otherwise, moisture can seep in, be absorbed by the circuit boards; and then when they get into the soldering operations, bad things can happen like delamination, cracking, and other things. So, you don't want to expose your boards to moisture.

IPC 1601 addresses handling and storage of PCBs and essentially you're going to treat them just like moisture sensitive devices and components.

That means the PCBs will come sealed in a bag; and when you take them out of the bag, you will only have so much time to put them through all of the soldering operations. If you exceed that time, you have to bake them.

The bottom line: "Keep it in the bag. Keep them sealed. Don't take them out of the bag any longer then you have to." And if you know that you've got an open bag of boards, a partial bag left over after a build, and you know you're not going to be able to assemble them for some time, either quickly reseal them into a moisture barrier bag with a desiccant just as you would MSD components or put them in a dry box. Some people have initially said, well I'm just going to treat a board like a Level 4 MSD, which would give you 72 hours out of the bag exposure time at nominal temperature and humidity conditions.

Phil ›› So, it's a good point. The concern has been brought up, and I think the concern is because of the laminate materials for lead-free in the higher reflow and soldering temperatures. Lead-free is just making all the problems with delamination worse, so the moisture issue becomes more critical and now we're going to have to abide by it.

Pin-in-Paste Calculations

(solder paste, reflow, stencils, aperture, reflow of through-hole, intrusive soldering, pin-in-paste, step-stencil, over-print)

Phil ›› What's today's question, Jim?

Jim ›› Well, Phil, this is a pertinent question because it falls right into your field of expertise, published research, and all the other wonderful things about you. This is about reflow of pin-in-paste, reflow of through-hole, intrusive soldering, whatever you want to call it. This is where we're going to try to create a through-hold solder joint by reflow soldering it. And the question is one of the most pertinent.

"We are about to implement pin-in-paste technology. How can we insure proper plated hole fill during the stencil printing process? Will the process require a different solder paste then the one we were using for SMT assemblies?"

So now our resident R.O.T. or reflow of through-hole expert, Phil Z.   P.S: Soapbox Alert!

Phil ›› This is definitely one of my favorite subjects, has been for a long time; and although I do have to say that one of the terminologies used, intrusive soldering always sounded kind of rude and pushy, it can be an essential process.

I did a study of this many, many years ago back around very early '90s when I was at GSS/ARRAY. While I was doing my study at GSS/ARRAY Technologies, our good friend and now ITM colleague, Joe Belmonte was hard at work doing the same thing at

Motorola-Codex. And about that same time, I believe our good friend Bob Willis was also working on this process in his lab in an undisclosed location in England. Long story short, we all, independently came up with essentially the same methodology and similar formulas.

The idea of getting enough solder into the gap between the lead and the inside barrel of the hole was through over-printing. I think a lot of people freak out when they hear overprint because they think: "Oh man, whenever I have slight misprint of my solder, I get solder balls". But this is the way to do it.

Jim ›› Perhaps we should be really basic with our audience out there and say that overprinting means using an aperture in your stencil that is larger than the pad on the circuit board. In this case, larger than the outer diameter of the annular ring or land around the plated through-hole.

Phil ›› And being that the solder paste is a continuous mass, it will flow together, with the capillary action pulling it into the barrel of the PTH. There are calculations that are done with regard to thickness of your stencil, how much overprint, to get enough solder to fill that gap between the outer diameter of the component lead and the inner barrel/diameter of hole.

Jim ›› Is there any place that people can go to get more specific information?

Phil ›› As a matter of fact, if you go the ITM website, you will see in the papers and articles section the paper that I did a number of years ago with the formulas as well as Joe's paper. You can find Bob Willis' treatise on his website (though he does tend to use that funny British vernacular.)

Jim ›› Formulas, exact calculations, select estimate calculations.

Phil ›› Yeah, hard to believe - something like that coming from me.

One very important thing is that if you look at IPC-610 (Workmanship Standards), even going back to Rev C as well as Rev D, you'll find that it's not necessary to have a big positive fillet on both sides to comprise an acceptable through-hole solder joint.

That big ol' positive-fillet-on-both-sides-of-the-PCB-joint is what we are used to with regard to wave and hand soldering. Reflow is a different animal. So even getting something that's actually flat with a surface, even slightly concave is usually more than enough strength - that joint is not going anywhere. As long as you've attained a minimum of 75% hole fill.

Jim ›› Well certainly that's really great information, Phil; and I'm sure RL will be very happy. Obviously, this is a very complex subject.

How To Calculate Component Standoff Height

(reflow, component, stencil, solder paste, BTC)

Phil

Jim, what's our question today?

Jim ›› Measuring component height after reflow, or what we might call "standoff." This is from C.S. who writes, "I have an SMT component that has a height of eight millimeters, a stencil thickness of 0.5 millimeters. We are using a lead-free paste. The pad size is 11" by .054" The question, is there a method of determining the overall height of the component on the board after reflow.

I have to believe that the pad dimensions of 11" by 0.054" is incorrect. I would have to guess if that's supposed to be 0.011" or 0.110". It's probably 0.110"

Phil, how would you answer C.S.?

Phil ›› The answer is yes, there is a method for determining the overall height of the component on the board after reflow. But from the information given, whether that one dimension was accurate or not, you don't really give us enough information, C.S. What do we need to know to do that, Jim?

Jim ›› Well, I don't know that I could do it anyway. This is a multi-parameter mission. You've provided some of the details, the component thickness. You've given us the thickness of the stencil. The stencil, 0.5 millimeters that would be a 20 mil thick stencil.

Phil ›› What are we soldering here?

Jim ›› Stencils are usually 4 to 8 mils thick, not 20 mils thick.

Phil ›› What are the parameters we're looking for?

Jim ›› He's given us the pad size, the thickness of the stencil, assuming we know what that is. We'd have to know what the aperture is relative to the size of the pad. But most importantly, he doesn't tell us what type of component it is.

Jim ›› Is this a QFP? A QFN? Is this a chip? Is this a BGA?

You also want to know the weight of the component. But even then, doing an exact calculation is pretty difficult.

Phil ›› Most people, I believe, who are interested in this data will actually do some physical measurements for their system. If you're using it to predict the thickness of a stencil, again, you'd probably want to go on some correlation.

Jim ›› Also, I want to point out that he's talking the height of the component. Typically, we talk about that in terms of standoff. That is the distance between the board and the bottom surface of the component. Of course, we could just add that to this eight millimeter thick component. But does that height include the leads if this is a leaded component or BGA? So, more information is needed.

Phil ›› Well, there you go. That's a full baked answer to a half-baked question.

Cleaning No Clean Boards With IPA

(cleaning, solvent, alcohol, no-clean, flux, residue)

Jim ›› Today, we're working at the car wash

Phil ›› Working at the car wash. That's right. We've got some clean questions and clean thoughts for you.

What do we have here? Well, here is a question R.P. who asks: "In our company, all our products are RoHS compliant. For some of them, we're using lead-free no clean flux and lead-free solder. Is there a specific IPA, isopropyl alcohol, to clean lead-free PCBs? Is it needed?"

Jim ›› It's a good question.

There are a lot of issues here and we're just going to cover them briefly. First off, IPA refers to isopropyl alcohol. It's just a specific chemical. If you're talking about a solvent blend, of which there are many, the answer is yes, there are specific solvents. Some of them use IPA. Some of them don't. We'll just call them specific cleaning solvents or cleaning materials, which can remove virtually any flux.

The problem is there are no universal ones. So, you need to know exactly what you're doing, what flux you're using, in order to choose the right solvent and the right cleaning process.

Let's talk some generalities. No clean fluxes are designed not to be cleaned. Generally, they're designed to have a residue that's safe to leave on the board without any other coating.

So typically, they're designed not to absorb moisture. So, they're not very soluble in water. So, most of the water-based things, which include a lot of the IPA blends, are not particularly good.

You have to decide do you really need to clean it? If you are, why are you using a no clean. Should you go to a cleanable, water soluble flux that's designed to be cleaned?

But assuming that you have your reasons for cleaning no clean you need to realize that it's going to be more difficult, and the fact that you're soldering for lead-free, therefore, you're soldering at temperatures that are probably 30 degrees higher. Therefore, in general, the residues are going to be more difficult to clean.

So, understanding that you've created a situation where you've stacked the dice against yourself, you've raised your degree of difficulty, you've got a no clean flux, which is harder to clean, you've got lead-free temperatures, which make the residues typically harder to clean.

That being said, you need to find a solvent that is specific for the flux that you're using, whether it's a wave soldering flux or whether you're reflow soldering and it's in a paste. You need to talk to your solder paste manufacturer or the flux supplier, and then to one of the cleaning chemical companies. They're probably the best source because that's their job to supply you with cleaning chemicals. They should know what is good and best for your specific flux that you're using. They'll probably run some tests for you.

Phil ›› If you're going to endeavor to clean the no clean, as we said, for whatever reason, you definitely want the right tool for the job. And IPA, it's kind of squeezing by.

Jim ›› IPA will not clean a lot of flux residues. There's a lot of confusion, People say, "Oh, IPA cleans everything." This is really typical at the repair and rework benches. They get IPA, throw it on there, and it cleans it. In a lot of cases, it just doesn't. So, don't make that mistake, and particularly for no clean. If you've got a no clean, you're going to have to find the specific system.

Some of them may require a heating, agitation, multiple soaks, and so forth, because, again, many of the no clean residues are not designed to be cleaned.

Phil ›› As Jim mentioned before, there are specific solvents made for doing exactly what you need. Go to the experts. Go to the companies that exist just for this purpose, companies like Kyzen, Zestron, and some of the others. They're the experts on the area. They have the right stuff that will work with a particular formulation that you're using.

Jim ›› The worst thing you want to do is use something that sort of dissolves this stuff and spreads it around on the board and maybe de-encapsulate some of the active chemicals. So, the bottom line is if you use the wrong solvent, you can end up with a board that's, in chemical terms, dirtier than you started with because the active chemicals are no longer encapsulated as they would be with a properly activated no clean residue.

Phil ›› So use the right formulation. Or you will be wishing you did.

What is an Acceptable Level of Exposed Copper?

(surface finish, OSP, corrosion, oxidation, ENIG, solderability, reflow, wetting, procurement, PCB Fab)

Jim ›› Phil, this is an anonymous question. We don't even have the initials of the perpetrator of this question. It relates to the surface finishes on printed circuit boards.

The question is: "Is there a general specification for an acceptable level of exposed copper for circuit conductors on circuit boards where all the copper surfaces are gold plated? And a further question is: What problems could we see if there are very small non-contact areas on some conductors that have exposed copper?"

Phil ›› Well let's see, the answer to the first question, general specification: yes - generally speaking there shouldn't be any exposed copper. As far as potential problems you could see, well obviously that copper can corrode, discolor.

The thing here is, we would politely say, This a process indicator. It's also a supplier indicator. What kind of crappy boards are you buying? What's with this exposed copper?

Hey, it's supposed to be gold plated, why the hell is the copper showing through here? You know what's going on here? This is a process out of control.

Jim ›› But let's apply some logic to this, Brother Phil. What is special about gold?

It's expensive. So, in the fab process that calls for gold coating, obviously any supplier doesn't want to put anymore gold on than they absolutely have to.

Now what happens in real life? Some board fabricators are reasonable about that, they try to keep it low, but well within the specs. Others try to take it right to the limit of the spec.

Phil ›› And cross over the line.

Jim ›› So one thing might be here as a process indicator, you might want to measure the average thickness of the gold on the other conductors. Is it not only exposed on little edges and so forth, but is it really thin on the other places so you can't see it, but whereas it might not give you 100% protection? The question I would have is: Are you getting good soldering on all of your joints that are supposedly fully protected by this gold coating?

Phil ›› And I'd particularly concerned also about the inside barrels of the through-holes and vias. If you're seeing it on the surface, one can only wonder what's beneath. If it's exposed copper, wow, the guys even skipping on the nickel for crying out loud. What is this world coming to, Jim?

Jim ›› Well remember, we don't know that. There are flash gold finishes that go right over copper, Phil, so we don't know that specifically here. We typically think of an ENIG finish where we get a nickel barrier, and I agree with Phil, but we don't have data here to make that claim.

If it is a ENIG finish and you got exposed copper, then Phil's right; not only did they not get the gold on, but they didn't get the nickel on, which brings us to another thing that you have to ask is: Was it not a problem with the gold being too thin but rather the fact that the copper wasn't cleaned adequately underneath, and that's death with any finish. Just remember, I don't care what your surface finish is - OSP, Immersion Silver, HASL or anything, you're starting with bare copper and you've got to get that copper clean.

All of the surface coating methodologies start by actually etching a little bit of the copper off to get any deep-seated corrosion. You get down to really virgin copper. So whatever finish you put on gold or nickel or whatever, you can get a good complete coverage.

Phil ›› So coming or going, it's a process out of control. This case it could be poor cleaning at one end and/or skimping on the gold at the back end. Nevertheless, it might be time to look for another vendor or get this one in line.

Jim ›› Yes, unfortunately where so much of the PCB fab has gone offshore, the supply link is longer, and problems have increased.

What Causes Blow Holes?

(wave soldering, flux, profiling, defects, voids, component, entrapment, thermocouple)

Phil ›› Today, we've got a question from M.J. out there in wave solder land. M.J. asks, "When wave soldering radial lead LEDs, we are seeing blow holes. We have found that loosening the clinch applied by the placement machine resolved the blow hole issue. Any idea why the tight clinch might be closing blow holes?" Well, this is interesting.

Jim ›› Let's get back to basics. Blow holes are caused by trapping solvents in the flux inside the hole. When they hit the wave, the solvents boil rapidly and expand. They form a bubble and blow solder out of the hole.

The traditional causes are inadequate preheat. You're not boiling off all the solvent deep in those holes or you've got too much flux. Contamination can also be an issue.

The fact that you have been able to resolve it by loosening the clinch tells us that in the initial setup, the clinch was obstructing the hole and preventing the solvent and flux from getting out of the hole during the preheat and trapping some amount of liquid flux and solvent.

So that when you hit the wave, it exploded and gave you a blow hole. That could be the only reason if you've resolved it completely by loosening the clinch.

You obviously now have more clearance around that hole at the bottom where the principal amount of the evaporation is taking place. It's allowing that extra flux and solvent to be boiled out during preheat.

It surprises me that tight clinching would cause this problem. But I guess if the whole clearance was pretty tight when you clinched the lead over close to the board surface, it could restrict the flow of liquid and gas during the preheat process.

Phil ›› Let's say hypothetically it isn't totally resolved, that maybe it starts reoccurring again, particularly in those radial parts.

Jim ›› One possibility would be that the radial parts are heavier than the other parts that you're inserting, and the preheat was marginal so that you were not completely heating all the joints because the extra mass in these radial parts.

What's unique about the radial parts? Were they heavier? Are the leads heavier. So maybe your preheat was on the marginal side.

Phil ›› You can certainly determine that by running a thermocouple on that particular part.

Jim ›› That's right. Put it on the top side and make sure it was at least 100 degrees C for alcohol flux or 120 degrees C for VOC free water base fluxes.

Phil ›› We also don't know if we're running a no-clean or a water soluble. Of course, it brings up a question of the amount of flux going on, and if the penetration is correct.

Jim ›› One of the classic things of blow holes is too much flux.

Phil ›› Wave soldering never goes away. Wouldn't it be great if we could just retire it to its noble place and put it up in the museum?

Leaded Parts Through a Lead-free Wave

(SnPb, Pb-free, wave soldering, profiling, solder pot, temperature, pre-heat, contamination, solder, RoHS)

Phil ›› We're coming to you today from high atop Mt. Rialto here with a very cloud obscured view of we're not sure what. Today's question is from J.B.: "We will be assembling circuit boards using a RoHS compliant assembly line; however, the customer does not have a RoHS lead-free requirement. Are there any concerns if we use a few leaded components in this process? Are we likely to contaminate our wave solder bath?

Jim and **Phil** ›› The answer is YES. Don't take the chance!

Jim ›› This is a classic example of not wanting to introduce anymore variability or chances into your process. Could you put tin lead plated parts through your lead-free wave soldering? Lead is going to get into that pot. Your limit is 0.1%. Yeah, could you get away with a few parts? Sure.

Is it a good idea? No, it's because sooner or later the contamination build up in that pot will come back to harm you; and if you contaminate that pot; if you get too much lead in it; you will have to completely drain the pot and flush it.

It's just a very complex and a costly procedure to get that pot back again. But thinking in a more philosophical vein; don't enter variability into your process. It's not a good idea. You got a lead-free process; you want to keep it lead-free.

Do not allow any contamination anywhere on the line - parts, stencil printer, anyplace that contamination can occur. You're taking a risk, and you don't want to introduce additional risks into your process if you don't have to.

Phil ›› Now, chances are you're probably not auditing your incoming components. It would be great if you were, but chances are you're probably not (if you're like most people) and there's a possibility you could already be running some leaded parts through that bath.

So, we recommend that in order to get a feel for what's going on, that you send a sample from your bath out for analysis to your solder company or analysis lab to monitor to the various levels of contaminates in your solder bath.

You should do this more frequently at the front end until you get a good feel for what's going on and then back off to an appropriate sampling interval.

Jim ›› Right - but keeping tin lead and lead-free separate has been a continuing logistical problem. Don't take any chances. And with process concerns such as contaminating a wave pot, taking risk is just not worth it.

Pick and Place, Thermal Issues and Cleaning

Can Pick and Place Systems Insert Radial Lead Devices?

(pick and place, through-hole, components, feeders)

Phil ›› Today's questions is from K.A. who asks, "Are there standard SMT pick and places that can also insert radial lead devices?" Now what an interesting question.

Jim ›› I think before we go any farther, my general opinion is NO.

Phil ›› I would rate it a qualified YES.

Jim ›› That's all right, and we're not here to agree. We're here to give information. The reason is that handling radial parts which have either two or principally three leads, most radials have three leads, takes a lot of lead preparation and lead handling, and typically there are dedicated machines to do this, radial inserters made by Universal and some of the Japanese companies, Panasonic, TDK, Sanyo.

And having been with Dynapert many years ago when they were attempting to and never successfully build a radial machine, I understand how difficult it is to do this reliably in an automated machine. So, my feeling is, yes, there are placement machines that can do some insertion. They typically call it odd-form insertion. But we're usually dealing with connectors and things like that that have fixed, very stable leads that don't need any lead handling.

A radial package needs a tremendous amount of lead preparation and typically you have to hold the leads in alignment while you insert them. It's more extra mechanism than is practical to provide in a pick and place machine. Pick and place machines achieve significant speed and cost effectiveness because they're doing a relatively simple operation, whereas insertion machines have been more expensive and much more limited because of the dedicated nature of handling leads.

Phil ›› So what you're going to want to do is ask among the different pick and place manufacturers out there to see if they can do odd form, and most of the time the odd form they're referring to is exactly what Jim was talking about, connectors, things with rigid, fixed lead patterns.

If they can do radial, you're going to have to ask what the care and feeding of said components are going to have to be. How are you going to have to prep them within specific tolerances for the machine to handle it and also in terms of how are you going to feed it? Then you've got to ask yourself, as Jim was saying, whether it's all worth it or, geez, let's hand insert, or if there's high volume, look at getting a machine purposely designed for doing that, mainly a radial inserter.

Jim ›› I doubt very sincerely that you will find a pick and place company that will just say, "Yes, here's a piece of off-the-shelf hardware that will take a variety of radial parts, form them, lead prep them, and insert them for you as part of the normal pick and place program." Don't know for sure, haven't looked in a long time, but I really doubt it.

Phil ›› Well, I say "seek and thou just might find".

Conductive Epoxy: Pros and Cons

(conductive epoxy, adhesives, soldering, reliability)

Phil ›› Today's question is from a R.H., Jim, what's his question?

Jim ›› His question is "what are the advantages and disadvantages of electrically conductive epoxies?" We have a lot of questions about this, Phil, and I know that this is something you have a deep and significant knowledge and wisdom about. So please enlighten us.

Phil ›› I would be glad to. I probably have this stuff running through my veins, especially ever since I cut myself. Conductive epoxies are typically polymers that contain conductive materials. Those materials can be tin, copper, graphite, gold, and silver, etc.. The idea here is that they're used as a connectivity compound for forming electrically conductive joints, for lack of a better word, but we're not really talking about traditional joint connections.

Typically, they're in the form of a liquid, a viscous liquid that you would apply by either dispensing or printing. There's another type. It's a film type that we'll talk about another time (anisotropic). But concentrating on the liquid ones, most commonly they're printed on and as I said, they can be dispensed.

Some of the advantages of conductive epoxies? Well, first of all, one advantage is they're lead-free. How about that?

The second advantage is that they're also no-clean. We're not reflowing. We're not using a flux. We're basically setting up this material, curing it, if you will. Another advantage is that cure temperature - typically, the schedules call for temperatures that are much, much lower than reflow temperatures. We've seen quite a few that cure at under 100 degrees centigrade.

So those are the advantages. Now, of course, your immediate reaction is, "Wow, wouldn't this be a fantastic material to use instead of leaded solder?" Well, yeah, maybe. But there are some limitations.

One limitation is that conductive epoxies tend to be very, very expensive. I don't know what the current pricing is, but I know a number of years ago, when we seriously evaluated it as a possible substitute for leaded solder, the price for the silver filled conductive epoxies was approximately ten times per gram that of tin/lead solder. So that's kind of a limitation right there.

Second of all, a lot of these epoxies work very well for steady-state temperature environments particularly at extreme temperatures. However, in terms of applications where you have thermal cycling, they typically don't do as well.

The third disadvantage is that there is sometimes an inconsistency not only from vendor to vendor in terms of the conductivity and resistivity of the materials, but even from batch to batch.

But it's a good material to know about. It's a good material to have, particularly if you're ever in a situation where you have a thermal limitation in terms of dealing with a material.

Jim ›› What about rework, Phil?

Phil ›› They could definitely be used for rework.

Jim ›› But can you rework them when they've been put down initially?

Phil ›› Qualified, yes. There's basically two types of conductive epoxies. One is what's called "thermoset." That is a very rigid plastic. That is very, very difficult to rework.

Jim ›› It's like a two-part epoxy or something like that.

Phil ›› Exactly. Those of you who have ever had to use them for holding passives for your pick and place, that's the type that you have to basically use a chisel to get the component out.

The other type, which is thermo-plastic, is more of something where you reheat it and it becomes pliable and you can actually remove the component. It kind of resembles Tupperware, if you will.

Jim ›› "Tupperware", another scientific evaluation from Phil Zarrow.

Phil ›› Yeah, well, you know, what can I say? Just common science of the common man. Well, anyway, that's about as far as I'm going today.

Jim ›› Another thing, getting back to the cost issue, the traditional ones that have been used successfully in aerospace and so forth are silver and gold filled. They are very expensive. A lot of work has been done and there still remains a question of whether you can do it with copper filled. Obviously, if you can it would be a lot cheaper. But I've not heard anybody who's gotten complete confidence in using a copper filled conductive epoxy.

Is There a Standard Usage Rate for Stencils?

(stencils, printing, squeegee, apertures)

Phil ›› Today we're speaking to you from the technical archives of ITM, which most other places pass as a dumpster

Today's question is from S.C. who asks a three-part question. The first question is, "Is there a recommended or a standard usage rate for stencils?"

The second question is, "Should I expect different usage rates for metal, rubber, or plastic?" I assume S.C.'s referring to squeegees, because I haven't seen any rubber stencils lately.

And the last question is, "Is there a specific way to determine when it's time to replace a squeegee?"

All right let's do these in order. First of all, as far as recommended or standard usage rate for a stencil, the answer is NO because there are just so many variables. These can include the shape of the apertures, how many apertures there are, as well as some of the inputs from your printer itself, such as squeegee pressure and some of the variables there.

Jim ›› Most important, squeegee pressure and how thick the stencil is. A thicker stencil is going to last a lot longer than a thinner stencil.

But I think what you said in design, sharp edges, cut outs, and so forth, there are a number of things you can do in design of stencils to extend their life, but certainly not having excessive squeegee pressure is probably the most significant in increasing the life of your stencil. And handling. I mean handling these things. When you take them on and off, they're stretched in that web in your stencil and if you're not careful with them, you bang them, you scratch them just by handling.

Phil ›› That's right. It's not hard to ding one.

Usually the answer to that question is the stencil pattern will be obsolete long before the stencil itself is worn out.

Jim ›› I think that's typically right, unless you're in a very high-volume product it's much more common to lose a stencil because of mishandling.

Phil ›› And even then, we don't really have any numbers. I know there's some instances where I've experienced a quarter of a million prints from a given stencil.

Jim ›› The difference in usage rates with a metal, rubber, or plastic squeegee. If you are using a rubber squeegee, you probably can expect a reasonable life on pure cyclical use, but to be real honest, we don't find a lot of people using rubber squeegees and certainly not for high volume.

Phil ›› Yeah, and a number of reasons. I mean one of the reasons we moved away from rubber in the first place, besides the wear factor, was the fact that you need a different hardness or durometer for depending upon the pitch that you're printing. In most boards today, we have a wide range of print, so metal was a one-size fits all as far as pitch goes and the metal itself is pretty long lasting. Again, unless you drop it, in which case it's time for a new one.

Jim ›› But it leads us into the third question, "Is there a specific way to determine if it's time to replace a squeegee?" And that was the problem with rubber. When did it need to be replaced? When was it getting a little worn or out of there? That was very difficult. Replacement is much more clear-cut with a stainless steel squeegee where unless it goes out of flat or unless it gets dinged, it's probably okay. So, it's much easier to see defects and wear that's significant to cause you to replace a stainless steel squeegee.

Phil ›› Right. On top of that, there's also a few aftermarket squeegees that are available that are the metal, of course, that have various treatments on them that supposedly extend the life of the squeegee in terms of number of print cycles by quite a large percentage, according to the respective manufacturers' claims. But again, a lot of it has to do with setting everything else up right and have good proper care and treatment.

Jim ›› Right, and with squeegees as with stencils, most of them have to be replaced because of mishandling, not because you ran too many good quality, well-adjusted prints on them. And so, if you're having a concern, questions like this, "why do we have to replace our squeegees and/or stencils?" I would certainly look at your handling and your set up procedures because that's much more likely the cause of early replacement.

All right. Well, you've wasted another five or six minutes of your valuable time listening to us drone on about our knowledge of printing and all the other various sundry aspects of electronic assembly.

Phil ›› But we did answer all three questions, so you've got to credit us that.

Jim ›› We did. You got your money's worth.

Is There a Passive Component Solder Void Limit?

(soldering, voids, components, printing, reflow, solder paste)

Phil ›› What is in our mailbag today, Jim?

Jim ›› Today we hear from H.M. "I know about voids in BGA solder joints, but is there a quality criterion for the solder voids in passive components, including resistors, capacitors, etc.?"

Well, when it comes to specifications, we always refer to IPC 610. In IPC 610 in Section 5.2.2 called Solder Anomalies, it talks about pinholes and blowholes, but also addresses voids. It defines a defect for Class II and Class III products as pinholes, blowholes, or voids which reduce the connection below the minimum requirements.

The requirements for chip components, resistors and capacitors is given in IPC 610 in Section 8.2.2. There are many different categories, but they talk basically about coverage on the pads and on the terminations and a number of them give percentages.

So theoretically, according to IPC, you could measure the void. If it's an internal void you'll need to use an x-ray machine. If it's an external void such as a blowhole, you could just measure it with a microscope. And then you could apply that to the joint category such as 50% coverage, 75% coverage, and so forth that are listed in the 8.2.2 sections.

These measurements are theoretically possible, but they are typically judgment calls.

Phil ›› When we look at these specs, we're basically comparing contact area voids with things like misalignments, skewed components, things along those lines.

Jim ›› Say you had a void near the toe of a solder fillet and the spec says that you need to have at least 75% coverage. So, you look at the coverage and if a void was bigger than 25%, that would reduce your total to less than 75%.

That's easy to say here quoting numbers off the top of our heads, but I think in real life, it's subjective. But to answer your question, yes, there are criteria and they are defined in the IPC.

Phil ›› The trick is to determine if voids are a symptom or a defect, particularly before you go about doing any actual reworking and manipulation where you could do more harm than good.

Jim ›› That initial spec, 5.2.2, defines all voids, blowholes, and pinholes as a process indicator. So, if you're seeing them, they're telling you that maybe there's something wrong. Whether a specific void causes you to reject a part or rework it is often a judgment call against the criteria in 8.2.2.

Maximum Time Between Soldering and Cleaning

(soldering, cleaning, reflow, water soluble, No-Clean)

Phil ›› Today we have a question on cleaning.

Jim ›› This is from J.T.: "What is the maximum staging time permissible for PCBA's between wave soldering and cleaning?"

I'm aware that ideally it should be ASAP in order to reduce white residue and stain formation, but in many cases, our manufacturing processes are not robust enough for immediate turnaround. Some PCBA's are staged up to 24 hours prior to cleaning. Is there an industry standard specification?

Phil ›› Well, we're not aware of a standard, at least we haven't come across any, but you are correct about the time factor. Temperature also comes into play, but then again, we're wondering if that's somewhat negated. Right, Jim?

Jim ›› Well, theoretically, if you've burned off all your solvents in your wave soldering operation, then all you're doing is hardening. So, once you reach room temperature, theoretically that should be it. But we know that that's not absolutely true in real life.

One question you have to ask is what kind of flux are you using? Is it water based or is it alcohol based? Obviously, alcohol would evaporate and dry out a lot faster. But you wrote up an interesting historical fact about organic acid fluxes, Phil.

Phil ›› This is going back quite a few years; I'd say about 20 years ago. It took place at a company in Boston. What happened was this contact of mine had been running a wave flux on both wave and reflow, and they had run a batch of boards and the surface finish on the boards were immersion gold. What happened was as they finished this batch of boards coming out of the wave solder machine, their cleaner crapped out.

It took about 24 hours to get the cleaner up and running and these boards were sitting there with OA flux residue for 24 hours. After they cleaned the boards my contact told me that there had been degradation of the gold finish attributed to the acid flux.

Jim ›› That was some powerful acid.

Phil ›› That was the powerful acid flux, so don't get any on your fingers or hands or God knows what it'll do to you.

Jim ›› There are a lot of other stuff besides gold finishes on boards that can be degraded by OA fluxes. So, if you do have an OA flux in your system, then you may want to reduce that time allowance for concerns about degradation, corrosion, and so forth. But there are no industry standards. The longer you wait, the harder it's going to be to get the stuff off.

Can Ultrasonic Cleaning Damage Sensitive Components?

(cleaning, solvents, ultra-sonic, cracking)

Phil ›› Jim, what's today's question?

Jim ›› Okay, today's question comes from NL: "Currently, we are using ultrasonic cleaning to remove no clean solder paste and it works fine. However, the use of ultrasonic system causes damage to one ultra-sensitive SMT component. Can you recommend a method we could use to prevent damage to this component caused by the ultrasonic cleaning process?"

Phil ›› First of all, don't put it in the ultrasonic cleaner. Okay, that was kind of trite. I think ultrasonic cleaning for a long time got a bad rap. This would be one for Myth Busters but it's a little too esoteric. The theory was you put components into the ultrasonic cleaner and the ultrasonics would cause wire bonds to break on IC's and sometimes it would crack capacitors.

Probably the most informative study was done quite a few years ago by a friend of mine with a major capacitor company. He was doing a study for a very large OEM client at the time. He tested at various frequencies through the spectrum that ultrasonic cleaners might operate that indeed there was no damage promoted by the immersion of these components on boards into the ultrasonic cleaner regardless of the medium.

Jim ›› It really doesn't matter because this is an answer that you'll never prove 100 percent. The basic physics is that ultrasonics operate typically a certain frequency and if you have something in any particular component that resonates at that frequency, the potential for damage is there.

The potential internal construction of components is infinitely varied so you could never test every possible component. So, it's very possible that for your system, particularly if you don't have the chance to use different frequencies or if your system doesn't vary the frequency by itself, that you just happened to hit a component that has something in it that's resonating at the frequency of your cleaner.

Phil ›› Hence the key appears to use a sweep frequency ultrasonic rather than a fixed frequency.

There's another possibility. You may be uncovering a latent defect in that component itself. One of the other things our aforementioned friend discovered was that in many cases where the dielectric was not co-fired properly, ultimately there would be cracks induced in that component. All the ultrasonics did was to accelerate the development of that "eventual" crack. So, think of it almost like extremely accelerated life testing.

Jim ›› If you think about wire bonding, if your wire bonds aren't completely encapsulated when they do the over molding, maybe it's good that it breaks them before they get out in the field? But if you're seeing this consistently, it's probably a system-level problem.

Phil ›› Be sure it actually is the ultrasonics that's causing this problem.

Jim ›› But there are still many people who say don't use ultrasonics. There's just a certain amount of risk that you'll never be able to mitigate.

Thermocouple Attachment Review

(reflow, soldering, thermocouples, profiling, wave-soldering)

Phil ›› We're coming to you today from the roof of the ITM building on beautiful Mount Rialto.

For those of you who are regular listeners to Board Talk, you will know that we've discussed talked attaching thermocouples to PCBAs for the purpose of profiling that board on a reflow machine or a wave machine.

Jim ›› We got on one of our sacred, holy soapboxes and said we don't like tape and we like to glue down thermocouples using high-temperature solder because it's more permanent.

We got a number well thought out responses, people saying, "Hey, we can't do that in our environment. We can't sacrifice a board. We've got to use tape." A lot of people are saying, "We like aluminum tape." And so, we just thought we would weigh in and review.

With any temperature measurement, the key element is to get the thermocouple itself in good contact with what you're trying to measure and to do so in a way that does not modify the area with a lot of extra mass or material that's going to give you an inaccurate reading. So, if you have to use tape, make sure that the thermocouple is in good contact with what you're trying to measure, be it a material or a solder joint or whatever. Try to strain relief it with some other tape before you put the tape over the thermocouple so there's no pressure on the tape holding down the thermocouple.

So, when the tape does heat up and the adhesive may get a little weak, there's no pressure to lift that thermocouple up. Be careful that the location, the shape and the size of the piece of tape you use do not affect the heating of what you're trying to measure.

Phil ›› Right, and that same principle applies to if you are indeed using the preferred method of conductive epoxy or high-temp solder in that you don't use an inordinate amount or volume of solder or conductive epoxy. Because for that same reason Jim just outlined, you're going to affect the readings in a bad way.

Jim ›› You want to measure the temperature of the solder joint, not the temperature of a big piece of tape sitting on top of a circuit board, not the temperature of a big blob of high-temperature solder sitting on the circuit board or a big blob of adhesive.

Is There a Thermal Cycle Limit?

(soldering, components, PCB, temperature, profiling, reflow, wave-soldering, selective soldering, Rework and Repair, thermal cycling, intermetallic, reliability, delamination, thermal considerations)

Phil ›› We have a theory question today, Jim.

Jim ›› The question is from P.W. and the wording is, "How many thermal cycles can we expose a Class 3 printed wiring assembly to before it no longer maintains a Class 3 rating?" P.W. is referring to IPC Class 3 as spelled out in the "Holy Bible" of our industry, IPC 610D.

This is the highest rating for critical electronics. The question continues, "In general, how many cycles should we allow at a given location on a circuit board, such as a BGA site, before we should consider the assembly compromised and thus be unreliable at any class rating?"

Now these are really good questions.

First off, we're assuming when we say, "thermal cycles", we're talking about soldering cycles, be it reflow, wave or hand soldering.

Phil ›› Let's say if we were putting down an SOIC, that's one thermal cycle. And let's say we have to repair it, that's another thermal cycle to remove it and another thermal cycle to replace it.

If it's on the A or first side of the board, it would have gone through one initial thermal cycle to reflow it onto the board, and a second thermal cycle while the second side of the board gets reflowed.

Jim ›› So the answer is that any given site can potentially see a lot of thermal cycles and what happens? Well, one thing that can happen, particularly if you're dealing with anything but an ENIG surface, the copper tin intermetallic will continue to grow and get thicker every time you heat that joint.

We all know that the copper tin inner metallic is strong but brittle, so you want a thin layer, not a thick layer. So, as you continue to heat this through repair and multiple reflow and wave soldering cycles, you stand a chance of making that inner metallic too thick and reducing the ultimate reliability of the solder joint.

This is greatly reduced if you're using an ENIG finish, electroless nickel with immersion gold, because you're not soldering to copper, you're soldering to nickel and the nickel tin inner metallic doesn't tend to form nearly as quickly.

The other issue is the circuit board. What about the materials underneath the pads? What about the adhesive material that's bonding the copper pads down to the PCB and what about the PCB materials, the laminate materials, and the vias in the same area?

Phil ›› The thermal cycling will affect the Z axis, as well as the X and Y axes.

Jim ›› And of course the key consideration here is a BGA site because when you get into BGA repair, you have one or two reflow cycles up front. Then you've got to take the BGA off and then you've got to get in and scrub the excess solder off and then you've got to put stuff down and then you have to reflow it again.

Phil ›› So, there's a lot of concern about damage to the BGA pads in the BGA areas because when removing them, you tend to have to heat them quite intensely to make sure you melt all the joints before you pull the BGA off. The BGA repair sequence raises the bar, raises the concern.

Jim ›› As Phil said, unfortunately, we don't have any numbers. IPC doesn't seem to publish it, but people have come up with their own numbers, although I can't recall off the top of my head the methodology they went through.

You can compromise a local area of a circuit board, by applying too many heat cycles and the rework cycles are particularly a concern, especially with area arrays are where you've got to get in and really heat them to get the parts off and then scrub them to get the excess solder off the pads before you do the repair.

P.W., you're on the right track. I'm sorry we don't have any hard numbers for you, but I would say think about it and certainly think about how many BGA repairs you want to allow on a given site.

Phil ›› If you're talking about BGA repair, think about minimizing the intensity and duration of every one of those heating cycles because none of that heat is doing you any good. That's the bottom line with any of these materials. Extra heat cycles do you no good.

Help With Defective Solder Joints

(soldering, reliability, defects, reflow, wave-soldering, selective soldering, PCB finish, HASL, PCB fabrication, contamination)

Phil ›› Jim, what's today's question?

Jim ›› It's about defective solder joints on a HASL boards. HASL, of course, is hot air solder leveled. The question goes, "What is the possible cause of incomplete soldering after surface mount reflow?

The bare circuit boards in question are hot air solder leveled. At the problem areas, we notice a yellow stain on the hot air leveled surface on the PCB"

Phil ›› Before we get into our usual diatribe, the straight answer to your question is you are suffering from a case of contaminating residue and pollutants, or CRAP, in your HASL process.

So, it's obviously something your fabrication shop is throwing into the works.

Jim ›› The one thing that HASL has always had going for it is it solders well, even after it's been stored, it has a long shelf life. You've got to remember that solder leveling is a very rigorous process. It starts with a bare circuit board, bare copper, scrupulously cleaned, washed and dried.

Then it's coated with a water-soluble flux. Then it's preheated. Then dipped into a solder pot. It's pulled out. It's blasted with the air nozzles to blow excess solder off the surface pads and out of the plated through holes.

At that point, it's completely covered with flux residue and whatever else has been blowing around in the air knife chamber. It has to be cleaned very scrupulously. Likewise, on the front end of the process, that water soluble flux has to be properly preheated before it goes into the solder pot.

Phil ›› So, it's a complex process, but it should give you a really good solderable surface. If you're seeing stains, something was amiss in the way they operated the HASL process, most likely in the final cleaning, but maybe some combination of preheat and airflow or something else, just general contamination.

We're not big fans of using HASL for many surface mount applications. It's kind of an archaic process. It was developed originally for through hole. One of the things that trips people up is the unevenness of the surface you get with HASL.

When you start getting below 25 mil pitch parts the topography of the board surface can really throw you for a loop. Another reason you might want to look towards surface finishes other than HASL.

Jim ›› But to be fair, a HASL process, if done properly, should give you a very solderable surface and you should have no problems getting good wetting. The intermetallic bond has already been formed.

All you're doing is melting the solder on the surface of the pad with the solder in the paste. So, it's really a much easier task in terms of soldering if the HASL was done right.

Phil ›› It's always a good practice to assure that your PCB fabricator is not giving you CRAP !

Mixed Cleaning - No Clean and Water Soluble

(reflow, cleaning, no-clean, water soluble, wave-soldering, selective soldering, flux, solder, residue)

Phil ›› Today's question comes from a Mr. P.H who writes,

Jim ›› "I have a closed-loop batch wash system used in SMT, running a water-soluble process. An associate wants to clean assemblies that were hand-soldered with a no-clean through our batch wash.

The solder alloy is the same, 63/37, but the manufacturers are different. Of course, one is no-clean, and one is water-soluble. Does this pose potential problems for the assembly or equipment? I prefer not to introduce the no-clean into my SMT environment, since the system is closed-loop."

Phil ›› Well, the most important thing, though, is that he's not going to clean his no-clean residues with a straight water cleaner. If he does, he's likely going to make one hell of a mess.

Jim ›› Well, he might. It really depends on the individual no-clean chemistry. No-clean is not one thing, it is a wide family of many different formulations using many chemicals.

Some can be cleaned with water and a saponifier, others require very special solvents and cleaning processes, so you have to match the cleaning processes for no-clean to the specific no-clean flux formulation you're dealing with.

Phil ›› There is no universal solvent, IPA, or anything else that's going to get it all off. It's a common mistake that any people make. But most importantly you're not going to clean it with pure water.

Phil ›› So that's the bottom line. If you want to introduce your boards with a no-clean flux for cleaning, you have to introduce a saponifier to the system.

As far as changing it over from running straight aqueous, he would have to talk to the saponifier companies as to what concentration of what specific saponifier to put in there.

Jim ›› I suppose that you could say, "I'll run everything with a saponifier," but that's an additional cost and maintenance, and you've got to make sure that your cleaner and closed-loop system will handle it. There are just a whole lot of issues. I guess our advice is no, don't try it. It's not going to clean a no-clean, and it could potentially mess up your pure water batch system, even with a closed-loop.

What Causes Exploding Solder Joints?

(soldering, defects, wave-soldering, selective soldering, flux, voids)

Phil ›› Today's question is from G.V. and it's a wave solder question.

"We have seen joint voids that look like explosions after wave soldering, some members of the team believe the problem is caused by humidity brought to the process by the bare board. The problem was solved by changing the bare board lot.

Have you seen this problem before? Do you agree that the cause is likely due to moisture absorption in the bare boards? Can this suspicious lot of boards be salvaged?"

Jim ›› The answer is technically YES to everything. It's very interesting in that we're talking about voids, blowholes - explosions in wave soldering joints.

There was an article by Alpha Solder on this very problem and it was explained in detail. It states no less than 36 specific potential causes for blowholes. So, I'm sure you could find anything you want on that list.

Phil ›› Certainly the most common ones are flux problems. Either the flux is not properly preheated so that there is residual solvents hitting the wave and exploding and getting trapped within the barrel of the hole and then exploding when they hit the wave.

Or there is too much flux that just can't get completely activated by preheat. Certainly, moisture could be a problem and the aforementioned paper lists that as one of the issues. If you did see the problem isolated to a specific board lot, that might be it.

It could also be problems with the plating on the plated through holes and some of the other contamination issues that are listed in this article. You might try baking the boards, but you might want to do some contamination investigations on the plating, particularly the barrel of the holes to see if that could be the cause.

Jim ›› There are, at least, 36 potential candidates for what could be causing it. Good luck.

Do We Still Need SMT Adhesives?

(soldering, adhesives, components, BTC, reflow, wave-soldering, apertures)

Phil ›› Jim, what's today's question and who's it from?

Jim ›› Well, it's from D.A. The question is: "If double-sided surface mount assemblies are the way of the future - weren't they the way of the past - should we anticipate a growing or declining need for surface mount adhesives?"

This is interesting because there could be two questions here, depending on the interpretation of the term surface mount adhesives. Are they asking, because we're going to double-sided reflow, will I be gluing fewer chip components on the bottoms of my boards and wave soldering and therefore I will need less surface mount adhesives?

Or are they asking because of double-sided assembly - am I going to need more adhesive to glue the parts on the side of the board which ends up on the bottom during the second reflow pass.

Phil ›› I would say much to the chagrin of the adhesive companies, the answer to that is YES and NO. Yes, you will be using less because running surface mount components through the wave solder process has become very out of vogue. It frankly was never a good idea and never defect-free by any means, and that's been kind of frowned upon for a long time.

And as we see the increase in the use of aperture pallets and more and more select soldering systems, wave soldering surface mount components has gone away. So, using adhesive for that purpose certainly is on a decline.

Jim, differentiate what we mean by side A and side B, first side and second side. Warning: Soapbox Alert!

Jim ›› There is absolutely no universal terminology. So, let's define it for our conversation today. We say the bottom side of the assembly is the side we reflow first and the parts end up on the bottom side during second reflow. The top side is the side we reflow second.

Phil ›› So, on those surface mount components that are being re-reflowed, the old theory was that they would fall off when they would be re-reflowed. However, what people soon discovered, the truth of the matter is they don't most of the time.

Because the surface tension via the molten solder is a lot greater than wet solder paste. So, what they found was it really depended upon the ratio of the surface area of the cumulative leads and the mass of the component.

There were some experiments done and the formula we generally use is you take the mass of a component in grams and you divide it by the total pad surface area in square inches and if you come out with, on the conservative side, a ratio of less than 35 grams per square inch, that part's not going to fall off.

We've even gone higher. We actually did some connectors that were in excess of 44 grams per square inch. But at the 35 grams per square inch, you're typically talking about just about any QFP, most non-ceramic BTCs and area arrays (BGAs) and certainly fine pitch.

Jim ›› It's counter-intuitive to the people who first looked at it. They'd look at the small parts and say well they don't weigh very much, therefore they won't fall off. But the big parts will.

And it's really the opposite because the big parts, for the most part, tend to have many leads and each one of those leads and pads adds its own surface tension, so the cumulative surface tension is more than enough to hold the part on.

The only exceptions, and there are some, tend to be large heavy parts ceramic parts that only have a few leads.

Phil ›› In most design schemes a good DFM practice is for the more massive components to be on the second side, the top side. But when you are faced with them being on the bottom side, take a look, do this ratio and don't do any unnecessary process steps, particularly gluing them.

Can Silver or Gold Filled Epoxies Replace Solder?

(soldering, alloys, conductive epoxies, reflow, solder, reliability)

Phil ›› Today's question is: "Can conductive epoxies be considered a viable RoHS substitute for tin lead solder?"

It's a question that's been asked many times over the ages, especially since the original advent of RoHS appearing on the horizon. It's something we've touched on before in one of our other diatribes on conductive epoxy. Fundamentally yeah, you could consider it, but from a practical standpoint, not really.

This was originally examined back in the early days of getting ready for RoHS. Motorola Schaumberg IL, did some major investigation into this at the time and they decided - no. There's a number of limitations with conductive epoxies regarding how they fare in terms of robustness compared to tin lead solder. Jim, do you want to elaborate on that a little bit?

Jim ›> Probably the most predominant concern is that the conductivity of the material degrades over time. That is, the net contact resistance goes up. So, for many applications that can eventually damage your signal flow through your circuit. That's the biggest one.

Other issues that are raised are difficulties reworking, and some of the structural properties. Depending upon what your failure modes are, in some cases the epoxies can be more robust. But in others, cycling or vibration and so forth, they are less robust.

The final issue is cost. Most of the ones that work successfully are filled with silver or gold. Silver is expensive. Phil, did that Motorola study have a rough estimate, even back in those days when metals were cheap?

Phil ›> Yeah, the study was done back in the early 2000s and the cost of silver-filled conductive epoxy was at that point about 10 times the cost per gram of tin-lead solder.

On the other hand, gold-filled conductive epoxies were used for electrical interconnections on the Lunar Rover. It lived (and is still living) in a steady-state very, very cold- near absolute aero environment. But can you imagine what the gold-filled epoxy cost? And then we left the thing up there…

Jim ›> One of the possibilities that has been tested many times is a copper-filled material, but nobody has mastered how to achieve the reliability level of silver-filled.

Phil ›> So, on the surface (pun intended), the idea looks really good. It's no-clean, it's lead-free, you don't have to worry about VOCs, no cadmium, chromium or mercury.

But it is really going to depend upon the application, it's working environment and other factors as to whether it makes sense. But remember, things tend to change and improve, so, you never know.

Will High Humidity Affect Reflow Soldering?

(soldering, reflow, humidity, solder paste, flux, profiling, moisture)

Phil ›> Let's see, what do we have today, my brother?

Jim ›> Well, Phil, today from S.A. we have a concern about high humidity. The question is, "Will higher than normal humidity in our facility affect reflow soldering? What impact might it be?"

The second question, "Are there special concerns regarding our solder paste when we are exposed to high humidity environment?"

Phil ›> The answer to that is YES, YES, and yeah, most likely.

Of course, in terms of solder paste, all solder pastes, whether they're no-clean or OA - water soluble, are hygroscopic which means they're absorbing moisture from the air as they sit out there on your stencil, on your board, basically during the work life of the solder paste.

And as they absorb various degrees of moisture, that of course is going to affect the chemistry of the flux itself or of the solder paste. So, it is going to have an effect on things and generally you'll find solder paste has a specification, an upper and lower limit in terms of the comfort index.

What do we usually see on the specs about an upper limit of, what, about 65%, 70% RH?

Jim ›› Some pastes are formulated specifically for higher humidity environments. If that's a concern, you can look for it. And on the low end, typically it's 20% to 30%. Which can be a problem up here in New England and other Snow Belt regions when we turn the heat on, and it tends to dry things out.

Phil ›› One solder paste "malfunction" that may be humidity driven, is slump or bleeding after printing. There is, of course, our good friend solder ball, it's just another cause of solder balls. And because basically the flux is being somewhat diluted, if you will, you may see an effect on wetting. The ability of the flux to wet properly, because of the chemistry being altered as we mentioned before.

Jim ›› As Phil said, both no-clean and water soluble pastes are hygroscopic. These humidity effects tend to be more pronounced in water soluble paste because they have alcohol or water-based solvent systems. Although the paste manufacturers have been working hard to minimize those effects.

With regard to solder paste in general, you also need to think back into your stencil printing. If you get too much humidity, moisture absorbed from humidity while it's on the stencil, it can affect the printing properties as well as what happens when you try to reflow.

This is particularly true in low humidity when the evaporation of solvents can raise the viscosity, cause drying of the paste, plugged apertures and all those unpleasant occurrences in our stencil printing operation.

Phil ›› So, pay very close attention to the specification of the solder paste you're using, do your due diligence in terms of trying to control your relative humidity and, of course, your temperature in your work facility. If you are in a situation beyond control, consult your solder company to see if they have a formulation for those extreme humidity situations.

Problems with Counterfeit Components

(components, counterfeit, materials, x-ray, procurement, reliability)

Jim ›› Today we have a question that I'm surprised we don't get more often. The question says, "We are just learning about the infiltration of counterfeit components. We are an EMS and we are very concerned. Is this legitimate? What can we do to protect ourselves and our customers?"

Phil ›› Wow, where to begin? Welcome to the greatest scourge upon our industry in who knows how long. The four horseman of the assembly apocalypse, whatever you want to call it. Yeah, be very afraid. Be very, very afraid.

Basically, there's been all kinds of estimates. There was as many as $8 billion worth of counterfeit parts back in 2008. There's estimates of 12 percent of product out in the field are affected, but, Jim, nobody really knows.

Jim ›› People don't want to talk about it.

If I'm this EMS and I start saying, "I'm concerned about counterfeit components," how am I going tell my customers, unless I have something airtight to back it up.

My customers say, "Oh, my God," and my competitor down the street says, "Oh, no, we take care of counterfeit components, because we only buy from reputable suppliers."

Phil ›› We know in spite of this, we hear a lot of incidents. Big companies, small companies, OEM's, CEM's, all areas of products, and what surprises me, though, is there's an awareness.

People know about incidents, and yet there's a complacency about doing anything about it. I think this is based on the myth that, we're going to let our component distributor take care of things. We deal with one of the big component distributors and they claim that they're clearing and certifying their parts. Therefore, how can we go wrong?

Well, there's a lot of ways they can go wrong.

Jim ›› The one that I've heard before is that a very competent and conscientious certified distributor has their inventory compromised through returns.

They sell good parts to Company A. Company A buys them, but they have a temporary large order, so they have to go on the gray market and buy some extra parts of the same part number.

They mix their inventory. Now, an order gets canceled, so they have to return some parts to the registered distributor, but what happens is some of the gray market parts, which turn out to be counterfeit, get returned to the certified distributor, who does not conscientiously check the returns.

They're only worried about counterfeit coming in from the supply side. And unbeknownst to them, totally unconsciously, their inventory gets compromised.

There was a discussion held on the floor of Productronica about counterfeit components. One of the panelists said it's everywhere and you're never going to stop it.

He said people are doing it because there are profits to be made. You can sell counterfeit components for regular prices and make a lot of money. He said once you introduce that, the potential for compromise is anywhere in the supply chain.

Consider the ordinary handling clerk in a stock room. You don't think about them. All of a sudden, this person needs to be a secured person. He cited a known example of a company that manufactured components, and some enterprising person within the company went to the scrap bin, grabbed some parts that were scrap, but still fully marked, so you couldn't identify them.

They had not yet been ground up. Takes them down to the stock room and substitutes them for good parts. Takes the good parts, goes and sells them. But now at the very manufacturing site, you've got a contaminated inventory. And when you think about shipping and handling and so forth, it's not something we typically think of as a controlled job.

When there are profits to be made, people will get bought off. The potential is huge.

Phil ›› Trust no one. We'll be talking about the counterfeit subject quite a bit in upcoming Board Talks. In the meantime, we highly recommend an article from the October 2, 2008 edition of Business Week entitled "Dangerous Fakes". One of the best pieces of investigative journalism and it is centered upon our dear industry. This is "required reading" assignment from the Assembly Brothers.

How To Determine Stencil Thickness

(soldering, reflow, aperture, stencil, area ratio, aperture ratio, reliability)

Phil ›› Today's question is a good one. "On what basis is stencil thickness decided in the case of BGA's or fine pitch components?"

Jim ›› Most of us are aware of the issues of the different size and style of components that need to be processed on the same board, and the need to have different volumes of solder paste for different components, creating the need for different thicknesses of stencils.

Some people call it "mixed print" or "broadband". There are a number of names for it. Okay, I've got particular components. What thickness stencil should I use if I have a 50 mil pitch BGA? What thickness stencil should I use if I have a 0.4 millimeter CSP?

As we're designing apertures, we have to calculate aspect ratios and so forth to make sure we get good printing. As you really analyze this topic and start to think about calculations and deciding on stencil thicknesses and apertures, the most obvious thing that comes out in terms of the data that you need to make this analysis is the volume of solder paste required for a specific joint.

If I have a 50 mil pitch QFP, and I have a particular pad geometry, what is the volume of solder paste, or the range of the volume of solder paste, that will give me an acceptable joint?

From the qualitative side, I know if I use this stencil too thin, I won't get enough paste and I won't have good fillets. Likewise, on a small fine pitch part, if I use a stencil that's too thick, I will get too much paste.

We talk about aperture reduction and area and aspect ratios based upon the printing parameters. But there's the other issue of how much do I need to reduce the aperture to give me the proper volume of solder paste.

Phil ›› It comes back to what do you need in terms of the volume of solder paste. And to be quite frank, is there a source that can supply that answer?

I've talked to a number of people in the industry and when we finally get around to hemming and hawing and talking about it, nobody can provide any answers. I have looked at some IPC specs and stencil design and I honestly don't remember the number off the top of my head, but it talked about an aperture for using a 6 mil stencil and a 4 mil stencil.

I calculated the ratio between those two stencils, both of which they were proposing as acceptable. It was over 2:1 in terms of the volume that we'd get from the different stencil thicknesses and aperture design.

Again, it's only qualitative and it seems too big a range, and keeps begging the question, what is the appropriate volume for a given components and given pad sizes.

Phil ›› So we're all looking for a holy grail of calculator that will automatically calculate for a given part what that volume should be.

Jim ›› If there is a spec out there, IPC or anybody else we plead ignorance. But as I said, we've talked to a number of pretty knowledgeable people and nobody can answer it.

Phil ›› Maybe if we get desperate enough, our colleague Ron Lasky can come to the industry's rescue and come up with the volume coach. Calling Dr. Lasky…paging Dr. Lasky…stat!

Issues With Components Near PCB Edges

(DFM, soldering, components, reflow, BGA, PCBA, reliability, cracking)

Phil ›› Jim, what is today's question?

Jim ›› "What issues are we likely to see when we place BGA components very close to the PCB edges? What impact might it have on reliability? Will, equipment, screening, placement, or re-flow require modification?"

The first thing is you have to be quantitative about this. What do you mean by very close?

Phil ›› Yeah. We've seen some real goofy things in the last 30 years. It was that one cell phone manufacturer, remember that? They wanted components literally right up to the edge.

Jim ›› They wanted to build a batch of single cell phone boards without a panel through all their processing and they wanted to put components literally right on the edges.

Phil ›› Why don't they put them on the edge itself? You know, the side of the board. By the way, that process never happened and they weren't in the cellphone business too long…

Jim ›› The general answer is any given process is going to have some limitation on how close you can get to the board edge.

Screening depends upon what type board hold down is used. If your board hold down clamps the board from the top, there's some definite keep out area. Even if you're doing edge clamping, you can't count on the pressure and the squeegee to be absolutely identical, right out to the very edge. Now, is that, 3 mils, 5 mils, 10 mils, You should talk to your screen printing manufacturer.

Phil ›› Likewise, placement equipment will not typically place right out to the exact edges of the board. Think about this, think about trying to support that edge. I guess if you have a single sided board, you can use flat plate supports, but still, how are you gripping your board?

You might find equipment that would be more tolerant. With reflow, most of us are using edge conveyors. They're designed to have a minimal thermal impact, but, boy, you try putting a large component like a BGA very close to the edge, so that the balls end up right over the pin of a chain that's carrying the board. You're taking risks.

Jim ›› And what about the impact on reliability? You're always concerned about edge singulation.

Phil ›› I think when the board is out in the field, a good solder joint is going to be a good solder joint, but again, it depends on the environment it's living with and whether that card is going to be flexed when it's put into an enclosure or whatever. In our consulting practice, probably one of the most cause of ceramic component cracking, as well as other strain related defects, comes from singulation where components are too close to the V-groove edge of the PCBA.

So, let's assume this board is being built in an array and there's going to be some sort of singulation. How close to the edge can you get? I know that one of the "pizza cutter" manufacturers recommends that the component be no closer than 5 millimeters to the V score of the board because of the stresses. So that's not only BGA's, but think about ceramic capacitors, those little hot patooties.

Jim ›› So I guess my overriding comment is really think about whether this is a good idea. You are going to increase the risk of problems with your process, or perhaps reliability, depending upon final handling. You could probably find equipment that is more tolerant than others, but I think you're going to find that most pieces of equipment; printers, placement machines and soldering equipment, are going to have some level of keep out area, at least desirable.

I think you should really ask is this necessary? Is having components very close to the edge giving us such benefits, that we're willing to take these other risks and additional costs for special equipment and so forth.

Contamination from an Aluminum Flux Tank

(soldering, wave-soldering, flux, contamination, corrosion, materials)

Phil ›› Today's question is from S.S.: "If we use a flux tank with our wave soldering system that is constructed from aluminum, and we use water-soluble flux, could the flux become contaminated by contact with the aluminum tank? Well, I guess the question here, Jim, is: What the flux is going on?

Jim ›› On a totally technical standpoint, I would say, yes, there's some concern. The bigger question is, which water-soluble flux? What is this formulation, and what is its reactivity with aluminum? The real thing that jumps out here is why are you asking us this?

We did not formulate the flux. We don't know what's in it. We don't have any technical data on the flux. Water-soluble is a very generic name. These fluxes are formulated from a very complex mixture of a lot of different chemicals to give you the exact properties that you want to perform well throughout the whole wave soldering operation; flux application, pre-heating, soldering, de-bridging, and so forth.

Phil ›› Why hasn't your flux supplier given you this information? All manufacturers of materials, such as fluxes, pastes, solders, and equipment for that matter, maintain a technical service department for answering technical questions about the application of their products to individual customers.

We can only assume that you haven't established that relationship with the technical services from your flux supplier, or your flux manufacturer, and that's why you're having a question like this.

Perhaps you buy directly through a sales representative that may not have this technical information, but it is certainly worthwhile, and I would say required with any materials to find out all critical specifications, certainly critical materials like flux.

Jim ›› When you start using a new flux, or preferably before you start using it, you establish a relationship with the technical service people from the manufacturer. They're the ones who are going to know how they react with aluminum or any other materials in the conditions that you're going to be operating.

You should do this before you have a problem, because it may take some time. It may take some phone calls getting to the right person who has the actual technical knowledge.

Sooner or later, you're going to have questions like this and the ability to get that information quickly can be very valuable operating an efficient and cost-effective manufacturing process.

I remember that time I was out in the desert in Arizona, and we had a problem with a flux that was being used by one of our customers. We were on a conference call and we called the supplier, and the technical expert that we knew was on vacation.

We had to get somebody else and it was painful, because this person didn't know us. This was a technical person. He was very concerned about talking openly about potential problems. Whereas, if we had been able to contact the person who we had a relationship with, we know that person would've been much more open giving us honest, complete technical support.

Phil ›› You, as a customer, SS, are entitled to full disclosure of how the material that you're buying is interacting with anything else you have. We're fortunate in our industry that we have very good data sheets. In general, if a data sheet comes up short, call the applications person.

You'll be serving two purposes; one, you're going to find out the information needed, and two, you're going to keep somebody employed somewhere and give them a sense of self-valuation.

Jim ›› And giving them the feedback regarding situations that their customers are actually dealing with when they try to apply their materials.

Phil ›› So, don't be shy.

Can You Trust Pick & Place Machine Ratings?

(pick and place, components, de-rating, throughput)

Phil ›› Today our topic is on Pick and Place.

Jim ›› The topic comes from Q.R. who asks, "We're setting-up an SMT line. In estimating the capacity for equipment selections, why can't we use the Pick and Place manufacturer's rating for components per hour? They design the machines, don't they?"

Phil ›› Oh, yes, they do and they're trying to sell you machines. I think the real answer to your question is we don't live in an ideal world. Bear in mind that Jim and I have both spent a portion of our careers with equipment manufacturers, including Component Placement equipment suppliers. Been there, done that, own the polo shirts…

Let's look at it from two major components.

First, the Pick and Place machine manufacturer, is trying to sell a machine. He's got to demonstrate the machine at some specific rate.

Cycle rate is ridiculous, because that would be putting down the same component in the same place in the same location, and we all know that's totally meaningless. So, generally, what they do is they have some rate they designate, and it might qualify if you're doing passives or simple ICs.

Generally, when you go and look at the machine, you'll see a demo board, and the demo board is usually optimized for the machine under ideal conditions. There have been attempts to come up with standardized boards. The IPC has worked on it, but they're not widely used.

Let's face it, from the manufacturer's perspective, before we get a lot of nasty-grams from them, there are no two applications that are the same. So, where do you benchmark it? How do you benchmark it?

So, we have what we call de-rating factors. The biggest thing with the de-rating factor is the real world, your environment, and there's a lot of things going on here.

Let's start with your factory. If we're taking an eight hour shift, are you really working eight hours? Well, most likely you're not. Your employees take lunch. Do you give them breaks?

Maybe there are a few slave masters out there that don't in certain parts of the world. What about change-over time? That's probably one of the biggest killers. In addition to change-over time, even if you're running high volume of a single board, there's transfer time, or from the printer to the pick-and-place machine.

Typical conveyor transfer time is about four to six seconds? So, this is all adding up. There's of course, what we call bumbling time, or what we at ITM Consulting call "floundering time."

Jim ›› We should start with the more generic term of "unscheduled down time". This occurs when you're attempting to run the machine, you're all set-up, there's a board waiting to go, or there's a board in the machine, but something happens.

Of course, we all know, what is the thing that happens most of the time? The feeders jam, the feeder runs out, the tape doesn't peel-back right. The machine stops, an operator comes over, ideally very quickly, fixes the problem, and pushes the reset button and away you go.

How often does that happen? Once an hour? Once every half hour? Once every 15 minutes? And you start subtracting this significant percentage of the available operating time, and that all takes away from capacity.

Phil ›› The sad fact of the matter is, if you were to look at overall efficiencies, typical machine throughput rates running 20% to 40% of what was originally specified?

Jim ›› The actual capacity rated over the time that the machine is theoretically available, if you can get above 25%, that's very good.

I wanted to elaborate on "floundering time". It is when a machine goes down, an operator comes and doesn't know what to do. So, they walk around trying to find somebody who understands the problem, trying to call a maintenance person, trying to call the supervisor, and the bottom line is capacity is lost.

When you average these out over a significant length of time, what you need to do to estimate your capacity for a new line, you find that you're actually only going to get 25 percent of the machine's capacity.

Phil ›› So, that's the difference between what you might read on paper and might get in the real world.

We Need Leaded BGAs, But They're Only Available Lead-Free

(Pb-free, BGA, components, re-balling, soldering, reflow, alloys, reliability, RoHS)

Phil ›› Today's topic of discussion is orientated to you poor, lost souls who are the exemptees for lead-free and have to cope with a lead-free world.

Jim ›› We've been advising our customers, the exemptees, people out of scope, who have to assemble Tin/Lead products for reliability and other issues. And, of course, one of the hugest issues that comes up is BGAs with lead-free balls on them. Typically, SAC 405,

305, or some of the newer ones, 105. How do you deal with the backward compatibility issue?

I'm trying to maintain a tin/lead process, but I have a need for BGA packages for my assembly, and I can only get them with lead-free SAC balls on them. What do I do?

Phil ›› There are many strategies. A lot of people have fooled around or have tested and validated specific processes for soldering SAC balls with tin/lead paste by changing re-flow profiles and so forth. But, we've always taken a very strong stand that these techniques are very specific to the individual type of component, the environment it's going to see, the size of the pad, the volume of the paste, and so forth.

Jim ›› And so, we have never accepted a strategy of just raising re-flow temperatures as an across-the-board silver bullet solution. I've always said, for a variety of components, you have to maintain the reliability. The best thing is to re-ball the BGAs. Take the SAC balls off of them and put tin/lead balls on them, and then solder them in a regular tin/lead process.

We've been saying that, and I feel that the published literature is validating us. If you look at the technical proceedings, SMTAI, APEX and so forth, we're seeing more and more very comprehensive technical evaluations of the reliability of re-balled BGAs, including sheer testing, x-ray inspection for voids, and inner metallic layers. Thermal cycle testing after assembled units after they've been re-balled, drop and sheer testing looking for delamination inside the BGA package resulting from the re-balling operation.

The fact that we're seeing these is a strong vindication to us that, yes, re-balling is an important and in some cases we feel the most viable technique for mitigating this backward compatibility issue with lead-free BGAs.

Are There Standards Governing Polarity Marks?

(DFM, components, polarity, standards, IC, pick and place)

Jim ›› Today's question comes from S.B. "Is there some standard that governs the polarity marks which are used to denote the orientation of an SMT LED component, PCB silkscreen, and on assembly drawings? Examples, cathode or anode in the case of an LED, Pin 1 in an IC. Must the mark be visible from the top, etc.?"

S.B. sent us a very detailed explanation, and I'll just summarize it for you.

They've been building equipment for a while and have not had a problem, but they're building a board that had two different color LEDs on it. There were no questions with the assembly with regards to LED orientation during visual and automated inspection, until ICT. In circuit test says one LED is backwards on every PCB.

I look at all the information and cannot understand why. Based on the data sheet from each LED, the polarity mark denotes the anode on one LED and the cathode on the other LED. Needless to say, I was confused.

Phil ›› All right, well, where to begin…

Jim ›› Warning – Soapbox Alert!

Phil ›› Well S.B., welcome to the wide and wonderful world of surface mount technology and electronic manufacturing in general, because whether we're talking about LEDs, QFPs, QFNs, even PLCCs, SOICs, there is no standard marking for denoting Pin 1 on active components, I mean ICs, and certainly on polarized components. There's a lack of standardization there.

As you have found out the hard way and are paying tuition for that lesson. Yes, on some polarized capacitors and diodes, you will see a band or a color dot typically denoting the anode end.

Believe it or not, surface mount having been around for about 30 years now in this wonderful industry, there is no standard on demarcation of polarization. What can you do about it? Well, if you really feel so inclined, start a committee.

Why has JEDEC never really thoroughly addressed this? Unbelievable but true. Something as basic as denotation of pin-one location on an IC. And the problem manifests itself in exactly what you discovered, the fact that these could be arranged in different ways on your feed mechanisms, whether it's tape or matrix tray. And there's really no practical way for the pick and place machine to pre-detect it.

Jim ›› Think about the capability that is in your pick and place machine with the cameras, the vision recognition, the lighting, and everything else it can do to look at physical attributes of a component. The industry can't come up with the standardization that will allow it to accurately and repeatably denote the proper orientation.

Phil ›› All it would take is something like standardizing a dot placed in the vicinity of Pin 1 for ICs, or a dot will denote the anode end or cathode end, but let's standardize on it, and let's have some consistency, and therefore, repeatability. But alas, nobody's gotten around to doing it. And that's probably one of the biggest mysteries I think I've encountered in this industry. Something as simple and basic as this has been so severely neglected.

Jim ›› Phil, you've been talking about it as long as I've known you, which is well over 30 years now, and one would think that something would have happened. It just doesn't seem that illogical.

Phil ›› Well, this industry ponders on. But Jim and I do not "do" committees really well. That's why we work for ITM.

But anyway, in the meantime, we hope that somebody will champion this cause, and I think this type of thing is a little bit more important than some of the other things we see specification committees formed for. And on that note I will say "Harrumph!"

No-Clean Flux or Water Soluble - Which To Use?

(soldering, DFM, flux, cleaning, No-Clean, RMA, Water soluble, OA, reflow, wave-soldering, selective soldering, no-clean)

Phil ›› The question for today has to do with fluxes.

"What are the major differences between rosin-based fluxes and water-soluble fluxes? And, assuming we have updated equipment and cleaning systems to handle either process, under what circumstances should we use one process over the other?"

Jim ›› This is a very interesting question, but I want our readers to be careful about the statement at end of that question, "We have cleaning systems that can clean either." So, we are not considering a no-clean process. That's important because, if the question is between water-soluble and no-clean, that is a whole different issue.

If we are considering cleaning it is much more desirable to use water-soluble. Why? Because it's designed to be cleaned and in most cases it can be cleaned with heated water, without any additional chemistry.

Notice I said, "Most cases." Also, it gives us a much wider window on the activation that we can put in the flux. So, for getting more robust soldering, handling a wider range of solderability, of your materials, your leads and your circuit boards, water-soluble is typically a choice.

Most high-rel people, traditionally, have used water-soluble fluxes because they're stronger fluxes, they give a more robust soldering process and they're easier to clean. Because with rosin, you need to use some sort of chemistry, either a saponifier in a water-based system or another solvent.

Phil ›› Remember, the electronics world started out with all rosin-based fluxes and we cleaned them with Freons and Tri-Chlor. And that was great, but we can't use Freons and Tri-Chlor anymore, so we have to go to much more sophisticated and expensive solvents. Not that they don't work, but given a choice, we would traditionally use water-soluble.

However, the issue of water-soluble compatibility with lead-free soldering temperatures is something that is clouding the waters.

The basic scenario that many people are finding is that, at the higher soldering temperatures required for your lead-free alloys, most water-soluble formulas are no longer so easy to clean. And that the possibility of cleaning them with plain water, some people argue, is not reliable - that you have to have add some sort of chemistry.

Jim ›› There's a lot of information out there - claims being made - we're not going to support it. We're just reporting that, whereas for tin-lead, most people felt comfortable using water-soluble and getting good cleaning with just water at higher temperatures.

Another thing is low-profile components, such as QFNs. They have very small stand-offs that make them more difficult to clean with just water.

So, those issues are pushing us towards the use of chemistry, which may re-open the issue of using a rosin-based flux. Since you're going to clean, if you're using chemistry anyway, maybe it's more desirable.

I think, from a soldering standpoint, you'll prefer to use a water-soluble flux because of the potential of more, stronger acids.

Phil ›› Of course, with at least 75% of the electronics industry using a no-clean process, the solder paste manufacturers are putting a great deal of research and development into no-clean flux technology.

Stay tuned….

Contamination, Components and "Floundering Time"

Lead-free Solder Contamination Concern

(lead-free, soldering, alloy, contamination, wave-soldering, selective soldering, defects, profiling, thermocouples)

Phil ›› Today I believe we have another question on one of our favorite subjects - profiling. What is today's question, Jim?

Jim ›› From R.C.: "How about high-temperature solder, such as Sn5: 5 percent tin, 95 percent lead. If the solder does not melt in the wave solder because it's high-temperature and not meant to melt, will it contaminate a lead-free solder pot when using it to attach a profile TC, or is it just too risky? Is it okay if you're only attaching the TC to the top and not on the bottom using high-temp lead solder?"

Phil ›› Okay, that's a good question because, in the past, I have used high-temp solder for reflow. But with regard to wave-soldering, well, we're grateful the guy's actually profiling, but Jim, weigh in.

Jim ›› It's a good question, but I do think it's perhaps over-cautious. The TC will not melt. The solder will not melt while passing through the pot, so it will not contribute at all significantly to the amount of lead in the pot. That's what you're concerned about. You're concerned about getting lead contamination in a lead-free pot of either SAC or modified copper or tin/copper, such as SN100 and so forth.

Contrast to where we spoke before of running a tin-lead circuit boards through a lead-free pot, where you've got hundreds - perhaps thousands - of leads all coated with tin-lead, which is going to melt. That's why we say even with a few boards - you don't want to run them through a lead-free pot if they have tin-lead on them.

But a high-temp profiling TC, if you've only got one or two of them on the board, but they're not going to melt. If you went to an atomic level, I imagine a few molecules of lead will dissolve into your solder pot, but since you may have 1.5 to 2.5 cubic feet of your lead-free alloy, it's not a problem.

Phil ›› It's an interesting question on wave soldering because, in our recent experience we've been called to look at wave-soldering processes and we have been shocked at how many people were doing a significant amount of wave soldering on multiple products and not doing any profiling to set up their pre-heat.

What's true for reflow is certainly just as true for wave, and with wave, it's really critical that in your pre-heat you heat enough to activate your flux but not too much so that you've burned it off and consume the activators before you get through the solder pot.

You won't know how much you're heating, what your temperatures are going into the pot, unless you use profile thermocouple. In some cases, you can only look at the top. That's true, but in many cases, I would suggest in all cases, put a TC on the bottom because then you know what the thermal shock is for your PCB as it hits the wave.

Jim ›› There are different opinions, anywhere from 100 degrees to 140 degrees C. You should always profile, and it's not a bad idea to put a bottom-side TC on every board that you're profiling. High-temperature, high-lead solder is a very good way to attach those thermocouples so that they don't come loose when they come in direct contact with a wave.

Phil ›› It never ceases to amaze us how many people take this for granted, and I don't know if it's because they consider wave soldering a mature process or one that's very constant, and it's anything but. Everything is application-specific, and you can't do this by the seat of your pants. You've got to know you're dealing with a very, very high thermal excursion. Inquiring minds have to know.

Slope Calculation for Reflow Oven Profiles

(reflow soldering, ovens, alloys, profiling, flux, Temperature, throughput)

Phil ›› The question for today: "I have a question concerning the gradient for reflow profiles. Is there any specification or empirical value for the time period the gradient is calculated in, one second, ten seconds, etc.. JEDEC specifies a ramp-up, but it depends on the chosen time span."

Jim ›› It specifies three degrees per second.

Phil ›› We'll talk a little bit about how compatible that may or may not be, but the question is, basically, what's the right way here? How's it being calculated. Where is it?

Jim ›› He points out that, if he calculates it over a 10-second interval, he gets a gradient of 3.5 degrees per second, but if he calculates it over a 20-second interval, he gets a 2.8 degrees per second gradient.

Phil ›› This is important because a lot of things will be gradient- or slope-dependent. A lot of times we'll see, particularly with some of the lead-free solder pastes, where slope is extremely critical, spec limits under that three-degree-centigrade-per-second rate, too. So, Jim, how should it be measured?

Jim ›› The first thing we have to note is that this comment comes from Germany and we have to note the use of the word "gradient". Gradient is not a word that we typically use in the United States, and it can often be confusing. Having worked for a Dutch company, we had this problem, and the word "gradient" in Europe typically means what we call a slope or ramp rate in this country. So, I will call it "slope", and it is the rate at which temperature changes over time.

This question is profound. It is one that we've dealt with for many, many years and it has never been answered successfully to my satisfaction. The idea is, over what interval should I calculate the slope, and typically we're talking about the minimum interval that we're looking at. And so, we get a specification for a solder paste or a component, where we're concerned about heating or cooling too fast or, like, warping a BGA or cracking capacitor or something like that. We have these slope limits that we have to stay within when we set up our profile, and this could apply to both reflow and wave solder.

So, we go to calculate at a slope and over what interval are we concerned about? This used to be a problem when the profiling tools such as DataPak, KIC and ECD-Mole produced more sophisticated packages that calculated slope for you automatically, and they often had a feature that said, what is the maximum slope?

When they first came on, you would look at these and the maximum slope you set up a standard reflow profile and tell you that the maximum slope was 15 degrees per second. And you go and you look, and it goes, "That's crazy. I don't understand that. How can that be?"

Well, when we dug into it, we found that the profile was sampling the temperature once a second and it was calculating slopes for every one-second interval throughout the profile. And so, what it found is that, due to inaccuracy of some things that we'll talk about later, that some of the slopes for one-second intervals were extremely high, and some of them were extremely low. So, obviously, that wasn't practical, but it raises the question, what interval should I calculate it over?

If I'm talking about a solder paste, let's take a simple example. I have the solder paste and I want to create a straight-ramp profile. I'm going to go from ambient all the way up to peak temperature at one continuous slope. That's my objective, and my solder-paste manufacturer says, "That's fine. The paste will work that way and the range is between 0.5 degrees and two degrees per second."

Phil ›› So, I set up my profile. How do I measure the slope? Do I measure it average slope from ambient from entering the oven and ambient temperature, 25 degrees up to 220 or 245 if I'm doing a lead-free profile? Just take those two temperatures, subtract the times from my profiling data and calculate the average slope, or do I need to look at smaller intervals?

Jim ›› Why do we have slope specifications? To protect materials and make sure they work right. So, we're talking about a solder paste where the manufacturer's probably concerned that if we heat it too fast, and our slope is too high, we may boil the solvents and create solder balls and voids.

If we heat it too slow, we may dry out the solvents and use up the flux before we get to reflow. So, that's why they do it. But over what interval can this damage occur? Basically, we're trying to prevent things from damage and enhance the proper chemical reactions.

Let's look at a classic example in real life. We have a convection oven we know that there are limits to how low a temperature I can set in the first zone that is, the zone that the board sees when it first enters the oven. And what happens is, if we measure short-term profiles within that zone, we will often see that the slope is above the maximum rated by the manufacturer.

Take my example. My maximum slope is 2 degrees per second. our board comes in at 25 degrees C. we may like to set our first zone at 75 degrees C, but because of the thermodynamics of the oven thermal spill and so forth, parasitic heat transfer within the oven we can only set our first zone at 100 degrees.

So, what happens? The board comes into this zone. It's at 25 degrees. It gets hit by this 100-degree air and for at least the first part of the profile the slope is very high. Then, it levels off and the slope will drop off to its correct value in the next zone because we can set it at a reasonable temperature.

Phil ›› Should we be concerned about this short-term spike or steep part of the curve? And the answer is, we think so. We've never heard of that data produced or discussed by any material supplier.

Accordingly, with BGA components we're concerned about heating or cooling too fast. We should point out another common place this exists in the oven is in the first cooling zone, where most cooling zones don't have temperature control.

Jim ›› So, if we're coming out of a hot profile, particularly for lead-free, coming out of the last zone, which may be operating at 260 or 270 or hotter. The board is at 240, it hits the first cooling zone, which may be at 100 degrees or less and if we look at the first few seconds or even longer than that, the slope may be steeper than the 3 or 4 degree maximum cooling slope allowed.

So, the answer to your question is, we don't have an answer. Our personal feeling is that the only reasonable minimum interval should be the time that the product is in one zone because that's all we can control. The minimum effect we can have on the profile is the length of one zone, so we typically use that as my minimum time base.

It's just the reality of what we can do with the oven or the wave machine, and nobody has ever provided better specs.

It's been a topic talked about as long as we've both been involved reflow, which has been 30 years.

Can We Rework Lead-Free Boards with Leaded Solder?

(rework, lead-free, SnPb, alloys, soldering, hand-soldering, reflow, wave-soldering, selective soldering, Temperature, surface finish)

Phil ›› Today's question is a repair problem from J.T.

Jim ›› This question deals with mixed alloys, backward and forward compatibility. J.T. asks, "Can circuit board assemblies originally built with lead-free solder be reworked successfully with leaded solder? I realize that the assemblies may not comply with RoHS requirements, but will they be reliable?"

Phil ›› With all due respect to J.T., what are the circumstances, I hate to answer a question with a question, but if you've already assembled it with lead-free and it survives, obviously it's compatible with lead-free thermal excursions, why are you using tin lead? Why does this issue come up? I mean, maybe you have a good deal on the tin-lead solder, you know, kind of surplus or something.

But, putting that aside, let's attempt to answer your question.

Jim ›› Well certainly you can repair it. The question is reliability. There's two ways to look at this - two ways to approach it. You can be very scrupulous and carefully remove all of the lead-free solder from the joint or joints that you're going to rework, strip them down as close as you can to just the surface finishes, and then make the repair adding all of the necessary tin-lead solder. So, you're finished with a good standard tin-lead joint. So now you have a tin-lead joint.

Now will that be more or less reliable? The answer is maybe. Because, as we know from the work of Jean-Paul Clech, if the real life of your product induces high stresses on your product, then the tin-lead joint will probably be more reliable. If the service life of your product induces low stresses on the joints, then the tin-lead joint will be less reliable than the original lead-free joint.

Phil ›› If you're not as scrupulous in your repair and you add tin-lead solder to some volume of the remaining lead-free solder, you get a mixed alloy. And, in our humble opinion, you'll have no idea what the reliability will be because you don't know what the mix ratio is. There's been all kinds of varied outcomes of testing mixed alloys. So that would be the riskiest situation in terms of long-term reliability.

Jim ›› So again, safest thing to do use the same alloy as the original.

How Do You Inspect QFN Components?

(inspection, BTC, QFN, x-ray, soldering, defects, voids, lead-free, SnPb)

Jim ›› Our questioner today is G.V. "Is there any way to know if QFN components have sufficient wetting when doing non-destructive PCBA inspection. Can you provide guidelines for qualifying an assembly house for QFN assembly especially lead free."

Phil ›› Most of the time the most practical way to authenticate acceptable wetting is with x-ray.

Jim ›› We should say if you are fortunate enough to have a QFN that has a single row of perimeter leads and they have castellations around the side you can pretty well confirm wetting by noting the wetting up the side of the component or out on the edge.

Or if you can extend the pads out that can help you, but to know underneath the package you need a good x-ray machine with oblique angle viewing.

Top down alone is going to give you some indication, but not a really good indication of the wetting.

Phil ›› So with regard to your second question, what to look for, in this regard, when you are qualifying an EMS? When we are working with clients, to help qualify a board shop, we look to see if they have a good x-ray machine, just as Jim just described.

Not one of those ancient things and not one of those little cheap quickie machines.

Jim ›› We're talking about a fairly sophisticated system with reasonable resolution. It doesn't have to be micro-focused, but very good resolution and reasonable oblique angle viewing.

Phil ›› Oblique angle viewing is a must and it's been out for quite a few years now and it's a real must-have on x-ray, and definitely something to help qualify shop.

Jim ›› One simple question that I think you might ask when talking with an assembly house about QFN's, ask them what their experience and procedures and philosophy is with window paning because most QFN's have a large central ground or thermal plane.

The strategy for printing paste on that is a very complex. Most people find that some sort of window paning gets the best coverage with the least number of defects. If you ask that question and the people look at you like you're coming from outer space, then they probably don't have much experience with QFN's.

Phil ›› Or they're from outer space. Another area of qualifying the shop, what is their experience working with the devices and who are their references?

Phil ›› And don't solder like my brother.

Can Water Harm Electronic Components?

(components, flux, soldering, cleaning, rework, hand-soldering, wave-soldering, reflow, flux, solvents, OA, water soluble, no-clean)

Phil ›› What is our question today, Jim?

Jim ›› Well, the subject today comes from M.M. and it's on water cleaning. "Can water be harmful to electronic components? We have been reworking circuit boards for the past 30 years. After solder touch up, we remove the flux residues with ordinary alcohol, then clean with soap and water. Then dry each assembly with a blower. We have never encountered issues with microprocessors.

A new quality assurance engineer insists that electronic components, especially microprocessors should not be cleaned with water. Can you enlighten us?"

Phil ›› Yeah, we can, where did this guy come from? Where the heck has this guy been? New, new to what? New to the industry? I'm speechless.

Jim ›› Water has been used as a standard cleaning, particularly for high rel products. The use of water soluble flux being cleaned with, in the best cases, pure DI water, sometimes with saponifiers added, is a standard technique. Microprocessors are in standard electronic packages. We don't see why there should be any concern.

Phil ›› We'll qualify this by saying that dropping your cell phone in the dishwater in the sink is probably not a good idea. You know that in application in situ that's a bad way to clean your boards, but we've been using water cleaning for a long time.

Jim ›› The only explanation we can come up with. First, MM, you should have a little more confidence in yourself. You've been cleaning for 30 years with a very good process.

Alcohol cleaning, followed by water, with soap or a saponifier in its more generic sense, is a way to clean a board. You've had good experience, so we think you are very right to question this newcomer.

The only thing we can think of with microprocessors is that they are complex packages, usually in a BGA configuration. And there could be a concern about water not being able to get all the way under the part to flush out all of the residues.

Phil ›› In your case M.M., be certain to adjust the final rinse to get out the soap or saponifier in your final cleaning step, because, as we know, when you're using cleaning in chemistry such as soap or saponifiers, that leaving residues behind can be even more dangerous than the flux, because usually it has some of the flux chemicals dissolved in it.

Jim

So, if we think about it, you use the alcohol to dissolve the flux, and you are washing the alcohol residues with the soap and water, but now you've got to make sure that you get all of that soap residue out of there. But I was wondering what this new-fangled engineer was thinking of using as a cleaner? Maybe changing to some sort of solvent?

Phil ›› We know of one guy who tried to use Windex, but we won't go any further on that. The other question is where did this information come from anyway? I mean, one point is, have you guys had failures, have you had any decline in field reliability? If you've been doing this for a long time. So, what prompted this? What, if anything, changed?

Or did he read an article on the Internet? Another Popular Mechanics Engineer. Go by your experience and your data. What is your data telling you?

Jim ›› The general statement that electronic components should not be cleaned with water is, I'm sorry, it's just ludicrous.

Random Lifted Leads on QFP Components

(components, leads, defects, DFM, soldering, pick and place, handling)

Jim ›› Today's question comes from E.L:. "We have a number of QFP, quad flat pack, components on our circuit boards. After placement and reflow, we have a random lifted lead problem on some QFPs. The fallout rate is small at less than 1 percent of components. Is this fall our rate normal? What might be the cause? Where should we look?"

Phil ›› I guess there are three   popular areas that come to mind. The first of the more blatant ones is the popcorn effect due to improper MSD recognition and handling.

Jim ›› Exposing plastic parts for too long out of their moisture barrier bags before you do final reflow. Causing them to absorb moisture, to expand, crack the component. But I would think you would know the solution because a popcorned part is permanently damaged.

Phil ›› A more possible thing is coplanarity.

Jim ›› If you have a single or few leads at random locations, particularly in the middle of a row along one side of your QFP, I would say it's a coplanarity problem and that strictly a result of handling. Something somewhere in the handling of that package caused the lead to get bent and is not coplanar with the rest of the leads so it sticks up. You may not see it, but it's high enough that it's lifted.

Phil ›› The other possibility would be that component is not level, it's tilted, usually resulting from an improper placement operation, but there you would typically see it at the corners, or one side of the package all lifted because the entire package is tilted.

Those are the two factors and the solutions. The handling damage for coplanarity or improper placements through a clogged or worn nozzle or an off centered mechanism.

Jim ›› As far as the defect rate, 1% random coplanarity reject is probably not too high, even coming out of matrix trays, there is always some fall out. Some of your better placement machines have coplanarity checks on them before they'll place the part and they'll reject it if they are out of spec. Only some machines have that capability, and usually require relatively costly additions to hardware in the vision system.

Eliminate Tin Whiskers on Component Leads

(lead-free, SnPb, tin whiskers, defects, components, soldering, PCB surface finish, alloys)

Phil ›› Today we've got an interesting one from an aerospace guy.

Jim ›› This question is from E.B.: "We work with an aerospace manufacture on PCB assembly that includes lead free components, but no BGA's. We process using tin lead 60/40 solder. But this does not solve the issue with tin plating on the leads and the risk of tin whiskers. According to information on the nasa.gov whisker website (http://nepp.nasa.gov/whisker/), tin whisker formation is an issue on the exposed component leads outside the solder region.

Is there a process that can be used to re-plate component leads to add lead?"

Well, this is a very common topic which we discuss regularly in our technical workshops entitled "Lead Free for the Exemptee" where we have people dealing with backward compatibility.

Phil ›› Typically your brethren from aerospace military avionics, medical, and all you other guys thought you were going to get it easy when you didn't have to comply with lead-free, but we've found just the opposite.

Jim ›› The NASA website is absolutely correct. When you solder tin plated leads, even matte tin over nickel, the solder cannot be counted on to wick all the way up the lead, so you end up with a small section of lead close to the component body that still has tin coating on it. And it can cause whiskers.

If you look at the INEMI (http://www.inemi.org) recommendations for surface finishes, they say that matte tin over nickel is acceptable, but it's all under the caveat not for high-rel applications.

Phil ›› That's right, so Jim, what's an engineer to do?

Jim ›› The standard procedures are affectionately called strip and dip. Basically, a chemical or a metallurgical process is used to remove the tin coating and replace it with a tin lead coating. Some use chemistry and acids to strip the tin off and then usually they dip it to replace it. Some use sequential dips in a tin lead pots so each time you dip it you get a purer and purer tin lead coating on the leads. The bottom line is you end up with all of the lead completely coated with tin lead.

Phil ›› This has become quite a little bit of a cottage industry.

Jim ›› If you're doing a significant volume, there's automated equipment you can buy to do this yourself.

Risks of Mixing Tin-lead and Lead-free

(SnPb, lead-free, RoHS, alloys, soldering, reflow, wave-soldering, selective soldering)

Phil ›› Today we've got a lead-free question. It says, "What are the risks of mixing tin-lead and lead-free components on a board that does not have to be RoHS compliant?

What are some of the common pitfalls that one should be aware of?"

Jim ›› This question surprises me, but since its basic I think it's important if people are still learning the basics of the lead-free environment. To this specific question, unless you are just starting out opening a manufacturing facility, if you've been building boards over the last few years, you have been doing this.

If you've been building boards with a tin-lead process, you have been using lead-free components. Most manufacturers have eliminated tin-lead finishes on their components years ago. Panasonic, for instance, eliminated all leaded finishes in 2004 to be an aggressively green company in anticipation two years ahead of RoHS requirements.

Phil ›› Right. And they didn't ask your permission to do it, either.

Jim ›› And so in general terms we call this backwards compatible, when you get a lead-free component, and you're doing a tin-lead process. Virtually all components have no problems. They typically have a pure tin finish on the component leads. It solders perfectly well with tin-lead solders at tin-lead temperatures.

The tin diffuses into the tin-lead and you get essentially a typical tin-lead joint. The Hi-Rel people have some concerns about residual pure tin exposed in the leads for whiskering, but that's only in the very exotic Hi-Rel products.

The one issue that remains today that's still a problem is BGA components with lead-free balls on them. And there isn't any real resolution about this, is there Phil?

Phil ›› No, there isn't. And this is one of the most common areas of concern Hi-Rel customers deal with.

Jim ›› It's a huge topic. And we spent a lot of time on it in our normal lectures.

Phil ›› In our "Lead-free for the Exemptee" workshop, it's a major topic. People are coming looking for a silver bullet, and there are no silver bullets. In our humble opinion. The answer is nobody really knows yet. There's a lot of studies being done.

There's a lot of conflicting data. Stay tuned because more and more work is being done because it's a situation we have to deal with. There's still a lot of you out there that are not only exempt from RoHS compliance but are restricted from using lead-free materials. So, we've talked about this before.

Jim ›> So in general, for most components unless you have an ultra Hi-Rel issue, there's no problem with your lead-free components in your tin-lead assembly except for your BGAs with SAC balls.

Phil ›> Your best bet in the meantime, if you're working with BGAs with SAC balls, is to reflow them at lead-free temperatures.

Jim ›> If you want to be absolutely safe, you have to re-ball them too.

IR or Vapor Phase for Prototypes

(reflow, soldering, components, cleaning, convection dominant, Infra-red, vapor phase, low volume, alloys, DFM, surface finish)

Jim ›> What is the question today, Phil?

Phil ›> Today's question is from a Mr. P. B.: "Could you please compare the advantages of IR convection reflow and modern vapor phase reflow with polymer solvents for small-scale prototyping environments. There are many suppliers for batch ovens and it's hard to find spares of vapor phase equipment. That should normally mean that the supposed process control and environmental advantages, the vapor phase process has some important disadvantages about which the cognoscenti such as yourselves (flattery will get you everywhere) could expound. So please do."

Okay, so this is a vapor phase question, which means time for our vapor phase expert: Jim Hall, front and center.

Jim ›> Thank you, Dr. Phil. Yes, from a process standpoint vapor phase is superior to convection-based systems. Think about prototyping: you have maybe only one set of parts, you want to get a functional board to get it operational and you don't want to damage anything.

Vapor phase allows you to take any assembly, put it into the vapor phase system and completely reflow all of the joints without any risk of overheating anything and damaging it because of the inherent temperature control of the vapor phase process: 215 degrees for tin lead, 235 degrees for lead-free assembly.

Whereas with convention-based, first off we want to talk exception to the term "IR Convection." To us that means the old Vitronics panel IR-based systems, which are definitely inferior in the heating characteristics and are even worse for prototyping.

We hope that you are talking about modern convection-dominant systems that have powerful fans that transfer most of their heat by convention and give you a much better temperature uniformity and allow you to keep the temperatures lower and minimize the chance of overheating.

But still, with the prototype you may only get one shot. So, you've got to set up a recipe in your oven and you either have to be conservative and use a short cycle, or fast conveyor speed, and low heater temperatures to minimize the risk of overheating something and damaging it. In that case you may not get good reflow on all your joints. If it's underneath a BGA or another area array that could be a real problem in a prototype.

If you go the other way, and to ensure good soldering you have to use longer cycles or slower conveyor speeds and/or higher heater temperatures, in which case you take the risk, because you haven't had an opportunity to profile the board, of overheating and damaging something that may, as we say, be a one-up in a prototype environment. So, vapor phase is definitely better and safer and easier to get a good reflow first time, every time.

Why don't you find much vapor phase equipment? Quite simply because the equipment is expensive, and the fluids are expensive. With vapor phase even for a simplest system you have to have a lot of expensive hardware. You have to have a stainless steel high temperature tank, high temperature heaters, cooling coils with an active water circulating loop, either once in or recirculating. You've got to have a filtration system which adds a lot of money to the base cost, even for a relatively simple system to do small prototypes.

Also, the fluid is very expensive. Typically, $500.00 to $700.00 a gallon for tin lead fluids and for the lead-free fluids, which you have to boil at 235oC or 240oC there's only one supplier in the world that we know of. I've heard numbers above $1,500.00 a gallon.

Even with the best systems you're always losing a little, particularly in a prototyping system where you can't optimize your cycles and so forth. So, you have a high equipment cost, initially, and a high operating cost because of the expensive fluids. That is why you don't see a lot of small vapor phase systems, even though it has the advantage.

Most people feel that a good convection-dominant system is good enough, it gets them close enough, they understand it, they can get a profile that they feel comfortable and can give them reasonable soldering without overheating things. But there is always that risk, which you completely eliminate with a vapor phase system.

Phil ›› So maybe you might luck out and you find one of those ancient original batch systems that Jim used to build in the "old days". But whatever you do, as Jim said, stay away from IR convection. It's the antithesis of prototyping: there's a lot of trial and error, a lot of burning and the potential for overheating,

Can We Skip Cleaning After Rework?

(cleaning, rework, soldering, flux, no-clean, water soluble, reflow, wave-soldering, selective soldering, alloys, PCB surface finish, contamination, defects)

Jim ›› The question today is pretty fundamental. It's from D.B. and it goes: "What short-term and long-term concerns should we have with product reliability if we skip cleaning after rework? Our rework process will leave organic flux residues on our circuit boards. What do you mean by "organic"?"

Phil ›› Well first of all are we talking organic in the term of organically activated or organic acid flux? Or are we talking about organic in organic rosin fluxes? Or are we talking about free range fluxes? But we won't get into that today.

The more common way to talk about flux is, is it a no-clean flux or is it an OA water soluble flux? Is it designed for the residues to be left on the board, or is it designed to be washed off? If it is in fact an organic acid flux it needs to be removed from the board.

Jim ›› If you leave it, the materials are acids, they are active full-time even at room temperature, they will perhaps in the long-term and perhaps even in short-term, cause corrosion, promote electro-migration and dendritic growth and shorting, and damage. They're not designed to be left on the boards.

No-clean, on the other hand, which might include low concentrations of organic rosin are designed to be left on the board. But in rework, and this is something we deal with our customers a lot, a no clean flux is active when you put it on the board, and the only way that that residue becomes safe to leave on the board is if you properly heat it through a reflow, a wave, or in this case a rework cycle. And that means all of the flux, all of the flux volume.

Phil ›› So, when you are reworking you have to be really careful with no clean flux to make sure that you heat all of it so that you deactivate the active chemicals and the residue is safe to leave on the board. If you don't you can get into some of the same problems that you do with an OA flux is you have active chemicals around that that corrode things, attack things, cause electro-migration and so forth.

Jim ›› The real issue in no-clean flux, if you're talking about organic rosin no-clean fluxes, is don't put too much of them on the area, because if you use a lot of flux during rework, it's almost guaranteed you're never going to be able to heat all of that flux sufficiently to deactivate all of it. So therefore, you deactivate part of it, but you still have some of that flux hanging around that's got active chemicals that can damage the reliability of your board.

That leads us to cleaning no-cleans. And that's a whole other topic that we will leave for another day.

Solder Defects and Continuous Improvement

(soldering, defects, continuous improvement, Lean manufacturing, lean six-sigma, alloys, flux, cleaning, inspection)

Jim ›› Phil I'm looking at the responses and questions from our readers. We get an awful lot of questions about solder defects. Is that telling us something about what's going on, generally, in the industry?

Phil ›› Yeah, I think it really does. And I got to tell you: at least these guys are asking the questions. I got to grant them that. How about all the others that aren't asking? This is something that just pulls my rickshaw. The fact that there seems to be complacency out there, "I'm okay to live with mediocrity," the idea, "Oh, a certain level of defects, that's okay. Don't fix something that's not really broken."

Well it is broken, damn it. This whole thing flies in the face of what you and Dr. Ron and I are always talking about, Lean and Continuous Improvement. This is the opposite; I don't get it. I mean people are actually maintaining inventory in preparation for building scrap. This is insane. How did we evolve to this? Where did this come from?

Jim ›› Well perhaps people don't like to admit their mistakes, so they hide the rework people off in the back corner. We see this all the time - we deal with this very frequently in our consulting activities. People don't measure the defects; they don't keep totals, they don't keep accurate numbers: "Oh, it's hard!"

I think one of the problems is they don't want to know; they don't want to deal with DPMO, defects per million opportunities, percent first pass yield. They're taking first yield after you do touch-up. All these things contribute. I think it's just hiding a problem.

Phil ›› Yeah, I agree. I guess you could say these people were in denial or something here.

Jim ›› Warning – Soapbox Alert!

Phil ›› We have something we call the Consultant's Dilemma. Basically, we feel like we're car mechanics (with all respect and reverence to our Car Talk brothers). One of the things we have in common with them is what we typically see. People are experiencing a defect problem, but their initial reaction is:: "Maybe if I ignore it it'll go away," l This is like putting electrical tape over the Check Engine light or turning the radio up to hide a sound.

Then they go a little further: now it's starting to get a little bit more severe, kind of swerving from side to side, hitting the curb, things like that: "Well, let's try to fix it ourselves," oh, finally getting to do something. Sometimes they succeed; a lot of the times they don't, and it gets worse. And then maybe they'll call in the consultant.

The next step is to see if you can get the problem resolved for free. Ask Applications people from your equipment company, or your solder paste vendor. Or a magazine article and, of course, the internet- because everything you read on the internet is true, right?

But anyway, it's that first thing, that complacency, where they're living with a certain level of defects. How do we get this way? Is this not an indictment of our society and our whole culture?

Jim ›› It's not unique to the United States.

Phil ›› And a lot of people settle for, "Well, you know…," and they send this stuff overseas, cheap labor, and "Yeah, you got to expect a certain lack of quality." Why? Why are you settling for mediocrity?

Is De-paneling PCBs by Hand Acceptable?

(singulation, de-paneling, routing, "pizza-cutters", BTC, DFM, Components, cracking)

Jim ›› Today's question comes from R.M., and it's about de-paneling. The question, "Is it acceptable to hand break when de-panelizing our circuit boards. Are there any resources or papers that quantify the type of failures caused by hand breaking and stress?"

Phil ›› I have to say that is something we've encountered quite a bit in our consulting time. We've come across all types of de-paneling methods, and methods to certainly avoid. I would have to say that, in our experience, hand breaking is about the worst method we've seen.

This calls to mind the experience I had a number of years ago. We had a client, an American company, building satellite down-converters. The boards were being built for them in Taiwan. They were having a capacitor cracking problem. This pre-dates the days of common use of QFNs or I suppose would have been victimized as well.

They sent me some photographs and also some cross sectioning. Looking at the crack, it wasn't a thermal crack. It wasn't the wave solder or the reflow process, which they originally thought. Maybe it's dwelling on the wave too long, or something along those lines.

It was definitely a mechanical crack, so I said, "Can you send me more slides of your process?" And all of a sudden, there was one slide where a guy is holding the board, it was a four-up, and he was doing a karate chop to break it apart.

It wasn't a good thing for the boards. So "There's the problem." Common sense will tell you you're putting undue stress on a board, breaking them that way, even if you've scored the boards properly.

Most of the pizza cutter manufacturers recommend a keep-away distance from scored area of at least five millimeters. They're addressing specifically capacitors, but the same thing goes with regard to any kind of device, especially something as tender, and vulnerable, if you will, as a QFN, or even an area array.

Jim ›› Most of the issues we see are with cracked chip components, resistors and capacitors too close to the breaking zone because of localized flexing. Certainly, we're concerned with QFNs, having the weakest, least robust solder joints of any of the IC configurations.

I saw a presentation at a local SMTA chapter meeting, in Boston. It was by DFR Solutions, and they showed pictures of horizontally cracked joints in QFN components due to flexing of the board. I don't recall that they were specific about whether it was de-panelization, but we know that de-panelization can be one of the biggest sources of flexing in the assembly process.

Cleaning Solder Paste Misprint

(soldering, printing, cleaning, flux, solder paste, stencil, defects, solvents, misprint)

Jim ›› This question comes from M.H. and it has to do with post print inspection which is close to our hearts because it is something we always stress with our clients. We have had tremendous success helping our customers implement 3D post print inspection for the improvement of overall quality.

This question goes beyond the inspection process and asks, "What do you recommend we do when we find defects in the solder paste print on the second side. We currently do not have an adequate cleaning process and scrap the boards when we find second side pasting defects."

So, what are they saying? They have already reflowed components on the first side, what we call the bottom side. Now he is printing the second side and has a mistake on the print on this second side. He is saying they throw those boards away with all those valuable components.

Phil ›› Even if they were inexpensive boards it's a horrible waste of value added on the first side with components, time and energy invested. It's not necessary. It is a question that people wonder how to clean first side and second side.

We see a lot of improper cleaning of first side as well. The first thing you want to do is scrape off all the excess solder paste with a Kimwipe using some isopropyl or approved solvent.

Jim ›› Don't assume any solvent will do. You've got to use a solvent that is compatible with chemistry of the specific solder paste you are using.

Phil ›› This is where it gets a little tricky. A lot of people stop right there. If you were to examine the board under high magnification you would find that there is solder paste now diluted trapped between the solder mask and the pads, in vias. So how do you get it out of those little cracks.

A while back we did a lot of experimenting with this situation and we found the best way to clean solder paste misprints is to run boards though a water cleaner. If you don't have a water cleaner you may wish to use an ultrasonic cleaner.

Jim ›› Referring to the original question where M.H. states that they don't have an adequate cleaning process, perhaps a simple economic analysis of the value being thrown away might justify a cleaning process.

Tin-lead Reflowed at Lead-free Temps

(SnPb, soldering, reflow, lead-free, Temperature, PCB substrate, PCB surface finish, profiling, thermocouple, delamination, moisture, handling)

Phil ›› What's today's dilemma, Jim?

Jim ›› It's about using a lead-free profile on a tin-lead assembly.

The question, "We recently reflowed a batch of tin-lead soldered circuit board assemblies with a lead-free profile. This was a mistake.

The lead-free profile temperatures were significantly higher than specified for these tin-lead assemblies. The assemblies appear fine, but we're concerned about reliability. Would you scrap these board assemblies? What additional testing can we do to confirm the long-term reliability of these assemblies?"

Phil ›› I'll start off by saying before you get into the testing, you might have to do a bit of research.

We're assuming that the joints look okay from visual inspection and there is no conspicuous blistering of boards, or parts, or strange chemicals oozing around.

So, starting at that point, visually, at least, things look good. The concerns with the metal, Jim would be?

Jim ›› If you reflowed tin-lead solder it should be able to go to that higher temperature if they soldered well on the way up. My concern would be time above liquidous. You have to take that profile, and recalculate the time above liquidous for 183 C, instead of 217 C.

The higher temps might have exceeded your specifications, and then you would be concerned about inner metallics forming on your joints, unless you have a nickel-gold board, in which case, that would not be a problem.

Phil ›› The real concern that we have are components and the printed circuit board. For components, you should be able to go back to your spec sheets, and find out what the peak temperature rating is, and what the moisture sensitivity rating was.

If you had a part that was only rated as a tin-lead part, at a level three, and it was exposed for six days, so you're near the seven day limit for tin-lead, then you may very well have exceeded the moisture sensitivity limit by going to the higher temperature.

Jim ›› The only way to test that is a scanning electron microscopy. That is really the only testing that I know, short of accelerated life-testing them, and testing them to failure, and see how they correlate.

That's a really long, expensive, and rigorous process. So, should you throw them away? It depends on the reliability requirements, but I think you can get most of the way by looking at the material specs on your components, and your circuit board.

What was the T-Sub-G of the laminate used? And then, as Phil said, visual inspection, looking for blistering on the boards, bad solder joints, warping, cracking of your components due to moisture sensitivity. But regarding testing, there's not a lot of non-destructive testing you can do beyond C-SAM for internal delamination.

Circuit Board Moisture Sensitivity and Baking

(MSD, moisture, baking, reflow, wave-soldering, cleaning, selective soldering, hand-soldering, rework, handling and storage, components, IC)

Phil ›› What is the question du jour, Jim?

Jim ›› This is a question from B.D. It's on PCB handling and storage concerns.

"Regarding IPC 1601 Guidelines for Handling and Storage of Printed Circuit Boards, does anyone have a feeling for how well this is being accepted, and/or how many companies are implementing these new policies?"

Well, IPC 1601 has been out there for some time now and has been widely adapted.

But then, what happens with any IPC spec?

Phil ›› There are some people who treat all IPC specs as holy scripture, and there are others that just go their merry way doing anything they want. However, in terms of whether this should be adhered to, we think it's very important. It's been a long time coming.

We get this question asked a lot when we're doing process audits. There's moisture specifications for components. What about boards?

Jim ›› We should say for those of who are not familiar, IPC 1601 is the formal definition for dealing with moisture absorption in printed circuit boards.

It's very similar to IPC/JEDEC J-STD-033 Moisture Sensitivity and Handling in Components. This is the same kind of specifications for circuit boards.

Phil ›› Moisture in circuit boards, either the way they've been stored, the way they've been shipped, the way they're handled at incoming and receiving, and in the storage room. We think this is a good guideline, and there's some really good wisdom in this one. This is not superfluous at all.

Jim ›› And it defines formal baking schedules. People in the past have felt, "Jeez, my board has been exposed. I'm going to bake it...but how much... at what temperature... how long?

This spec will define that for you. You will have a formal reference to go and answer how long should you bake a board and at what temperature, before you go into the reflow, or wave, or selective, or conformal coating - whatever your downstream process is, this will formalize it. It's a concern because of the newer laminates for lead-free, which tend to absorb more moisture, coupled with the higher temperatures for lead-free soldering. So, there are many reasons we feel people should pay attention to this spec.

How To Eliminate Pesky Solder Balls?

(soldering, reflow, wave-soldering, hand-soldering, alloys, re-work, flux, profiling, thermocouples, temperature, DFM, stencils, apertures)

Phil ›› Today, we have a question D.P.

Jim ›› "We use a bench top convection oven for prototype SMD boards. Frequently, on the sides of chip capacitors, and resistors, there are solder balls that must be hand-removed. What is causing these to form?"

Phil ›› This is what we commonly call "mid-chip solder balls," or "mid-chip solder beads." I'm a little dubious about hand-removing them. You may be getting the big buggers removed, but what about the little guys? You might want to go to a more aggressive cleaning process.

The best thing would be to eliminate them to begin with, that's the true remedy. Given the way these form, you're obviously using square or rectangular pads for your chip capacitors. If you examine the body of a chip capacitor where the end termination is metal, the bottom is uneven.

So, what happens is when the chip is placed with your pick and place machine, a certain amount of solder that is close to the inside of the pad is squeezed underneath. During reflow what happens is it is basically separated from the main mass of solder on the pad, and it forms its own little solder ball.

You can remedy this by modifying your aperture, and hence your print shape, of the solder paste deposit for those ceramic capacitors.

The most common modification is what is called the "home plate aperture", as it looks like a baseball home plate with the point facing towards the inside of the capacitor. You would still follow the same area, in terms of the total reduction of your aperture to be sure you're getting enough volume.

There are also variations on the theme.

Jim ›› They're rounding apertures to control the volume giving better printing, more consistent print release, for the very small chips.

Understand, we read the questions completely, verbatim, as you send them to us. The solution that Phil and I have just proposed is universal, regardless of what kind of oven you're using, and whether it's a prototype, or a main board. It's a matter of the stencil printing, and the aperture, reducing the aperture to minimize that paste.

Does Your Assembly Line Suffer From Floundering Time?

(efficiency, floundering time, set-up, line balancing, optimization, components, pick and place, reflow, printing, wave-soldering, selective soldering, component prep, feeders, lean six-sigma)

Jim ›› What's our question today, Phil?

Phil ›› This is interesting. The question is online efficiency. This is from F.B. who writes, "At a recent workshop you presented at my company, you mentioned the term 'floundering time' as a specific category of downtime, which affects overall line efficiency. What does floundering time mean?"

Jim ›› The term "floundering time" was created and documented by Dr. Ron Lasky, professor at Dartmouth College and a Principal Consultant at (prestigious) ITM Consulting. In its simplest form, it means, when the line is stopped, and no action is taken because nobody knows what to do, or the appropriate person is not available.

A classic example would be," The line's down. That's Joe's responsibility." "Where is Joe?" Joe's not here". "Did you call Joe?" "Yes, but he didn't answer his phone. We sent him an e-mail, we sent him a page..." And 20 minutes later, the line still isn't running, and Joe hasn't responded, and nothing else gets done.

So, the organization flounders along. The line is not running, is not generating any value, it's not producing any product, and nothing is getting done. And a procedure isn't in place to find Joe, or to implement what should happen.

Phil ›› Dr. Lasky defined it as a specific form of downtime that is very real but doesn't necessarily fall into the typical categories of downtime, of unscheduled maintenance where something breaks, or assists where a feeder jams, or the solder paste on the stencil needs to be mixed, or changed, or the stencil needs to be cleaned.

Things like that, all of which stop the line, reduce overall efficiency, and require some action. But typically, people know what to do. A feeder's jammed, a specific person comes over, they know how to fix it. It's resolved in a reasonable period of time.

Jim ›› What we always ask when we're talking to people is, "Okay, you're fixing it, but are there things we can do to prevent those from happening?"

In case of feeders, feeder maintenance is a huge issue. Making sure that damaged feeders don't get put back on the machine, but are taken off and repaired properly, so that you don't have those continuing little stoppages that just eat away at your overall efficiency.

Phil ›› And if you just accept them, and nothing happens, and at the end of the day, you haven't assembled nearly as many boards as you can. Let's face it, only thing that makes money for your company is finished boards coming off the end of that line.

So, when anything stops the line, that's directly subtracting from the bottom line of productive output. Floundering is particularly bad because it can go into hours, or a half a day.

Jim ›› Professor Lasky often says, if you have a line down and your line worth $500,000, $1 million, $2 million depending on how big it is, if that line is down for more than 15 minutes, or half an hour, some time interval and nothing happens, there should be a defined procedure that escalates it back up ultimately to the plant manager's desk.

He's got a major assembly line sitting there not doing anything because the right people aren't involved. The foundering should be resolved.

Reflow and Reuse

Concerns with Flux During Vapor Phase Reflow

(reflow, soldering, vapor-phase, flux, wetting)

Phil ›› We have an interesting question today about reflow and vapor phase from B.K. who inquires, "In a vapor phase system, is there an issue with condensing fluids, removing flux from the items to be soldered?" I can't think of a better expert anywhere on vapor phase than our one and only, W. James Hall, known affectionately as Jim Hall.

Jim ›› Actually, this question is answered almost by itself. And it says, "Removing anything that is soluble in the fluid. One of the foundation premises of vapor phase is that the fluids which boil and condense on the board heating the board very uniformly, and rapidly, and all that good stuff; that these fluids are totally chemically inert.

That means they will not dissolve anything. Remember dissolution is basically a chemical reaction of a sort, and so, the answer is "NO." These fluids will condense on the boards. They will flow over the solder paste and they will not remove any of the flux.

So, there is no need to use a special flux. There have never been, to the best of my knowledge, any special fluxes that were formulated specifically for vapor phase. Perhaps, for a special temperature profiling issue, but even then, I've never known of a specific paste formulated for vapor phase.

One of the inherent advantages that you get as part of the process is this chemically inert fluid that doesn't damage or interact chemically with anything on the board.

Phil ›› Very good, that sums up. I notice you always get excited when we talk about vapor phase. It's like a blast from the past.

Jim ›› I probably should say, with respect for people who are considering vapor phase, that as the flux residue comes to the surface, some of it will be physically washed off into the vapor phase sump.

In any vapor phase system, you need to have some sort of filtration. Any good vapor phase system should have a filtration system to remove this flux that is physically washed into the liquid sump. This flux removal is happening after the soldering process, and it will not in any way, negatively impact the wetting.

Phil ›› Well, thanks, Jim, for enlightening us.

Jim ›› This is 30-year old technology that's come back. Everything that goes around, comes around.

What Causes Chip Blow Off During Reflow?

(reflow, solder paste, profiling, components, pre-heat, ovens, Convection Dominant, maintenance, defects)

Jim ›› Today's question comes from D.L.: "What can cause a 0603 passive component to blow off the circuit board during reflow as if a firecracker was put underneath?" That's a pretty graphic description.

Phil ›› That's radical. Well, the first thing that comes to mind is a firecracker under the component. Maybe you have some prankster in your assembly department.

A couple thoughts on this. The question we want to know is if it is accompanied by splattered solder paste?

Jim ›› I am curious why this person would choose to use the words "as if a firecracker blew off" because I'm thinking of how you're going to know this. The board goes into the reflow. It comes out. The part is missing. Why would you describe it as a firecracker unless there was some evidence of some sort of explosion, which would lead us to believe that it would be solder paste-related.

Phil ›› Generally, we think of solder paste-related violence - eruptions of a volcanic nature. Typically, we find this is similar to out-gassing and that's usually due to too rapid a preheat.

Jim ›› Preheat slope too high.

Phil ›› Now, what if there isn't any solder paste there? The component's is gone.

Jim ›› My experience as a former oven manufacturer, listening to complaining customers, is that many displaced components relate from oven problems. Conveyor vibration has always been the biggest.

Align your conveyors, lubricate your conveyors, because if they're vibrating during the reflow cycle, during the ramp-up and before you actually start wetting, those components can move.

Phil ›› The key word here being "blow off" is improperly set or maladjusted convection. Either the blower's set too high, somebody's tooled around with the buffers and some of the other stuff, or since a number of machines have adjustable convection levels, somebody cranked it up too high.

Jim ›› Or a more benign maintenance issue is you've got some flux or other materials blocking up some of your hole/nozzle pattern causing a high-velocity jet or an improperly directed jet in one part of the furnace. So, your 0603 goes under there, gets hit by this blast of air and, whoosh, it's gone.

Phil ›› Make sure you're really profiling the actual board you're running. Put a thermocouple on the area; the type of chip that you see being blown off; measure what the real, actual preheat slope is. If you've got conveyor vibration, you can usually feel it by just observing it. Air flow issues are a little more subtle to diagnose.

Problems With Wave Solder Lead Bridging

(wave-soldering, selective soldering, bridging, solder, nitrogen, defects, optimization)

Phil ›› Jim, it looks like we have wave soldering question.

Jim ›› "We are wave soldering very close pitch through-hole components and see bridging. What is the finest pitch for through-hole components that can be successfully wave soldered? Is there anything you can recommend so we can reduce bridging on this component?"

Phil ›› Where to begin? You're talking about a technology that's essentially something like 50, 60 years old. And there has never been zero-defects with wave-soldering!

Jim ›› Even with 100-mil pitch, you still see some bridging. So, what is your acceptable level of bridging? With fine pitch connectors bridging can be 100 percent and can be a real issue. So, what do you do, Phil?

Phil ›› There's been all sorts of innovations, or "duct tape" if you will, on the wave soldering process, trying to keep up with this stuff. First off, obviously, tuning your wave soldering process, getting your flux down, getting your lead lengths cut, doing everything you can on the front end of the process to optimize it.

Solder pot cleanliness, solder pot temperature. All those can affect bridging in general, so they'll help the situation. But then you have to get onto something else.

Over the decades, there have been all kinds of things. Hollis Wave Soldering was famous in the 70s. I remember working with peanut oil and one of the supposed advantages was for de-bridging.

Other things that may be more practical; possibly worth a try? One is inerting the solder pot, if you haven't done that already. A number of studies that were done many years ago by both Soltec and Electrovert gave very credible data that shows inerting helps the solder go where it's supposed to go. This is done by reducing the tendency towards oxidation and, thus, enhancing the surface tension of the molten solder.

Jim ›› We've talked a little bit about other approaches before, and they're not really popular.

Air knife de-bridging tools may be something you have to look at. They are available from some companies, and this may be the situation where you have to grin and bear the reality of paying for that tool and learning how to use it to achieve a reasonable level of bridging.

Phil ›› The ultimate answer may to give this old technology a ride and take a look at selective soldering with the various new systems that are out there. As well as exploring whether this application might be feasible for intrusive soldering.

Jim ›› Pin and paste, reflow of through-hole, intrusive soldering, whatever name you want to call it. Bridging and wave soldering is a way of life. You manage it. You never eliminate bridging 100 percent, regardless of the pitch. Obviously, it gets worse at small pitch, and I agree with Phil. At some point, you're just going to have to say, wave soldering is not the way to handle this component.

What is the Shelf Life of Solder Paste?

(solder paste, storage, handling, flux, procurement)

Phil ›› Jim, what's our inquiry today?

Jim ›› It comes from D.P., and it has to do with the shelf life of solder paste. "What is the practical shelf life of a syringe of solder paste, and what symptoms would one see when the syringe is getting too old?"

Phil ›› Take a look at the data sheet for the solder paste in question. Also, if still in doubt, talk to your solder paste manufacturer's Technical Support people. The shelf lives are longer with some formulations than with others. Of course, there is the shelf life for unopened containers (cartridge or jar) versus once the container has been opened and exposed to ambient temperature and relative humidity. Some practitioners will tell you that you shouldn't have it out, once it has been opened for more than a week. Others come in and say, "Well, we've done it for a month," or, "No, no, no; only a day." Check with the manufacturer! They know the chemistries of their formulations. They know what they have and that's what you want to follow.

I want to congratulate you for getting syringes because that certainly helps, as opposed to when you have a jar that you're constantly opening and exposing larger amounts of the paste to the ambient humidity and temperature.

But even in a syringe, there are probably maximum exposure recommendations that vary among the different manufacturers. They may also have recommendations in how you store it, whether you're storing it vertically or horizontally. So, check with them.

Another thing - look at the quantity you're buying. If you're going to have it out for long times, you might be buying them in too large a quantity. Penny-wise, pound foolish. If you're using only very small amounts, order them in smaller syringes.

If you're ordering 500 gram syringes, consider 100 gram syringes or even 50 gram syringes. Another trick you could do is place a blanket order. Basically, forecast how much solder paste you'll be using in, say, a year, and then tell them how you want it allocated per month. That way you're not carrying huge inventories of solder paste long-term. You're turning your inventory, and that's a key thing there, too.

Jim ›› Solder paste is the most critical material you deal with in your process. Don't fool around with it! Don't take chances on saving a few pennies here and there by trying to use it longer, because what are the risks of defects?

It's going to give you solder balls and voids. Worst case, it's going to settle. If it settles in the syringe, you know it's bad. But a lot of times it'll look fine, but you put it on the board, and you get poor soldering. You get voids. If you're doing BGAs, you may not see it.

Don't take a chance. It's too critical a material. Buy it in the sizes that you're going to use it, even if it costs you a little more up front. The longer-term economics are much better.

Phil ›› Absolutely. My brother speaks wisdom.

Is Baking Required After Water Cleaning?

(cleaning, baking, flux, reflow, OA, water soluble)

Phil ›› Jim, what's the question du jour?

Jim ›› Comes from C.W. "Is baking required after aqueous cleaning? Do circuit board assemblies need to be baked after routine aqueous cleaning? If so, how long and at what temperature?"

Phil ›› Well, the answer to the first question - NO! Moving right along here... That answers the second question, too, doesn't it? That's pretty good.

Jim ›› The absorption of moisture by the resins in either components or circuit boards takes place very slowly. So, the time the PCBA is being blasted with water in a cleaner is only a couple of minutes.

Think about it this way: regardless of humidity - even in high humidity environment - for packaging and kitting and handling, both components and boards are considered to be okay for an hour out of dry cabin or a moisture barrier bag before you start a clock on them.

The couple minutes in the cleaner does not absorb enough moisture to be significant. It's a long duration over a long period of time.

Phil ›› This is a question we get asked quite frequently, especially when we're working with clients with regard to MSD. As there's more and more MSD cognizance, it's a question that comes up more often. And now, thanks to Jim, you know the reason why it's not a concern.

Jim ›› That was an easy question. Every now and then, we get a break, don't we?

Phil ›› Yes, every now and then. One additional caveat – be sure that your cleaning system is adequately drying your PCBAs. No residual moisture on those babies!

What Causes Non-wetting of OSP Test Pads?

(OSP, In-circuit Testing, PCB surface finish, reflow, soldering, wetting)

Phil ›› Jim, today's question is from P.M.

Jim ›› The question is about non-wetting test pads. "What are all the probable causes of non-wetting for OSP board test pads when the circuit boards are run through our wave solder bath?"

Do you want all the reasons? We'll give you a few.

Phil ›› Since we're talking about wave soldering the obvious one is are you fluxing them?

If you're using a spray fluxer, are you programming exactly where the flux is being applied, are you remembering to program the spray fluxer to put flux on test pads?

The non-wetting, or poor wetting, with OSP has always been a touchy subject and a very subjective one.

An obvious problem with wave soldering is previous heating cycles. Have these assemblies seen one or two previous reflow cycles, which could have degraded the OSP coating, causing them to have poor solderability when you get to the wave, typically being the final soldering operation?

Jim ›› Take a look at IPC Specification 1601 on handling of printed circuit boards. We've touted it before because it addresses the issues of moisture absorption and baking.

Within the recommendations they do not bake OSP boards. So, a question for P.M. would be, had you baked these boards before assembly?

Obviously, we would like more data; are the through-holes soldering and not the test pads? Because if it's baking or previous heat cycles (that is degrading the OSP finish), then you shouldn't be filling your through-holes, either.

Phil ›› Handling being a touchy subject (bad pun intended), you always want to exercise care. As with any kind of surface finish, keep the human contamination out. So, there are some of the reasons, if not all of them, and hope that helps.

High Temperature Reflow Soldering

(reflow, alloys, lead-free, profiling, DFM, BGA, BTC, components, thermal considerations, full-liquidus)

Phil ›› Let's see, what do we have today - a reflow question.

Jim ›› Phil, this one is very interesting. "You mentioned that vapor-phase soldering uses temperatures of 235 to 240 C for lead-free soldering. We use a 0.8 millimeter RoHS BGA that states, it is recommended to apply a soldering temperature higher than 250 C.

Could we use vapor-phase system for this part? Do you have any idea why the part recommends temperatures higher than 250?"

The answer is, NO.

I don't know of anybody who makes a vapor-phase fluid higher than 250 C, and I have no idea why a component manufacturer would specify a soldering temperature of over 250 C.

I don't know of any solder ball alloy that requires 250 C to collapse.

Phil ›› I'm surprised the component manufacturer would want to subject their component to such sustained temperature. Unless they want to sell you a lot of components.

Jim ›› The answer to the question is get back to this component manufacturer, and if you can find intelligent life there, which is the first challenge, and we'll give you points for that, you can ask them why. The highest temperature SAC alloy (low silver) melt at 227 C. So, maybe you want to take them up to 240-245 C.

What about the package? If you warp the package and create a bunch of Head-in-Pillow defects is the vendor going to cover for you and help you out? I would really look at that part, talk to the people who are making it and be sure that that's what's required, because most of the other things on the board aren't going to allow you to go to that temperature - even if you had a vapor-phase fluid. What else on the board wants to go up to that temperature?

Phil ›› I have to say, this is not the first time Jim and I have encountered application notes from component manufactures that were way out in space somewhere. So, you're very right to question this. Trying to find intelligent life among those component people - lots of luck.

Stencil Printing and Humidity

(printing, solder paste, humidity, work-life)

Phil ›› Jim looks like we have a printing question.

Jim ›› It is a printing question. "We noticed solder paste is drying out after being inside a screen printer a short time. Humidity inside the printer is 35% while humidity outside our screen printer is 50%. The question is how can we increase humidity inside the screen printer to help slow the drying of our solder paste?

Phil ›› This is a double-barreled question. Your first questions relates to your solder paste range RH range. We think 35% should be within the humidity window of the solder paste. Check the specs on the solder paste, at 35% it shouldn't be drying out.

The other question is why is the humidity inside your printer much lower than ambient humidity in your facility? We're guessing on this since we don't know the manufacturer, but you could be generating excess heat within the printer. If you are using some type of conditioning system inside the printer is it blowing too hard? I remember seeing this in some of the earlier systems.

But since you have actually measured the humidity, consult the equipment manufacturer.

Jim ›› This should not be happening. It's a matter of finding a problem and correcting it rather than looking for an alternative mechanism to add humidity to your printing environment. Check your paste and check out your machine.

How To Control Flux When Hand Soldering?

(hand-soldering, soldering, Temperature, flux, wire-core solder, thermal considerations)

Phil ›› Today we have a hand soldering problem.

Jim ›› It comes from P.D.: "Do you guys know of any tools or materials that will allow for precision application of no-clean flux for hand soldering operations? We are looking for something that has more precision than the tradition flux pens and don't want to use flux bottles if we cannot control the amount of flux applied. Any information assistance will be greatly appreciated."

Phil ›› Well, first off, I'd like to say bravo and kudos to you P.D. for realizing that you should not be using flux bottles.

Even flux pens are under question. It is really important to control the amount of flux, particularly no-clean flux, that we apply for hand soldering. The principle reason is that if we're not going to clean off the flux we've got to make sure that any of the residues left after the hand soldering operation are safe.

All no-clean fluxes work on the same principle. They start off with active chemistry that is deactivated by the thermal heating cycle regardless of whether it's reflow, wave or hand soldering.

Jim ›› And, of course with hand soldering and liquid flux it's a huge problem. Too much flux moving away from the joint, not being properly heated. If it's not cleaned off the board, you now have no-clean flux materials that are still active because they have not been heated sufficiently to deactivate them.

So, the traditional solution is to not use any additional flux, either a bottle or a pen, but to use cored solder wire. The basic mechanism is that flux only comes out when you heat the wire, therefore all of the flux will be reasonably well heated and therefore deactivated properly so that the residue you leave is safe.

You can get solder wire in different diameters, and you can also get different concentrations and amounts of flux within the wire. That is the traditional book technique that is used, but we thought of some other ones, haven't we, Phil?

Phil ›› One other possibility would be to use a very small syringe of solder paste for your manual soldering operations. First of all, you're going be using the same formulation you're using for your reflow soldering, mass soldering methodology.

And second, you know the ratio's going to be right. Typically using, say, a 50 gram syringe or larger, though 50 grams is easy to use at the hand soldering locations, should probably accomplish that.

Jim ›› Remember, because the flux is mixed with the solder it will all be heated when you melt the paste. You don't have the issues with liquid flux or the stuff from flux pens where liquid flux can move away from the joint and not be heated properly.

Problems with Pin-In-Paste

(soldering, intrusive reflow, Pin-in-Paste, Reflow-of-Through-hole, stencil, apertures, Hole-fill, components, Over-print, Through-hole)

Phil ›› We're coming to you from high atop Mt. Rialto at Board Talk Intergalactic Headquarters And what area of question do we have today?

Jim ›› This is about reflow of through hole, or if you like, pin-in-paste, or pin-in-hole, or intrusive soldering. Whatever you wish to call this technique. And the question comes from M.I.

"I have this USB four pin connector using a pin-in-paste process in one of our high runner boards." High runner means large volume manufacturing I assume. I just noticed it today after 1200 boards that the solder paste being pushed out of the four pins at the bottom side is dripping and accumulating inside our oven. Mostly on the second and third zones whose temperatures are operating at 120 and 140C respectively in a 12 zone oven. The question is, Is this normal, or what is normal inside the oven for pin-in-paste process? The protrusions of the four pins at the bottom side is 1 millimeter or 40 mils."

Phil ›› The first question, "What's normal?" I don't know what's normal. But we won't get philosophical here. I think one of the key problems here is the protrusion of your leads below the board being .040" is probably excessive. If it's at all possible, it would be best to require the connectors or pre-trim them to a maximum of .030" to alleviate the dripping problem.

The other question to ask yourself, assuming you put up with the tidiness question here with regard to the dripping solder, What do the joints look like? Are you losing solder volume?

Jim ›› What is your hole fill ratio?

Phil ›› That's right. Are you filling the hole? What do the fillets look like? Knowing that, you don't necessarily have to have a positive fillet on either side. That's been proven. But are you getting adequate joints? So, if you can live with the sloppiness factor I guess you could say, that's fine, but ideally you want to limit that protrusion to between 0.020" and 0.030" below the lower surface of the board.

Jim ›› But, do understand, it is perfectly normal to have some amount of dripping solder paste falling off the bottom of the leads, because when you print over the hole with a paste process, then insert your part, you're going to knock some small volume of paste onto the pin, and some of that is bound to fall off. You just need to make sure that it's not degrading the integrity of your final joints.

Phil ›› The only other thing I want to add is this also applies to both reflow ovens and vapor phase.

Understanding Reflow for Metal Core PCBs

(DFM, PCB, reflow, thermal considerations, profiling, materials, warpage, soldering)

Jim ›› This comes from P.B. "How does the reflow process for a metal core PCB differ from an FR4 laminate PCB? We've never processed a metal core before, and I would be grateful for any useful advice."

Phil ›› Your profiling procedures are going to become more difficult, and more complex. It would be wonderful to be able to solder the components on the surface without conducting a lot of heat into the metal core, but that's generally impossible because most boards that use metal core are designed to use the solder joints to help conduct the heat from the active components down into the metal core.

Jim ›› Regardless of what technique you use, a lot of heat is going to be conducted down into that metal core, therefore your profile is going to be longer.

You're going to have to heat slower. You may have to add a soak section before liquidus to allow the heat to penetrate into that metal core so that you can safely reflow all the components on the surface without too great a Delta T.

That means achieving full liquidus temperature on all the solder joints without overheating any of the components and materials. It's been used extensively, but you have to anticipate longer profiles, slower ramp rates, and perhaps soak sections or longer soak sections.

Phil ›› Now this is probably going to bring a smile to certain people with "vested interests" but wouldn't this probably be a good candidate for a vapor phase, Jim?

Jim ›› Absolutely. Metal core boards were one of the first assemblies we started processing in vapor phase and continued to process in the early 1980's when vapor phase was the principle reflow technique.

Phil ›› I remember in the early days of convection-IR when we would see an application like this we would go, "Oh, just use vapor phase." But, again, if you don't have a vapor phase system, hopefully you have a good convection oven with lots of zones.

Jim ›› Slow it down. Remember, you don't want to heat too rapidly because if you heat too rapidly, you can warp and delaminate these boards.

Phil ›› We want to complement our questioner. The fact that you've recognized that a metal core board is going to be different is a kudo for you.

Jim ›› To some people, a board is a board and they just try to profile it normally and they get into trouble, so you were right, intelligent and astute to question us.

What is Causing Intermittent BGA Failures?

(BGA, soldering, SPI, solder paste, printing, aperture, design, stencils, insufficients, Head-in-Pillow, defects. warpage, fine-pitch, surface finish, HASL)

Phil ›› I believe today we have a solder defect question, Jim, and BGA related.

Jim ›› This comes from M.S. "We're having problems with some BGA devices after SMT assembly. During testing, the BGA devices are failing. However, if we press lightly on top of the problem BGA device during testing, the board passes. What is the likely cause? Is it likely to be a solder joint failure, or something internal within the BGA package?"

Phil ›› That old enigma – the intermittent.. Well, I hate to tell you, it is most likely your process. And there's a number of different causes.

The first one that comes to my mind is inadequate solder paste height. So, the question I have to ask you, "Are you measuring your solder paste height?"

If you are indeed measuring it, are you holding it to intelligent levels? Because that's another mistake we've seen often where people have very wide divergence on the low side.

You definitely want to make sure you've got realistic levels and you're controlling it and you're not just recording it. You're actually looking at the data, because that's going to tell you a lot right there. So, that's the first thing that comes to mind.

Jim ›› One might tend to think about a head-in-pillow, but I would suspect not since you're getting an open circuit on initial test. Typically, with a head in pillow, there's enough contact. Although they're not soldered together, they is usually enough physical contact after the board has cooled down to give you continuity and passing tests.

That's one of the biggest problems with head-in-pillow, they seem to pass tests, but then they become intermittent later on. But I do suspect inadequate solder volume coupled with perhaps some amount of warpage of the package.

Look at your heating profile and your cooling profiles and your BGA packages. Make sure you are fulfilling all of the BGA manufacturer's requirements in your reflow profiles.

Phil ›› I'm also going to add that I hope you're not using a HASL finish on your board, because that can also add topographical variance which could lead to intermittents.

Jim ›› Lack of coplanarity on the substrate itself.

Phil ›› I don't care how good they say the HASL process is, or whatever the alloy is. When you start getting down to the finer pitches, it just isn't repeatable enough. So, good, so we hope that helps and steers you off in the right direction.

And let's not overlook possible warpage of the BGA package itself!

When Should You Use Underfill?

(BGA, CSP, flip-chip, underfill, PCB, materials, components, DFM, reliability, thermal cycling, fine-pitch, cracking, adhesives)

Phil ›› I believe we have a very interesting question today Jim.

Jim ›› This question comes from T.Y., and is, "When should we use underfill? We have a circuit board assembly with a wafer level chip scale package. The package is 2 x 2 millimeters with 20 balls. The diameter is 0.2 millimeter, and the standoff is 0.16 millimeter."

I would assume that's with a 0.2mm ball, that that's probably a 0.4mm pitch, but that's a guess. But the question is, "Under what circumstances should we use underfill? What type of underfill material do you suggest?"

Phil ›› When should you underfill? - - - When the board without underfill does not meet your reliability requirements either through thermal cycling, or vibration or shock; whatever you use to validate this product.

Jim ›› If these very small solder joints from the 20, 0.2mm balls are cracking, or not holding up under the service life of the product, then you can use an underfill material to improve the structural integrity of those joints and hopefully meet the reliability requirement.

Underfill is continuously evolving science, new materials are being brought out every day. I suggest you talk to the major suppliers such as Henkel Loctite and give them your specs, the size of the component, and standoff and so-forth.

Look at the type of process you're going to use to apply the underfill, the type of dispenser, whether or not you want to use heating during the process while you're dispensing, the cure cycle, and chose the best material that's available specifically for your application. I wouldn't attempt to give you a specific recommendation. How about you, Phil?

Phil ›› The only other thing I'll say is typically we found that chip scale packages using an elastomer interposer, such as those covered by the Tessera approach, generally do not require underfill, but I can't tell you if I'd take that to the bank, so you definitely want to check.

The bottom line is reliability. What are you seeing in your reliability testing? So, we hope this helps answers your question.

Jim ›› Typically underfill has been used for flip chips and not for advanced of packages that have more robust soldered joints.

As we're shrinking packages into wafer scale or chip scale packages, the solder balls and solder joints are getting smaller and smaller, we're converging with the tiny soldered joints on flip chips and experiencing some problems. The joints are just not strong enough to survive all the service conditions in the normal product life, and underfill is a viable solution for some. I can't say it's a panacea.

What is the Best Way to Reduce Dross?

(wave-soldering, soldering, nitrogen, alloys, lead-free, SnPb, dross)

Jim ›› You know Phil, we forget that there are a lot of people out there who are new to the industry. What may be basic to us, are questions to some people. We've had several requests come in about reducing dross in a wave soldering machine.

What is the best way to reduce dross? What are all the possible options to cut down on solder dross? First, I think it's appropriate we do a little overview!

Phil ›› Wave soldering is a process that has been around over 70 years. Dross has been an ongoing problem. For those of you who don't know what dross is, it's basically oxidized solder. You have a turbulent condition where a molten solder bath is going through a fountain and the wave tends to oxidize the solder

Jim ›› That's a good point. Molten solder will oxidize, even without movement, but it's grossly aggravated by the motion of the wave.

And that leads us to some of the basics of reducing and minimizing dross.

1. Don't turn on your solder wave unless you're actually processing boards. Most machines have controls that allow this.

2. Don't pump your wave any harder, higher, or faster than you have to, because that will increase the dross.

3. Don't use your chip wave unless you have to for glued on surface mount components or other reasons, because that increases the exposure of liquid solder to oxygen and increases dross.

4. There are a variety of chemical processes that have been advocated to apply to the wave, or float on top of the wave. Some people have had good success with it. We're not here to sell anybody's product, but you might want to look at what's available.

Phil ›› What we understand is in some cases these chemical additives work really well, but in other cases may offer no benefit at all. A lot is apparently relative to design of the solder pot and the wave itself.

One of the things we certainly recommend in the wave process, differentiating from reflow, is the use of a nitrogen, inert atmosphere in the solder fountain area.

Jim ›› But, Phil! Nitrogen costs money!

Phil ›› It does add cost due to the consumption of the nitrogen, but we're talking about a very small area, compared to reflow, as we're only inerting over the wave area. We're generally talking about using a nitrogen gas bottle as opposed to having one of those big towers out back.

The savings you will realize - even just with reduction of SnPb dross pays for the nitrogen itself. When you start talking about lead-free, particularly SAC305, it may pay for itself and actually help the process.

Jim ›› If you choose to explore nitrogen, understand that you must set it up properly and you must maintain it. Many people become disappointed with the results from nitrogen because they don't maintain it. They don't clean the distribution pipes. They don't make sure that their flows are correct at the solder pot and check the level of oxygen over the pot.

So, it can be very beneficial - a tremendous savings achieved over the cost of nitrogen, but you've got to set it up, and you've got to maintain it. If you're not willing to do that, I suggest don't try it. Use the other means.

Many people waste a lot of nitrogen because they don't set it up right and don't maintain the system.

Phil ›› Whatever you do, you've got to be very diligent about dross removal. You should have a schedule. Often at the beginning of each shift or at the end of each shift, the dross is removed from the solder pot. Dross is the "pond scum" of the solder pot. And you don't want it there. You want to remove it.

Board Deflection During Pick-and-Place

(PCB, pick-and-place, warpage, tombstoning)

Phil ›› We actually have a pick-and-place question today! How appropriate!

Jim ›› This comes from D.H.: "I was on the shop floor and noticed deflection in the 8x8 inch panel being populated. Would the deflection in the middle of the panel cause components to sit higher on the paste and thus have a slightly higher solder joint height than components near the support rails?"

Phil ›› Whoa, deflection!

Jim ›› The bottom line is deflection is not good in any process.

There are two concerns here. Is this deflection in the board by itself just sitting on the conveyor system before it's being populated? Or is this deflection that's occurring because of the Z-axis forces of the placement machine? And I'll say it right now - neither one is any good.

Phil ›› It's a bad situation either way. One of the worst causes would the deflection caused by the pick-and-place head coming down. And there's a number of things going on here. Typically, that would be any improper Z-axis location, or excessive Z-axis force due to a programming error. If that's it, it should be rectified right away.

Besides potentially smashing your component, you're probably displacing solder paste. I wouldn't be surprised if you see solder balls or inadequate solder joints.

Jim ›› If the board is deflected by itself - without the placement forces, then it's really up to your placement machine. Some of them can correct for this using force sensing to place the component.

You need to support your boards during placement, also during printing, and also during dispensing. And to some extent during reflow because deflection of the board is not a good thing.

In printing or placement it can cause errors such as Phil just described, paste getting squished out underneath causing solder balls. If the deflection is down in the middle, and the placement head doesn't compensate for it, you can get parts sitting on top of the solder paste not properly inserted into the paste. That's a recipe for tombstones on chip components, and potentially a poor wetting or opens on any component.

Phil ›› So you want to look at developing proper board support throughout your placement operations.

So, D.H., on your pick-and-place machine, check out that parts' smashing operation and make sure you've got adequate support.

Jim ›› This is a universal problem that we see throughout the industry and our consulting business. People just don't have support fixtures, or they don't put them in. They don't put the pins in the right places, and it introduces variability and related defects.

Round or Square Stencil Apertures?

(printing, solder paste, apertures, DFM, stencils)

Jim ›› We have a question about stencil printing. "What is your opinion using round versus square apertures for BGA patterns in our solder paste stencils?"

Phil ›› Of course, in printing the big trick is to get consistent fill and, more importantly, consistent release of solder paste from every aperture in a stencil, all those thousands of little holes in there. If any one of them doesn't release completely every time, and you have the potential for inadequate soldering defects.

Jim ›› So, as apertures get smaller, the question has been around for a long time. Is it more efficient to use a round aperture or a square aperture, particularly when you're dealing with BGAs where the pads tend to be round anyway?

Many years ago, I think more people favored round apertures. Based upon the published studies and hands-on experience that I've seen with our customers, I feel that for smaller apertures, 0.5 millimeter, 20 mil pitch and smaller chip components, 0402s, 0201s, and so forth. I think that Square wins!

Although the area ratio would tend to favor a round aperture having less perimeter per unit area, more of the data tend to support square or rectangular apertures for more consistent transfer efficiency, which means more consistent release of paste from the small apertures.

Phil ›› Let's face it in printing, that's what it's all about. This is a kind of a related subject, but with regard to non-BGA pads, some of the other pads people work with so-called "Roundy" pads.

Jim ›› Most of them are based upon square or rectangular pads. Then modified with radius corners to get the home plate or reverse home plate style of pattern. We're talking about changing the shape of the aperture other than a pure circle or a pure square or rectangle. That's a more complex subject than we can get into at this point now.

Phil ›› Remember, in printing, the bottom line is fill and release and the idea of getting a consistent, proper solder volume.

Rules for Reusing Electronic Components

(Rework and Repair, components, BGA, BTC, thermal considerations, reliability, MSD, cracking)

Phil ›› Jim, what's today's question?

Jim ›> This comes from DW. Very interesting... "What are the rules regarding reusing a component? If you remove a component from a circuit board, and the component is functional and not physically damaged, can it be reused on another circuit board?

Phil ›> The answer is MAYBE. Used components, or reused components, are very common. In fact, there's a whole industry to supply them. But the question is how reliable are they? Are they fully functional? And are they going to stand up and meet the product expectations for either the new or repaired product.

Jim ›> It really depends upon what you expect for the product the reused component is going into. If it's just a consumer product, not exposed to harsh conditions, that would be one thing.

Is the reused component going to be used to repair a piece of military avionics, which is a day-to-day thing for the military? And you can't get brand new parts for it. You have to use used parts. What tests do you do? There are laboratories that validate used or out-of-date old components and they put them through a variety of tests. Some test companies go as far as utilizing original manufacturer's specified tests.

So, yes, certainly you can reuse used components or scavenged components but making sure that they are reliable enough to meet the demands can be challenging. Particularly if it's going into a higher reliability product.

Phil ›> And there's also a concern with the level of operator skill of the folks who will be removing the components in the first place. This is paramount/

Jim ›> High temperatures do no good to any of the electronic components or materials, so limit heating during the removal process.

If you're talking about plastic ICs, make sure they are baked before being removed because those components are likely to be saturated from atmosphere moisture.

Phil ›> If you're going to use a hot air system that's going to heat the whole body of the component, you need to bake the board to remove the moisture or you're going to cause moisture sensitivity damage, popcorning, etc.

Even if you can't see it - remember you can have internal delamination and cracking in a component that you can only see through C-SAM or x-ray. Are you going to do that to the part before you reuse it?

SMT Components Popping Off During Reflow

(reflow, components, MSD, defects, ovens)

Phil ›> Jim, what do we have today?

Jim ›> A thing dear to our heart as we're old oven guys. The question relates to SMT components popping off during reflow and comes from D.L.:

"One particular SMT component is popping off during the reflow process leaving indentations in the solder. Could the fans in our convection reflow oven be blowing the part of the PCB, or is it more likely due to a component moisture problem?"

In this case we're assuming that if you're talking about moisture damage, you're probably talking about a plastic IC package. And the answer to your specific question is it could be either.

Phil ›› It could be a fan problem, or more likely a diffuser or nozzle plate problem. Most convection ovens are designed to give you pretty uniform gas flow and will not blow of components, particularly larger components. So, the question, has somebody been tinkering with the oven internal setups?

Jim ›› Or have you gotten some flux or other contaminant material into the oven such that it's plugged up some of the holes and caused a high velocity of gas to come out of one hole because adjacent holes are plugged up.

Certainly we have seen moisture cause parts to blow of boards, to be lifted off their pads causing indentations. If that's true, you should be able to look at the part after it comes out of oven. You may have to open the oven after it's cooled off and find the component inside.

Phil ›› You should be able to see permanent damage, popcorning type cracking on the bottom side of QFP, SOIC or BGA components. You'll find that the bottom has bulged, usually with permanent cracks, and that's what's typically called popcorning because you usually can hear a pop inside the oven.

Jim ›› You can also stand near your oven when the parts are going through and listen to hear the popping.

Phil ›› That would be a challenge to hear the popping above the sound of the fans and everything else. But if you hear popping, that means you have a moisture sensitivity control program that has gone astray or is nonexistent and that's another whole topic area.

Jim ›› If parts are blowing off I would suspect moisture sensitivity because it's one of the most universal problems that we see in our consulting business. We have been in only one facility in our many years of combined consulting experiences where we have observed a fool-proof MSD program. Many people have MSD programs and some of them are pretty good, but we've always been able to find holes in them where something can slip through the cracks.

Phil ›› With more parts being thinner, plastic, larger dies, and higher temperatures for lead-free - all of those have made the potential for moisture damage greater. So, look for those popped off parts, see if they aren't bulging.

Jim ›› If not, go back to your oven, turn it on and try to locate physically where the condition is happening in the oven. Check the flow uniformity out of the diffuser and nozzle plate on the top side of the board.

Moisture and bad solder paste might also be the cause. But if the paste was generating the explosive force I would anticipate you wouldn't see indentations. You'd see solder balls.

What are the Pros and Cons of Cleaning No-Clean?

(soldering, flux, no-clean, conformal coating, cleaning, components, BTC, solvents)

Jim ›› A question from A.S. about the pros and cons of cleaning no-clean.

"We are working with our contract manufacturer to develop the best process for our boards. With today's newer chemistries, what are the pros and cons of cleaning circuit boards assembled using a no-clean process?"

Phil ›› A very good question. Of course, the first thing is why are we cleaning no-clean in the first place? It sounds like an oxymoron, but we know better, and we know there are situations in circuit board applications where we do have to clean the no-clean. These include very high frequency microwave products where the residue will degrade the circuit performance.

In cases where certain conformable coatings won't adhere to the no-clean residue.

Jim ›› And some people with high-rel products just want to clean their boards. Another reason might be poor reflow or wave processing that didn't fully deactivate the no-clean such that the residues are not safe to leave on the board. In that case you certainly would want to clean. Although it would beg the question, why don't you clean up your process and solder correctly leaving you with a safe residue?

I think we talked about this before when somebody asked about IPA. No-clean is not one thing. It is a very wide-ranging family of materials that use all different kinds of chemistries. The one bottom line is that if processed properly, you should be able to leave the residues on the board for most applications.

If, for any of the reasons that we talked about before, you need to clean the residue, make certain that you use an appropriate cleaning chemistry and a cleaning process that will remove the no-clean and leave no dangerous chemistries on the board.

Phil ›› One of the biggest mistakes we see is where people have not matched the cleaning solvent with the residues. There is no universal solvent. There are some that work with quite a wide range; some that work with a narrow range. If you haven't done the due diligence, you're going to be in trouble.

Jim ›› You need a cleaning system that's going to get completely under all of your components and around them. So, you're going to have to look at your low clearance or low standoff components. QFNs jump out as being one of the toughest to clean. Remember, one of the worse things you can do is to partially clean a no-clean.

Phil ›› All no-clean formulations produce a safe residue through some level of encapsulation. That means that there are certain active chemicals on the board, but if properly processed they are encapsulated in a resin system. That resin system is not water-soluble. That's why pure water will never clean a no-clean.

Jim ›› And the worse thing is to use an improper solvent that partially dissolves the resin and potentially exposes some of the previously encapsulated active materials. So, you end up with a board that's more dangerous, that's dirtier from a chemical standpoint, than when you started.

Phil ›› The predominant methodology being used for cleaning no-cleans today is what's known as engineered aqueous, and there's been a long evolution that's led up to this. What we highly recommend is that you consult the supplier of your particular engineered aqueous solvent. In this case the two leading suppliers are Kyzen and Zestron. They have generally done very good due diligence matching up their particular formulations with the various residues from no-clean fluxes.

Jim ›› Look seriously at your product. Will it perform correctly and have proper reliability if there is a safely-processed no-clean residue remaining on it? Cleaning is just another expense. It's just another process. There's no reason to do it if you can avoid it. Many of the products that we use every day are processed with no-clean materials and not cleaned. If you have to clean for whatever reason make sure you get the right solvent and the right process to completely clean it.

TSOP Component Soldering Problems

(components, solder paste, printing, apertures, DFM, stencils, humidity)

Jim ›› This question comes from D.D. "I supervise three high-speed, no-clean, lead-free SMT lines. Unfortunately, these lines are in an area with no control over humidity. We are seeing a high fallout due to insufficient paste application on TSOP components. We made changes to stencils, we clean the stencil routinely, and it helps, but we still have a fluctuating yield. Is there such a thing as a low-humidity, low-temp, lead-free, no-clean paste? What do you recommend?"

Phil, when I read, "Is there such a thing as a low-humidity, low-temp, lead-free, no-clean paste?" I think that's implying that temperature fluctuations are also important.

Phil ›› The real question here - is there a paste that's more compatible with your process and your environment? And the answer is, most likely YES.

So, the question we beg to ask is, hey, D.D, when was the last time you, or one of your colleagues, did a solder-paste evaluation and qualification? I'll bet it's been a while. And therein lies a possible solution, and that is to evaluate different solder-paste offerings and find the one that best fits your process environment in terms of humidity, equipment, your oven capability.

This is something people neglect. They have the "Legacy Syndrome", where they're using the same paste forever. Things change, and, most importantly, things improve.

Even the manufacturer you're buying your solder-paste from makes improvements. You've been probably using their formulas for a while - chances are, with the competitiveness of the solder-paste market, they have an improved formulation.

Jim ›› Particularly lead-free, no-clean, because that's the highest-volume area where most of the paste manufacturers have been putting their primary research and development efforts.

Phil ›› So we recommend you do a paste evaluation benchmarking against your existing paste. When you go to the different solder paste companies, explain what your environment is, that you are looking for a lead-free, no-clean paste compatible with your normal humidity range.

Answering the demands of the various environments, a number of the solder paste companies are offering formulations with extended processing windows at either end of the humidity spectrum. So, chances are, there's probably something new available for you there.

Jim ›› Taking a step back I want to compliment D.D. on being aware that the environment impacts your paste. It definitely does.

As part of your evaluations, you might want to look at the paste performance over the range of humidity and/or temperature conditions that you typically experience. You could do a design of experiments, in which you would vary the humidity and see, for any given paste, if it has an impact.

Ideally you would want a paste that has no impact, that is insensitive to your humidity and/or temperature changes, but, if it did, you could use that information from your design-of-experiments results, to optimize in the middle of your environmental ranges so that you should have a minimum amount of degradation as humidity in your environment varies to its extremes.

Phil ›› You stated that a symptom that you're seeing is insufficient deposits on your TSOPs, and you're doing stencil cleaning and all that. The other thing to make sure that you have proper stencil-aperture design, that your apertures are correct.

Jim ›› Phil, wait a minute! He said, "We have made changes to the stencil." I assume that implied they were optimizing the apertures, but that's a good point.

Phil ›› Maybe they've reduced the apertures so much that it's making even more problems. As Jim likes to say, the "Too Tall-Too Narrow" aperture syndrome.

Chip Component Cracking During Component Placement

(components, pick-and-place, micro-passives, cracking, warpage)

Phil ›› Today's question comes from D.C. It states, "Occasionally we notice chip resistor cracking during placement. Most often the cracks are in the center of 0201 and 0402 size chips."

Wow! How the heck do you see them? "Does your experience indicate this is typically a placement equipment adjustment problem, excessive force, or could it be a component design issue?"

Well, let me start off by saying there has been occasions in the past, not frequent, where components come in partially cracked, so that even nominal placement or any handling can crack them. They might have been co-fired incorrectly, but how would you inspect them? You could have some poor sap in incoming looking at the reels, especially 0402s and 0201s, looking for cracks…

Jim ›› So you could look at the history of the failures and determine if it's a materials problem.

Phil ›› We're assuming that you have inspected these components after placement, prior to reflow, and prior to singulation, thus eliminating other causes of cracking, and that they are indeed, from what you see, a mechanical crack.

Jim ›› The first thing I would recommend with chip handling in any placement machine is to look at the nozzles. Make sure you have the right nozzles, that they're not worn, and so forth.

Worn nozzles have been a source of many problems over the history of chip placement. Haven't necessarily heard it associated with cracking, but it's a good place to check it.

Learn how your specific placement machine handles z-axis control. Does it place strictly on pressure? Does it place on absolute z-axis position relative to a zero point? How does it establish that zero point?

Phil ›› Whatever your machine does, make sure you understand it, and that you're programming the machine correctly. Assuming you're doing that, then I would look at the board.

Board warpage is a common problem. In this case you would expect that it would be a bowing up such that the chip location in question, where the crack occurred, was actually located on the PCB in the z-axis direction slightly higher.

Jim ›› That would be a particular problem if your machine was placing on z-position rather than pressure. A machine that places on pure pressure should be more tolerant of warpage in the board

Warpage, in the board in any of your operations, is a potential problem, so you should try to minimize it. Always use proper board support in any of your machines, whether you're printing, placing, inspecting, doing ICT, dispensing - always use proper board support.

Anything you can do to minimize bowing in general would be a very valuable thing that might help you in this situation.

Excessive force can crack a chip.

Phil ›› Sometimes with these very small chip components it's very difficult to see, but if you're having excessive force, one of the symptoms you should see are solder balls.

As you come down in the z-axis, rather than placing the component approximately halfway or one third or two thirds of the way into the solder paste deposit, you're going to be bottoming out and, no doubt, splattering solder paste.

We're talking about very, very small components so it can be very challenging.

Bench Top Reflow or Inline Reflow?

(reflow, soldering, profiling, Convection Dominant, thermal considerations, ovens)

Jim ›› Today's question has to do with reflow. "We have been producing small batches of lead-free boards, using a bench-top reflow oven that we want to replace. We have narrowed down the options to either a draw-style batch oven, or a small conveyor-type reflow oven.

Both look like they will get the job done and have very similar specs and features. Assuming that all things are equal, which would be a better option, a conveyor-type oven or a batch type?

Phil ›› The operative word here is "looks" like they'll get the job done.

Being reflow guys, I believe you can use anything to reflow, and I have often said that you could use a toaster oven. But let's look at the technical and thermal issues.

Jim ›› The main way to judge any reflow system is its heating capability. The ability to heat uniformly with repeatability. The only way you're going to know is to run your actual boards with thermocouples and see how uniformly they're heated with the profiles you want.

What can this oven produce in terms of different profile shapes? Can it produce a straight ramp? That's the easiest for any heating system to produce. But what if you need a soak for thermal or process reasons? Can it provide an accurately controlled soak? What capability does it have for cooling? That's where you create the actual solder joint structure.

Phil ›› Those are the things that should guide you much more than whether it's a batch type or inline. Batch systems have limitations because of their fundamental inability to change temperatures quickly.

In a multi-zone convection oven, where you have good separation between zones, you can create very sharp slope changes in your profile and create good, accurate profiles. A batch system, with its typically slower response, will have some limitations.

You should also take into account ease of operation, ease of profiling, and a lot of it is going to depend on the thermal transfer mechanism. A lot of batch ovens, the smaller bench-top type, do not use a lot of convection. They depend on radiant energy. As two guys who hearken back to the days of convection IR and IR ovens, we can tell you, it's not a lot of fun to work with IR.

Jim ›› The result being lack of uniformity, particularly on complex boards, and lack of repeatability from one board to the next.

Phil ›› Much trial and error trying to get a solid profile. If it was my money, I would seriously consider a conveyor oven. For lead free, we're probably talking a minimum of six vertical zones to do it right.

Jim ›› I want to reinforce, what I said was you want good heating capability so you can heat uniformly and repeatably, and that ultimately means good quality higher-volume fans. Some of the systems that we've seen, both inline and batch heating, that have small fans, but they don't do a very effective job of moving air through the process chamber resulting in ineffective and nonuniform heating.

In our opinion, it's not a place to try to skimp. We've seen people who have skimped, and they've regretted it.

Phil ›› So we recommend you take your most difficult board, thermal-couple it, take your data recorder, and demo. Try them out. And that will give you the bottom line and help you come to a conclusion.

I would also add to the mix, consider a used conveyor oven - as long as it's fairly recent vintage. See what works best for you and, again, use your most complex board and your data recorder. I think we've said what we had to say about that. Jim?

Jim ›› We fried that one to death.

Test for Spray Fluxer Uniformity

(soldering, flux, wave-soldering, selective soldering, OA, no-clean, water soluble)

Phil ›› One of our listeners inquires:

"How can we verify that our spray fluxer is uniformly spraying flux over the entire surface of our circuit board?" And then the second question is, "What's new in the world of spray fluxing?"

Jim ›› I'm assuming we're talking about spray fluxing for a wave soldering machine.

Phil ›› Just as wave soldering is an ancient technique, so there is an ancient technique we recommend for verifying the coverage on a spray fluxer. It's the old paper test using something like litmus paper.

Jim ›› You're going to take a bare circuit board with no components on it. Choose a board that has through holes distributed over the entire board area. Take a piece of paper, put it on top of the board, clamp it down, tape it down, and then run that board over the fluxer. Look to see if the flux penetrates uniformly. Make sure it penetrates through all the holes.

If you have a water-soluble flux you can use a litmus paper. If you're using an alcohol-based flux, use the traditional thermal fax paper, if you can still get that stuff.

Phil ›› This is the most straightforward test you can do. You can actually watch it as it takes place. Beyond that, there may be some other tests germane to the particular flux you're using. I would recommend contacting the manufacturer of the wave soldering machine or certainly the fluxer system, if it's not the same as the wave soldering machine. See what methodologies they have for measuring, comparing, and calibrating that particular device.

Jim ›› With many spray fluxers, you can program to spray different amounts on specific areas of the board. Make sure that you understand how to program it properly. But, that being said, the foundation is, you have a sprayer that is either on or off and a transport mechanism that moves it back and forth across the axis of the conveyor. It works in concert with the speed of the conveyor to give you your coverage.

Phil ›› If you're not getting uniformity, there may be a problem with one of the nozzles. Every manufacturer will have maintenance procedures for checking, cleaning, and testing your nozzles. I'm sure that most manufacturers also have maintenance routines for checking the movement of your flux head.

Jim ›› The final question, what's new in fluxers? From our observations there are improvements in user-friendliness. Better controls, easier to remove nozzles, nozzles that are more reliable, that don't tend to get clogged up, that tend to give you better, more uniform coverage. Easier switch-over between different flux systems making them more reliable delivering a repeatable quality process from your spray fluxing.

Is There a Test for Black Pad?

(surface finishes, PCB, ENIG, soldering, reflow, PCB fabrication, reliability)

Jim ›› A question from P.C. who asks, "We have identified some black-pad problems and are concerned that they may extend to some PCBs that have already been assembled. The units test functionally okay, but we are concerned about premature failures in actual field installations."

The question - "Is there a nondestructive test that can be performed on these boards, which would identify problems without damaging any assemblies that do not have any black pads?" That's a really good question, isn't it, Phil?

Phil ›› Black pad is definitely one of the scourges of the industry. At least among those of us using ENIG.

Jim ›› We will not get into an in-depth description of black pad. Let's just say we're talking about ENIG finishes where they appear to be good, they appear to solder well, but after soldering it's found that the joints are weak because there has not been good intermetallic formation between the tin in the solder, and the nickel under the gold.

There's a whole rash of analysis about why this happens, but the question here is whether there a test that can tell us if the solder joints are okay that won't damage good boards.

Phil ›› In search of that silver bullet, sadly we have to report that at present, there is not a nondestructive method of determining whether black pad is present or not.

Jim ›› Short of actually removing BGA components and inspecting the pads and then re-soldering the parts which is risky and expensive, but there is good news on the horizon.

Phil ›› We have learned of a consortium being formed in the EU, I believe based in England, of people involved with fabrication and assembly. One of the main objectives is to come up with a nondestructive method of determining the presence of black pad.

Connected with this, they're also going to be looking at developing alternative finishes such as more advanced versions of OSP as a possible alternative to ENIG where black pad occurs.

One approach towards eliminating propagation of black-pad is adding palladium to the ENIG finish. Though adding additional cost, the ENIPIG finish seems to work very well.

Jim ›› This highlights a significant problem. Boards with black pad, may look okay, the gold seems to be covering the surface and it looks good, they seem to solder okay. You could do a moderate drop test and see if parts fall off.

But with any kind of stress testing, you have to be concerned that you may be reducing the service life or affecting the product in some negative way.

Phil ›› P.C. having identified black pad, hopefully you've gone back to your board supplier and see what they've done to rectify the process to avoid the instance of black pad.

Finishes and Fluxes

Is Alloy Mixing During Rework Acceptable?

(rework and repair, soldering, alloys, solder paste, Pb-free, reliability, RoHS)

Jim ›› Phil, today's question comes from J.M.: "We're an in-house repair facility for boards from various vendors. A board may bear a RoHS label, but the lead-free solder alloy is not known. What is the best rework procedure? Clean off the original solder residue first, or just use any lead-free alloy and not worry about the resulting mix?"

Phil ›› Obviously, the best practice in the ideal situation would be to clean off as much of the old stuff as possible, and that should be pretty straightforward. There are materials and tools available for that including soldering irons, solder wick, and all kinds of other fun stuff out there.

Jim ›› Taking the solder off and avoiding significant mixing takes time. A number of papers and technical tests have been published about mixing during rework, particularly for the manufacturers of the modified tin copper alloys. They're different from the SAC alloys and the concern of mixing is raised, and there's some good test data available.

When the JCAA/JGPP, military aerospace program was done (its most published author is Dave Hillman) where they were looking at - what's the military going to do in a changing lead-free world - in setting up their test evaluation, they anticipated that, in repair, alloys are going to get mixed. In their test matrix, where they did vibration, shock, thermal cycling through several different cycles, they have included repaired boards that have mixed alloys in them,.

Phil ›› So, you might want to check that out. I'm sure there are others available. What you really want to be careful about is that you don't get lead mixed in with lead-free solders. So, if you have a RoHS label, make sure that it really is lead free.

And don't forget what happens if your lead-free alloy happens to contain bismuth.

Jim ›› Yes, that's all the more reason for not allowing any lead to get anywhere near a lead-free assembly. Is it worthwhile to go through the trouble to wick off and move all of the existing original alloy and then replace it with a single alloy?

Phil ›› You're talking from a joint-strength and integrity standpoint. What's the quality of the product? What is the expected life? Is it a stereo system that's going to sit on somebody's shelf, or is it an industrial controller that's going to see a lot of vibration, shock and temperature cycling? So that can guide you in terms of making an economic decision whether you want to go to best practice and take off all of the existing alloy.

Conformal Coating Over No-clean Flux

(conformal coating, soldering, no-clean, flux, cleaning, residue, reliability, moisture)

Jim ›› This question comes from D.L.: "We have a new product and need to apply conformal coating to one circuit board assembly. We have not applied conformal coating before. Is it normally acceptable to apply conformal coating directly over circuit boards assembled with no clean flux?"

Phil ›› Very good question. When we do no-clean evaluations the conventional wisdom was that you tested for this. You built a few boards with your candidate no clean solder paste, have the conformal coating applied in the normal manner, and tested.

One of the simplest tests was the adhesion test. Print and reflow an unpopulated PCB and then apply the conformal coating and cure it. Then you cover the surface with packing tape and let it sit for a while – maybe an hour. Then, pull it off and check the PCB surface under a UV light. Even going back a number of years ago, we found that most of the no-cleans were compatible, Basically there was compatibility, whether it was acrylic, silicone, really any of them. However, now we fast forward to the modern days and, Jim, you have a different take.

Jim ›› Whatever is under that conformal coating is going to stay there. What could be wrong with a no clean residue? It may not have been completely deactivated during the reflow cycle. Remember, all no clean fluxes start out with some active chemistry. Ideally, through the reflow cycle, that chemistry gets deactivated or encapsulated so that the residue is safe. If that's true, then, as Phil said, putting a conformal coating over no-clean flux residue should not be a problem.

The issue is if you haven't perfectly deactivated all that solder paste flux, now you're capturing it. You can make the potential for damage even worse because, virtually all conformal coatings are not completely impervious to water. They will, over time, allow water to diffuse through them.

Phil ›› If you have some hydroscopic contaminant from your no clean residue, it will actually attract water, and concentrate that water under the conformal coating. So that's where the controversy comes up. But, certainly, many people are conformal coating over no clean residues. That's a very standard practice.

Jim ›› Like everything else, in my opinion, it comes down to what is the reliability level of your product? How critical a product is it? What is the potential, what's the life? Are these service environments going to be in high humidity? Why is it being conformally coated? It the product going to be subjected to a lot of moisture? All those questions will enter into the equation.

Phil ›› The fact that this issue recently came up is interesting because it used to be a non-issue going back a few years. We touched base with one of our favorite conformal coating gurus, Chris Palin who said that, indeed, things have changed in the flux chemistries themselves.

Back in the old days of the RMA and no clean fluxes with the 63/37 solder, there was good adhesion. But the chemistries in the fluxes, and hence, the residues, have changed so radically because of the higher thermal excursions, principally for lead-free. There is a bit of a game changer, if you will.

Jim ›› There is also the issue of smaller components where you need more flux to hang around so that you're sure you don't re-oxidize the pads and terminations on your ultra-fine resistors and capacitors.

Phil ›› It certainly behooves you when you're doing a solder paste evaluation to evaluate your conformal coating from a reliability standpoint. As Jim says, don't be surprised if you find yourself relegated to cleaning that no clean residue off.

Once again, it's application-driven.

How Do You Calculate Solder Paste Volume?

(solder paste, apertures, soldering, printing, stencils)

Jim ›› I think we've got a great question today, Phil. This comes from T.A.: "How do you calculate the volume of solder paste needed for screen printing PCB assemblies? Is there a simple formula?"

If we had an all-time-great-questions list, Phil, I would put this near the top. This is a great question, "How much paste do I need to get a good joint?" In my opinion, from our experience, there is no formula.

Phil ›› There are no standards to tell you for a given configuration - take, for instance, I've got a 20mil pitch QFP with gull wing leads, 0.5 millimeter pitch, and from the spec sheet I see that the foot of the lead has certain dimensions, and I design a pad that's 10 mils wide and so long.

How much paste do I have to put down on that pad in order to get a good reliable solder fillets for that configuration? What's the minimum and the maximum? And that's important because suppose that part is on a board with a bunch of big resistors and capacitors, I would tend to want to use a thicker stencil, maybe a 6-mil stencil.

Jim ›› What's the maximum paste that I can tolerate on that pad without getting into bridging and solder balls? On the other hand, suppose that that's the biggest part; I've got nothing but real small resistors and other fine-pitch parts, and I want to use a thin stencil, a 4-mil stencil? What's the minimum solder that I can tolerate on this gull wing lead and still get an adequate fillet?

In my experience, in my reading of the literature, we have never seen any standards for that. When we start designing stencils and talking about area reductions or overprinting, we really need those numbers.

Phil ›› You need to know what's the maximum amount of paste so that you can make your decisions on shaping your aperture sizes when you have these different combinations on the board.

We're probably going to get letters that say, "You boneheads! Of course, there's a calculation." But what Jim is saying and emphasizing, is that there are no standards for a given lead, say, on a 20-mil pitch SOIC, that you need this volume of solder there. As Jim says it can vary - there are variables.

Jim ›› We know there's a range. You look at the IPC in other specifications, they'll show you minimum amount of solder and maximum amount of solder. Below that, you have a chance of getting an insufficient joint; above that, you have a risk of solder balls and bridges.

But the question is, for any given configuration, how do you calculate those numbers? That's what T.A. is asking us, and my answer is I don't know.

Phil ›› I don't think I've ever seen a direct correlation saying that the ideal volume to get the ideal strength for that particular joint is thus. There is no standard.

Recommended Board Spacing During Reflow

(reflow, profiling, soldering, PCB, ovens, Convection dominant, IR, PCB Handling)

Jim ›› Phil, this comes from K.D. The question is, "When running boards through a convection re-flow oven, should there be a gap between boards of one board length, or will it typically make no difference to have boards running end-to-end in a continuous train to save time and energy? What would you advise?"

Phil ›› I guess this is where we put on our surface mount "Myth-Busters" hat. The old wisdom was to leave an absolute minimum of one board length in between boards, and that had a modicum of truth to it when we had far less efficient convection-IR reflow ovens. Now with forced convection, we have much higher heat transfer efficiency.

Boards are absorbing energy as they go through the oven. The concern was how quickly can the oven replenish it. In today's world, it's a different matter.

Jim ›› Obviously, for any given situation to be 100 percent sure, you should test your oven with your worst board. Take your heaviest board. Run it in between three or four other boards of equal size. Run them right next to each other and see if it changes the profile at all. That's the only way to know for sure.

I've designed ovens for many years and was involved in the initial advancements of high-level convection ovens, and we tested this all the time. I can tell you from my tests with very heavy assemblies that all of the major high-end ovens today can run heavy boards with an aggressive profile, without any space between them, and show no significant change in the thermal profile seen on any board.

Phil ›› The physical reality in actual production is you need to leave some space for handling reasons. Typically, board-on and board-off conveyors are not matched in the speed, and the worst thing you want to do is have boards crashing into one another or lapping over on top of one another.

Most people leave a couple of inches to allow for any inconsistencies in the on-load and off-load transfer, and that drives how big that gap has to be, not the thermal reaction of the oven.

Jim ›› As Phil says, modern convection ovens re-circulate so much gas, there's so much energy available at any instant in time that they recover and show no appreciable loss of energy, even when running back-to-back heavy boards.

Is Rework Acceptable or Unacceptable?

(rework and repair, soldering, workmanship standards, reliability, standards)

Phil ›› What is today's question, Jim?

Jim ›› Our question today comes from D.V.: "We have a customer who insists that circuit board assembly should not be re-worked in any way. They will not accept boards which have been re-worked. Is this practical?"

Phil ›› What do we mean by repair, and what do we mean by rework?

Jim ›› The standard terminology that I've always accepted is that a reworked board is a design change, something where it was changed from the original configuration, a wire was added, a path was changed, a component was substituted, or something like that.

If that's the case, then the customer should have been involved in that decision from the beginning.

But, I'm assuming that this customer is using rework interchangeably with repair and they're talking about boards that have been manufactured to specification, but have a problem, a solder joint, a bridge, an insufficient or something like that that was then repaired before it was shipped to the customer.

Then how would you describe that, Phil?

Phil ›› It sounds like your customer is expecting to get the proverbial zero defects. We don't see a lot of that going around, and chances are you probably don't see it at your facility, either.

So, when we do repair, just how bad is it, because we've heard various documents and specifications that some customers will give no more than one repair or two, but let's talk about the single repair. Typically, how much damage are we inflicting? We're going through a thermal excursion, or two thermal excursions.

Jim ›› Potentially, if there's a component removal and replacement or maybe three, if we're doing a pad cleaning operation with some solder wick, we're adding another cycle, so there are concerns.

IPC has a whole division that does nothing but certify repair technicians, and the basic accepted practice is that if your operators are certified, they know how to safely repair boards without damaging them. Now, the situation is to prove it and, unfortunately, there's very little data out there.

Phil ›› I would like to point out that the consortium for the aerospace and military people, which our good friend, Dave Hillman has produced some of the best and most comprehensive test data.

The program was a comparison of lead-free and tin lead, but within this matrix, the consortium included, repaired assemblies.

Jim ›› To the best of our knowledge, they did not find any reduction in reliability, and they did two different versions of thermal cycling. They did shock and vibration and a whole bunch of other military and aerospace related accelerated life testing, and they did not find any degradation of repaired assemblies. There is a concern because you are putting them through thermal cycles, you are handling it again, and so I understand your customer's concern. But, as Phil said, to expect zero defects from a process, particularly if you're doing through hole components.

Phil ›› One of the best safeguards you could have is to have very well-trained, well-skilled repair techs who are IPC certified.

Don't take any chances here, and that should give your customer a little bit more of a comfort level, and yourself, too, for that matter.

Jim ›› Also show to your customer any other custom procedures and work practices, and work instructions that you've developed for your repair operations, showing that it is controlled, and that it is, to the best of your ability, done in a fashion that's not going to damage or reduce the long-term reliability of the product.

Recommendations for Bare PCB Finish

(surface finish, soldering, reflow, wave-soldering, selective soldering, HASL, OSP, reliability, DFM)

Jim ›› This comes from D.G., Phil: "Our company is now looking into going lead-free. Our products are not very complex with some 25-mil pitch components but no BGAs.

The average board size is 3" x 3". We would like to order bare PCBs with a surface finish that will work with both our current leaded process and lead-free solder processes, once we make the change. We are currently using HASL. What finish do you recommend that will work with either soldering process?"

That's a simple question. They all work.

Phil ›› Yeah, they all do with both processes.

Jim ›› Most all the finishes are backward and forward compatible.

Phil ›› Your application and the particulars of your assemblies are going to point you in a direction.

Normally, we're not big fans of HASL because most of the industry started moving away from HASL years ago with the advent of fine-pitch components. However, you don't have fine-pitch.

Jim ›› There are people doing lead-free HASL. We don't like it because of the additional higher temperatures that you're exposing the bare PCB to, but it's available. Take a look at OSP. You can save yourself a lot of money, anybody can do it, but there are a number of questions, processing questions and storage questions, but OSP is widely used.

Phil ›› Other finishes include immersion silver and ENIG and they would all work. What works best for you is something you're going have to find out, but they're all backward compatible with your lead process.

So, what we recommend if you're going with HASL, the most common alloys being used right now are the modified tin copper alloys, as opposed to the SAC alloys.

Jim ›› Tin copper alloys that are being used widely for surface finishes and wave soldering. So, you really can't go wrong with any finish. It's a matter of cost and availability, and, as Phil said, storage, very important.

Phil ›› Think into the future - are you going to be able to stay with these simple components, or are you going to have to use BGA components someday, or use finer-pitch components, no-lead.

Those are questions which should all figure into your decision.

What Causes Wave Solder Bridging?

(wave-soldering, flux, nitrogen, DFM, components, defects, bridging, Selective soldering, pre-heat)

Phil ›› What do we have today?

Jim ›› A very generic problem, but it's very detailed. "We are having continual lead bridging problems with our wave soldering system. How would you rank the following most likely and least likely causes and areas to investigate? Here's the list: flux quantity; flux type; solder pot contamination; solder pot temperature; component angle through the wave; wave solder ramp angle; and other".

The first thing that jumps out is solder pot temperature. If your pot is too cool, the viscosity of the solder at the end of the wave is too high and the solder bridges don't fall off.

Phil ›› Remember, when your leads are in the pot, you have 100 percent bridges. Now, you're counting on the weight of the solder to cause the bridges to fall off. If the solder is too cool, the viscosity is too high, that doesn't happen.

Then the one that isn't on the list is preheat profile.

The flux has got to be preheated properly. You have to make sure it's fully activated, but not preheated so much that the activators are burned up and you get re-oxidation, because you're counting on your flux to hang around in the wave so that it helps the bridges to flow off.

There are also a lot of other factors like pad spacing, the length of the leads, the design.

Jim ›› If you've got bad pad spacing that's outside of the IPC guidelines, you're going to have bridges. If you're trying to wave solder some of these new connectors with 40-mil pitch or 25-mil pitch, you're also going to have bridging problems.

You may want to go to a selective soldering.

Phil ›› These are all important parameters that have to be controlled, whether they're affecting bridging or not. So, they should all be controlled including solder pot contamination. It may not affect the bridging but you better have that under control.

Jim ›› All of these things could contribute to bridging, so it's a good list. I think we've given you some input on what we feel is important but check them all.

When is it Time to Shift from Hand to Wave Soldering?

(wave-solder, DFM, soldering, hand-soldering, components, defects, Selective soldering, set-up, maintenance)

Phil ›› I believe we have a through-hole related question today Jim.

Jim ›› This comes from V.N. "We assemble simple through-hole circuit boards. What are the main factors to consider when shifting from hand soldering to wave soldering, and what factors should be used to justify continuing to hand solder versus switching to wave solder?"

Phil ›› Well, the first is: What's your budget? Are you ready to buy some equipment?

Jim ›› I think volume is typically the dominant factor that should be considered when changing from hand soldering to wave soldering. Obviously, with wave soldering you're going to have to buy a machine and set it up and maintain it.

You have a lot of fixed cost, so you have to be able to amortize those cost over the savings in manual labor, so that's the foundation of your decision.

Phil ›› Anytime you have a manual operation, which is what hand soldering is, there's an introduction of variability and a lot of that can be attributed to the people factor.

So even assuming you have very well-trained IPC certified technicians, the fact is with hand soldering, there's great variation.

Jim ›› Bad hair days.

Phil ›› One of the goals of automating is to have more consistent, repeatable results. Even with a machine, there's still operator dependency in terms that it's set up right, that correct levels are maintained. So, it's not like you're free and clear, but it is a more consistent, repeatable process.

Depending upon the pin count and the other characteristics of the board, you may consider going to selective soldering, as opposed to going full bore wave. Selective wave has received a lot of attention and acceptance in the last few years. It does depend how many through-hole pins you actually are soldering.

Jim ›› Selective soldering may not be the best solution for large volumes of through-hole joints. Nothing is going to come close to a wave soldering machine for speed and cost per joint.

But selective soldering allows you to get down to controlling the process at the single pin level. It has a lot of advantages.

If you're coming from strictly hand soldering, some fundamental things you're going to have to consider including:

- trimming of your leads before you go into the wave soldering machine

- your lead-to-hole ratios to get a proper hole fill by capillary action

- the orientation of the multi-pin connectors

Phil ›› And, of course, you're going to have to learn, buy, install, maintain, and optimize a wave soldering machine, which is a very complex device, including fluxing, pre-heating, and one or sometimes multiple waves.

So it's not something to be taken lightly. But if you have huge volumes of through-hole joints to solder, there are certain economic advantages.

Phil ›› So whichever way you go, be sure that you do your research. Get the proper technology for the type of work you're doing. There is full wave, selective wave, and there are other methodologies. They're a little less popular, but we have to give them an honorable mention: robotic soldering and laser soldering

Jim ›› And don't underestimate the maintenance required to keep a wave soldering process running repeatably.

Solder Paste Print Volume vs. Alignment?

(solder paste, apertures, SPI, components, DFM, reflow, stencils, pick-and-place, printing)

Jim ›› Here's an interesting, high level global question: "Which of these factors is more critical to the solder printing process, solder paste volume or solder print alignment?"

Phil ›› A very good question. Well, I'll answer it with a question. What's more important in your car, the engine or the brakes? The answer to your question is: they're both equally important. You can't really have one without the other if you want to have good printing.

I'm a little curious what spurred this question, because generally, by adjusting for solder paste volume and height, you should not be sacrificing anything in alignment, and vice versa. They are independently controlled parameters. Even if they were interrelated, you shouldn't have to sacrifice one over the other.

Jim ›› That's a really good point, that they are pretty much independent variables when you set up a printer.

Phil ›› Inadequate alignment could result in the same problems you would see with inadequate volume.

Jim ›› Stepping back farther, if the alignment is off, when you place the component - you might only partially be into the paste. The component could move before it got to reflow because it wasn't adequately held, there wasn't enough tack surface contact with the paste.

If it's off between adjacent fine pitch pads you could start to get bridging. Of course, volume is important, particularly on area array packages, where the joints are under the package and you can't visually inspect them, and they're very difficult to repair and touch up.

Phil ›› So the bottom line is that you want to do your design of experiment in your printer set up properly. You want to make sure that all of the proper parameters are set up, alignment, volume, print height. Ideally, all of these are checked at least on an AQL basis with post-print inspection.

QFN Rework: No-Clean or Water Soluble Flux?

(BTC, no-clean, flux, OA, water soluble, rework and repair, reflow, solvents, entrapment, cleaning)

Jim ›› This comes from M.D.: "No clean or water soluble for QFN components. We're replacing 32 lead QFN and 14 lead DFN components. We can use either a no clean or a water soluble process. Which do you suggest? Is there a formula or a standard that explains when to use a no-clean or water soluble process with these component types?"

Well, I don't know of any formula or standard, it's certainly done both ways.

Ideally, it would be wonderful to just use the no-clean and assume the residues are safe and not have to go to a cleaning process.

Phil ›› In many cases and in many applications that is the case. There are risks involved, particularly when we talk about QFNs.

Jim ›› A paper published by our favorite cleaning gurus, Terry Munson from Foresight showed that they removed QFNs that had been processed with no clean and found active residue under the paste.

Phil ›› Terry theorized in his paper that the component and all of the paste under it had in fact seen the proper time/temperature profile during the reflow process and therefore should have deactivated the paste.

But, because of the configuration of the QFN, with a large amount of solder paste in the center for the thermal pad, what was actually happening was the flux residue around the perimeter of the package was hardening sooner than the center, preventing the evaporation or the escape of the evaporated materials from the no-clean paste.

Jim ›› Remember, no cleans are deactivated by three mechanisms: chemical reaction, evaporation, and encapsulation. So even if we have the proper heating cycle, if you suppress that evaporation and trap those materials, you have the potential of having some corrosive materials. So, my instinct is to use a water soluble process.

You need to make sure that you use a saponifier, because in most cases the high surface tension of pure water alone will not penetrate under the QFNs to clean out all of the residues. And with a water soluble you must remove the residue.

Phil ›› So probably the best of all courses for QFN component rework is to use no-clean flux, however, clean the no-clean flux using an engineered aqueous saponifier. As our other favorite cleaning guru, mild mannered Mike Bixenman will tell you, you must be certain that you match the solvent - in this case the engineered aqueous, to the soil, and the residue of the no clean.

Jim ›› I absolutely agree with that, but it's always been my feeling, if I know I'm going to clean, why not use the water soluble which is designed to be cleaned, and not a no-clean which is designed not to be cleaned?

Now it's done all the time, but it seems to me if you've got this flexibility and you're going to end up with a cleaning process with an engineered chemistry and some sort of saponifier, that it always seemed more logical to me to go with a water soluble that's designed to be cleaned.

But check it out for yourself. Make sure you run the tests on your parts and your components with your solder paste.

Why is Our Selective Soldering Causing Blisters?

(soldering, selective soldering, PCB materials, thermal considerations, PCB handling, storage, baking, delamination, humidity, moisture, PCB Fabrication, storage)

Phil ›› Jim, what is today's question?

Jim ›› Well, it concerns selective soldering.

The question comes from K.K.: "Infrequently we see blisters (delamination) on a board around certain components after selective soldering. The location of the blisters is not always at the same locations. We've tried reducing solder temperature to a minimum, but the problem persists. What could be the root cause of our problem?"

Phil ›› Let's assume for the moment that you have your selective machine parameters set up correctly. And they're consistent.

So looking at the fact that the delamination is happening at random times, in different places, let's look at the board. The first thing that pops into our watery little minds, when we hear about delamination, especially under the conditions you're talking about, is moisture.

Jim ›› Moisture absorption into the board. Think about it, selective soldering is typically one of the last assembly processes, so the board may have been out of its moisture control bag for a re-flow cycle or two, maybe some touch-up, maybe some inspection. We don't know what your processes are. But there are concerns.

Your board is always going to absorb moisture, depending on temperature and humidity in the room, and this may be why it's a random problem.

Phil ›› So what you thought might have been related to the selective process itself, it comes back to your storage procedures and practices, particularly with regard to boards. And there is a recommendation for you in the form of IPC specification 1601.

Jim ›› People have talked about moisture absorption, baking boards, for as long as I've been in the industry, and that's over 30 years. IPC felt that, particularly with lead free and higher temperatures, it's gotten critical enough that they needed for formalize this. So they produced this document that was just released last September and it talks about measuring moisture, and storage conditions, and bagging boards and sealing them, and using desiccants and so forth.

So I strongly recommend that you take a look at that specification, and look at what you're doing in your process in terms of the time that your boards are exposed to ambient humidity up until the time that you're doing your selective soldering.

But I just had one other thought. Obviously, we're assuming that it isn't just a random defect in the fabrication of PCB itself. Because if you're having inconsistencies with lamination or materials at the vendor, that could certainly show up.

Phil ›› So cross your T's and dot your I's. Make sure your selective machine parameters are okay, and that you are following best practices with regard to storing and handling your PC boards.

Solder Residues and In-Circuit Test

(soldering, flux, In-circuit Testing, no-clean, reflow, residue, HiP)

Phil ›› Welcome to Board Talk. This is Jim Hall and Phil Zarrow of ITM Consulting, bringing you Board Talk. Let's see, this looks like a solder paste question.

Jim ›› This question comes from W.O.: "While running a solder paste comparison through our SMT and ICT processes (that's in circuit test) we found that one solder paste is harder than the other. Pin impact into the solder on test points was less on one type than the other. The two solder pastes use the same powder, a 63/37 Eutectic, but different carriers and actives.

One paste is designed to overcome poor wetting head-in-pillow effects that come with soldering lead-free components in a tin/lead SMT process. The other is a longstanding tin/lead solder paste. What could be causing the difference in solder joint hardness?

Phil ›› I assume that he's talking about penetrating the flux residue as opposed to making little dents in the solder joints.

Jim ›› If they're both 63/37, there should be absolutely no difference in penetration just into the metal. So, we're obviously talking about a residue.

What jumps out at me is that one paste is designed for a specific thing, overcoming head-in-pillow. The reality is that the chemistry of solder paste is very complex. All of the manufacturers would love to come up with the ultimate solder paste that minimizes all defects and gives you good processing parameters, including ICT test penetration in the residues. But the reality is they're not there yet, and I don't know if they ever will be. Nature doesn't tend to be completely harmonious, so there are tradeoffs.

Manufacturers optimize paste to get rid of one defect, and you tend to reduce some other parameters. It sounds like one of these pastes, and I'm guessing it's the one that was formulated to avoid head-in-pillow, has the chemistry that produces a harder residue which is more difficult for the test probes on your ICT, or bed of nails fixtures, to penetrate.

I want to compliment this questioner for doing a solder paste comparison. You are doing the right thing. You're trying to find the best paste for your process, and you're doing the tests that are important to you. That's excellent work. Now, armed with this information, I would talk to this paste vendor, or other paste vendors, and see if they have another formula that gives you a better compromise between ICT and head-in-pillow, if that's the defect you're addressing. Most solder manufacturers will be able to talk to you in a helpful way.

Phil ›› Maybe someday somebody will come out with a "TempurPedic®" solder flux residue that serves all purposes. In any given marketplace, whether we're talking about the Americas, Asia or Europe, there are at least 20 different solder paste manufacturers competing with each other, and they're all trying to out-do each other.

Jim ›› They are working to give you a better process, to make your life easier.

Phil ›› So I guess no matter whether you're going to be doing in-circuit testing, whatever you do when you solder those boards ...

Jim ›› Don't solder like my brother.

Phil ›› Please don't solder like my brother.

What Are the Benefits and Drawbacks of OSP Finish?

(surface finish, through-hole, OSP, wave-soldering, selective soldering, soldering, flux, hole-fill, oxidation, solderability)

Phil ›› Welcome to Board Talk this is Phil Zarrow and Jim Hall, the Assembly Brothers. Our special guest today Joe Belmonte.

Jim ›› We have a question about surface finishes on printed circuit boards. This comes from S.B. What are the advantages of using an OSP (Organic Solder Preservative) surface finish? What precautions should be taken when using circuit boards supplied with OSP finish?

Phil ›› The most obvious advantage is that it's cheap.

Jim ›› It provides an extremely flat finish for placing your components. Under the proper conditions can give you very reliable solder joints because you're actually forming the inter-metallic during the soldering process. On the other hand, it has some limitations. If the finish is not properly maintained and properly handled, the solderability may be reduced.

Phil ›› So there are a number of storage considerations to take into account. And questions in terms of the number of thermal excursions.

Jim ›› The feeling many people have with OSP on a complex board with double-sided reflow, being two reflow cycles followed by a wave soldering operation, is that they do not get adequate hole fill.

The argument is that during the first two reflow cycles the heat on the barrels of the hole breaks down the OSP. You get minor oxidation so when you wave solder, you don't get good hole fill.

Joe ›› We have to remember there are many OPS products and suppliers. There are different numbers of thermal excursions, so you need to balance that with the best OPS product.

Another difficult wave soldering problem is a think board with heavy grounds planes and OSP finish. The challenging is getting proper top side hole fill.

Phil ›› No matter what surface finish you use, don't solder like my brother …

Jim ›› And don't sound like my brother.

How Do You Evaluate a New Solder Paste?

(solder paste, printing, bridging, solder balls, wetting, tack, print-to-pause, work-life, slump, procurement)

Phil ›› Welcome to Board Talk. This is Phil Zarrow and Jim Hall, the Assembly Brothers. Today we're joined by Joe Belmonte. Jim, what's today's topic?

Jim ›› Phil, we get a lot of questions about soldering and solder paste for surface mount reflow. There's a tremendous amount of development going on in paste technology. New materials to deal with lead-free, head-and-pillow and so forth.

Bottom line is it's important that most everyone look at what's becoming available and be able to evaluate and qualify a new paste. Joe is such an expert in this field, so Joe expand on the importance and the general procedure for qualifying a new paste.

Joe ›› Here's my approach and my philosophy on qualifying a new solder paste.

First, I know that changing solder paste is a very significant activity. Once you lock into a paste that works for you, and you feel comfortable with it, it's performing as you hope, it's giving you the yields you want.

However, solder paste, as Jim mentioned, is advancing all the time. There's new solder paste coming to the market, so how do we periodically evaluate those new solder pastes?

When I first started in the industry, what we would do is replicate all the laboratory tests that were done by the world-class suppliers and do all those tests over again in the lab.

However, my philosophy now is buy into those test results. Believe in them because they're done by world-class, reputable organizations. What we focus on is the performance tests. I'll call those the process tests. How will the new paste perform in your process? What about printability, shelf life, tack etc..

So my philosophy is to focus on those tests and not replicate all the tests that are done by the paste manufacturer lab. And the way to execute those tests is a formal design of experiments.

Set up a brainstorming session, put together the right people, including the supplier, maybe a customer; whatever the right cast of folks is. Get in a room and we decide what characteristics in your process are critical for that paste to work for you. Look at things like tack time, shelf life, storage, solderability, so forth.

And then do a design of experiments (DOE). There is one DOE that's been done many times for paste. It was actually developed by Cookson Electronics many years ago called a 27-board challenge.

It allows you to test several parameters with a very small sample size. It's an economical and practical test. It's been in the industry for many years; used by many customers as a way to identify on the shop floor, in your process floor, what paste is going to give you the performance characteristics that you need.

Phil ›› I think the thing that Joe emphasizes is that these tests are done on the shop floor, in the environment that the solder paste will be subjected to and that's something that cannot be done generically.

Jim ›› We could go into infinite detail, but I think that's a really good, basic, very heartfelt endorsement and recommendation from Joe.

Phil ›› Well you have just wasted five minutes with Jim, Phil and Joe, the Assembly Brothers, who by day, go as ITM Consulting.

Jim ›› Whatever you do, don't solder like these guys.

Phil ›› Yeah, don't solder like these brothers.

Does Flux Volume Impact Solderability?

(soldering, flux, wave-soldering, selective soldering, hole-fill, solderability, No-clean, residues)

Phil ›› Welcome to Board Talk. This is Jim Hall, Phil Zarrow and our guest, Joe Belmonte, all of ITM Consulting. I believe today we have a wave soldering question.

Jim ›› We do. It comes from H J. "I'd like to hear your thoughts on the impact or balance of usage of flux to improve solderability and its impact on post-assembly processes, like in-circuit tests where excess flux can cause contact problems."

Phil ›› This is like the guys at the wave solder machine pouring flux all over the whole board saying, "Wow, we get enough flux, I can solder anything."

Jim ›› The real issue is that you've got a solderability problem. So, you'd like to have more flux. I don't think that's a good idea or a good practice. The manufacturers recommend the amount of flux that you should use and then if you put too much, you have to adjust your preheat or you may not get it all activated. You may have other problems.

Phil ›› Yeah, like a fire.

Jim ›› Certainly, in a no-clean process, you do not have that option. You can't put excess flux on, or you'll have a residue that's unacceptable. Likewise, if you're using a water-soluble flux and cleaning, you can choose a stronger, higher solids flux to counter solderability but, that's a slippery slope to go down.

If you have poor solderability, you should be dealing with that up front, not trying to solve it in the wave solder machine. With a water-soluble flux, you can use a stronger flux and maybe use a little more, but make sure you preheat it properly. But you should be cleaning before you go to in-circuit test.

So, if I read this correctly, if you have flux reside, that means you're using a no-clean and you should use what the manufacturer recommends. Joe, do you want to talk about the best way to make sure that you're using the right amount of flux while wave soldering?

Joe ›› Flux is a very sophisticated product. We know it's not beautiful. We know it's not glamorous and we know it doesn't smell very good, but please respect the sophistication of fluxes because they're designed to work within certain parameters. Now every specification for flux has what Jim just mentioned; the precise amount of flux that should be applied to the product.

So, the way that volume usage is checked is usually by weighing the circuit board assembly before and after. The second thing is to find out if the flux has been applied in the right place. The key here, is hole fill because the real problem with waste soldering is top-side hole fill, especially with thick, multi-layer boards that are lead-free. So, what do we do? There's many sophisticated tools on the market which you can research and they're wonderful tools.

One way to get started is just to take two boards with no components and put a piece of paper in between them, like a paper sandwich. You run this board sandwich over the wave system then then take the boards apart. You examine the paper to see if you got penetration of flux up through the holes onto the paper. This will ensure that you've got enough flux in those holes to get proper topside fillets.

There are many ways to apply flux. We have spray, we still have people using a static method, such as foam fluxing and wave flux, so all those things have to be put into consideration, but the key is to get the right amount of flux and get it where you need it.

Jim ›› Thank you, I think that sums it up very well. So, I hope we've answered your question.

Phil ›› So on that note, we'll get the flux outta here. This has been Phil Zarrow, Jim Hall and Joe Belmonte.

Jim ›› Special thanks to Joe and whatever you do, don't solder like my brothers.

Phil ›› Hey, don't solder like my brothers.

BGAs, J-Leads and Squeegees

How to Gauge Solder Paste Volume?

(solder paste, printing, stencil, set-up)

Phil ›› We have a printing question today. Today we are joined by our ITM colleague and "Other Brother", Joe Belmonte.

Jim ›› This question is about solder paste. It's from C.T. "How much solder paste should be applied when running a stencil printing system?" And the second part, "Should you print a PWB on the first pass, or should you work the paste a couple of cycles before running the first good board?"

Well, Joe, what do you have to say?

Joe ›› My recommendation is if you have equipment that has a dispenser, is to purchase your paste in tubes and use the dispenser. That way you can have a controlled bead. But obviously, there are many customers who have purchased paste in jars.

Phil ›› The three of us concur that a bead of about one half to three-quarters of an inch is the ideal. The more paste you put on, the more paste you're exposing to the atmosphere, weakening the paste where problems can occur.

Joe ›› We know that this happens sometimes because folks try to run lines with fewer operators who have several responsibilities. So they load up the paste on the stencil so they can go off to other responsibilities. But you really have to keep that paste bead to a minimum so not to expose the paste to the atmosphere. Make sure you get the proper rolling, to ensure the hole is filled that's required to get a good paste transfer.

Jim ›› I think that's very good. But as with all things, it's going to be somewhat paste-specific. It gets back to qualification. That's this other issue of what we'll call kneading the paste, getting it rolling before you actually start printing.

Some machines have a kneading feature on them which you can activate, and it will actually move the squeegee back and forth in both directions a couple of times to knead or activate the paste into a good rolling condition. Do you need that, or can you just go ahead and print on the first board? It's really a function of the paste. All the manufacturers try to formulate a paste so that as soon as you dispense it, your first pass should be good.

Phil ›› It's the kind of thing you should evaluate when you do your paste qualification.

To be safe, if you don't have a kneading feature, you can print a couple of cycles back and forth on a scrap board before you actually put in a good board to print.

It's something that you should determine for your conditions and the specific paste that you're using. We're talking about application specificity. The materials you're using, the actual application, the machine you're using, and your particular environment.

Jim ›› One another thing; most paste manufacturers work hard to make the paste less sensitive to the environment so that the problem of having too much paste and letting it sit is reduced. But it's still a good practice to minimize solder paste exposure.

Joe ›› Folks often underestimate the sophistication of solder paste. Solder paste is an amazingly sophisticated product. We're asking it to do a lot of things. To get the maximum value, you have to do the engineering work to get the best set of parameters to optimize the performance in the paste you're buying.

Phil ›› You may be buying it as a commodity, but in many respects it is anything but a commodity. Solder paste is to your PCBA as blood is to your body.

Jim ›› And don't push your paste any harder than you have to because most solder defects start with printing of paste.

Can We Add Weights to Components During Reflow?

(reflow, soldering, profiling, fine-pitch, micro-passives, BGA, warpage, Lean six-sigma)

Jim ›› Joining Phil and I today is our "Other Brother" and ITM colleague, Joe Belmonte. Today we have a question about reflow. This question comes to us from C.B. "We have issues with small, light BGAs. They often have opens after reflow. We have no problems with larger BGAs or fine pitch BGAs with higher ball counts. Do you think it makes sense to add a weight to the top of small BGAs during reflow to improve soldering and reduce opens? Any advice would be appreciated."

Phil ›› It sounds like any advice would be desperately needed at this point. Adding weights? I haven't run into that one, yet.

Jim ›› How about NO?

Phil ›› I would venture to guess a possible contributing factor could be to look at your solder paste deposits. Perhaps they're too thick for the pad size and you're getting the floating BGA syndrome. Also look at the Z down-force pressure on your pick and place machine. Are you putting it approximately halfway, one-third to two-thirds of the way into the solder paste as you should?

Jim ›› Since these are not fine pitch devices, they are light. But, I assume they're larger in the horizontal dimensions. You may have an incorrect re-flow profile that's causing excessive warpage, which is causing the opens to occur because the part is warping too much during the reflow process.

Phil ›› This is a situation where we really have to think about whether we are really understanding or working towards the root cause? So often in our travels, we see people "band-aiding" processes and doing things, such as this, which are not the right thing to do as opposed to doing the work that's required to find the root cause of the problem, come up with a solution, verify the solution, and then institutionalize it.

Jim ›› That is the proper approach to a problem like this because this is not an industry-wide problem. This is unique to you.

Joe ›› When I worked at Motorola, the job isn't done until you institutionalize the solution, because if you walk away before the documentation is updated, the equipment's updated, the training completed, whatever it happens to be, then you haven't completed the task.

So what you should do here is certainly start brainstorming possible causes. Bring your folks together, the appropriate technical folks, even your supplier. Maybe even your customer, because it could have something to do with board design. Brainstorm possible causes and start running experiments and studies to identify the root cause.

Phil ›› Come up with solutions, test the solutions, and then, as Joe recommends, institutionalize them

Jim ›› And that's true in any problem such as this.

Solder Paste and the 5 Ball Rule

(solder paste, apertures, stencil, micro-passives, fine-pitch, 5-ball Rule, printing, powder)

Phil ›› Welcome to Board Talk. This is Phil Zarrow with Jim Hall and Joe Belmonte of ITM Consulting coming to you today as Board Talk from the Board Talk Cave high atop Mount Rialto.

Today is solder paste day, isn't it? And we have a solder paste question.

Jim ›› This comes from S.S.: "For either Type III or Type IV solder paste, should there be a minimum number of solder spheres deposited on each surface mount pad?"

Phil ›› Who's gonna sit and count 'em? All right, let's figure out what S.S. really meant here. Jim, take a stab at it, first?

Jim ›› Thinking of the number of spheres, maybe this questioner was getting into printing for ultra-small components, such as 01005 chips or maybe 0.3 or .4 mm BGAs or CSPs and where we are concerned about the deposit on each pad is so small. The surface area is large, relative to the volume and you tend to exhaust the flux and get defects such as graping.

There isn't any easy answer to that. Most people feel they try to put down as much paste as they can get away with without bridging. There are pastes designed to minimize those problems even when the volume of paste or, in this case, the number of spheres is very small.

Joe ›› As Jim said, the key, especially for miniature components with such an incredibly small volume of solder paste, is to print as much paste as possible through the aperture. The way to do that is nothing new to most of the listening audience, is the area ratio calculation.

There's no question that many of the leading stencil suppliers are doing wonderful work to minimize the area ratio required to get the maximum release of paste so you certainly want to keep current on those developments. But as of right now in the industry, we still talk about a 0.6 area ratio to maximize the transfer of the paste from the aperture to the printed circuit board pattern. That's really the key to get repeatability.

Phil ›› One of the things we've talked to our clients quite a bit about in our travels is the term "what works." When we talk about something that works, we're talking about something on the production floor that works 24 hours a day, 7 days a week.

Joe ›› Some of these new technologies are wonderful. I'm certainly the last one to say you shouldn't look at them. You absolutely should, but you want to proceed with caution and do the proper experimentation and studies before you introduce any of these technologies to make sure they in fact work 24 hours a day, 7 days a week on the production floor.

Jim ›› The question mentions Type III and Type IV and we know that Type III has larger particle sizes than Type IV. The other question that might be implied here is the Five-Ball Rule for any given aperture. Five diameters of the largest particle in the paste should fit across the smallest dimension of the smallest aperture to ensure good fill.

Phil ›› We're not even worried about release, just to get good fill as the squeegee moves across the board. So the Five-Ball Rule is pretty well established for very small apertures and perhaps that's what S.S. is referring to.

Options for Wave Solder System Mods

(wave-soldering, soldering)

Phil ›› What's today's question, Jim?

Jim ›› It's an equipment question and it's from G.D. The question is, "Can we replace a lambda nozzle with a Z wave? I have seen both work and the only real difference that I can see is the lambda has a right-hand impeller and the Z-wave is left hand."

Phil ›› Well, in our experience, when you look at equipment modifications in general, you have to ask yourself why do you want to do it, and what are the benefits and costs. Talk to your equipment supplier to see if what you're thinking about has value, and what it may do to your equipment warranty.

Jim ›› We've both worked at equipment companies. A lot of time, effort, and intelligence goes into designing the features and the options available on any given piece of equipment.

To go and modify that may have unforeseen consequences, so check it out with your equipment supplier. Particularly something like a wave soldering machine where which the nozzles are going to be directing the flow of 250, 260 degree C molten solder. You really don't want to take any chances.

Phil ›› When you do contact your equipment supplier, be sure to have the serial number of the machine available because that is key information for the supplier. It will indicate when the machine was built, the specific features and construction, and they will also have the service records. They'll have a good picture of exactly what you're dealing with so they can consider your recommendation with all the available information.

Jim ›› Another issue is after modifications, the ability to get factory service. I know equipment companies I worked for, field service technicians were instructed if unauthorized modifications were made to our equipment, they would not work on it from a strictly legal perspective. So all those factors tend to make me say don't modify your machine if your manufacturer doesn't bless

Phil ›› Hey, and since we're on the topic of wave soldering, a Best Practice with regard to wave soldering is - don't use the chip wave if you don't need it! Shut it off. Hopefully, your designs are advanced enough that you're not trying to wave solder surface-mount components. I know some of you may be stuck with older designs, but if you're not running SMCs through the wave, don't have the chip wave on. It certainly extends your dwell in the highest thermal excursion you're going to see and in general, it's just not a good idea.

When Is It Time to Replace a Squeegee or Stencil?

(stencil, squeegee, printing)

Phil ›› Welcome to Board Talk. This is Phil Zarrow, Joe Belmonte and Jim Hall of ITM Consulting. What is our question du jour, Jim?

Jim ›› Our question today comes from K.B. who asks: "Is there a recommended usage rate for stencils? Is there a way to determine when it's time to replace a squeegee or a stencil?"

Phil ›› Many is the time that we've seen a stencil damaged because of improper handling, dinged or something, long before its reached its expiration, if you will. Same thing with squeegees and since the majority of people use stainless steel squeegees, don't drop that squeegee. Don't ding the squeegee. Don't use a dinged squeegee.

Jim ›› Is it fair to say that if you don't drop and ding your squeegees, they will last a long, long time and there is no real predictable end of life for a squeegee. Most of them are ended by being damaged?

Phil ›› Pretty much so. That's been mostly our experience.

Jim ›› But stencils are something else?

Joe ›› Jim and Phil, you're absolutely right. In my career, this is probably the question I've been asked most and unfortunately there's no answer. You have to remember when a person's using a stencil or a squeegee, the conditions vary greatly from one operation to the other, such as the paste they're using, the cycle time, the pressures, the squeegee speeds.

Phil ›› I've personally never seen a stencil wear out. Usually the design is obsolete due long before there is sufficient stencil wear. However, I've seen plenty of stencils damaged so the stencil is no longer viable.

Joe ›› So as both Jim and Phil said, a stencil and a squeegee should only be one of three places. It should be in the equipment being used, in the cleaner being cleaned, or in a well-designed storage rack. Anywhere else, like up against the bench, on top of a table, leaning up against the machine is an absolute no-no. The biggest enemies of stencils and squeegees are mishandling.

Jim ›› The first thing the printer operator should do before he or she start the print process is give a quick look over of the squeegee and the stencil. If there is any concern at all, they should notify the appropriate responsible engineer or technician who should take that out of service.

Phil ›› You have to remember these are, relatively speaking, low dollar items, low value items, a stencil and squeegee. Why would you risk using a suspect squeegee or stencil to produce defects which cost many, many times the cost of those low value items? I know that most people want to help their company, to preserve the life and save money by not having to buy things but believe me, the right thing to do is take them out of service is there any question at all.

Joe ›› Another point is this: for any high-volume product you have to have a backup stencil. Who wants to lose revenue because of delay for the cost of a relatively inexpensive stencil? For a few hundred dollars, it's a fantastic insurance policy.

Jim ›› I have a question for you guys. When you're using a stencil with a HASL coated board, hot air solder level, you're oftentimes coming in contact with domed pads. Have either of you ever seen the impact on stencil life because of the tendency to deflect the edges of the apertures as they're coming down on a non-flat surface?

Joe ›› Jim intuitively that makes sense, but I have never seen any definitive study that would support that, although in perception and logic, that seems to make sense. There are so many variables in the process, you'd have to run a very detailed, long and laborious experiment to come up with data.

Phil ›› I think, you would see the impact on print quality in terms of the solder paste height and if it's severe enough there would be an effect on gasketing. I never thought about the effect of domed pads but again, they're generally not around long enough.

Joe ›› We learn as we go.

What is Causing Poor Wetting on OSP Coated PCBs?

(PCB fabrication, surface finishes, OSP, soldering, procurement, wetting)

Phil ›› Hello and welcome to Board Talk. This is the three stooges, better known as the Pick and Place brothers. Phil Zarrow, Jim Hall, and our ITM colleague and "Other Brother", Joe Belmonte. "Pick", "Place" and "Feed" and we're up in Mount Rialto. What type of question do we have today, Jim?

**Jim ›› ** This comes from J.G.: "We are experiencing poor wetting on one OSP coated PCB using a lead-free, no clean paste. We see this problem on just one board part number. All other similar boards reflow fine. Where should we look to solve this problem?"

**Jim ›› ** To your supplier.

**Phil ›› ** That's right, it's a supply chain situation, specifically your board vendor or board vendors. We don't know if you're getting the boards from the same fabricator or different suppliers

**Jim ›› ** If this occurs on the same board part number from different vendors, that would be very unusual.

**Phil ›› ** This seems to be a classic example of the copper not being cleaned adequately before the OSP coating is put on. We see that a lot. Contamination or just sloppy practices – a process out of control.

**Joe ›› ** I certainly agree with my colleagues, Phil and Jim. This is a case where you have to look at a process. We talk quite a bit about this in our seminars, especially our new seminar called "Best Practices," that a process involves inputs, operating parameters and outputs and one of the key inputs, is the board itself.

**Jim ›› ** We have to understand every single input as well as the equipment that we're using and all of the other factors. Nowadays, people try to save every dollar they can but you can't shortcut understanding your supplier.

**Joe ›› ** Including going to that supplier and qualifying that supplier properly by asking the right questions, investigating their documentation, observing what they're doing, asking the right questions and spending enough time to fully understand the supplier. Lowest price is not the way to select a supplier. The way to select a supplier is by value. To understand you're getting the right quality for what you want, the right delivery and the right specifications. Remember, the least expensive price may cause you the most expensive problems.

**Phil ›› ** Of course, sometimes trying to convince management is an uphill battle but persevere, 'cause as Joe's saying, we see that so many times. Pay me now or pay me a lot more later.

**Jim ›› ** And document your defects so you can back yourself up.

How Do You Remove Oxidation from PCBs?

(PCB, PCB fabrication, cleaning, PCB handling, storage, baking, contamination, moisture, oxidation, solderability)

**Phil ›› ** Welcome to Board Talk with Phil Zarrow and Jim Hall and our "Other Brother", Joe Belmonte also of ITM Consulting coming to you today from high atop Mount Rialto. Today we have a board question.

Jim ›› This question comes from H.M.: "What would be the best method or product for cleaning bare PCBs that have a small amount of oxidation? I know that proper storage and handling may solve the problem, but what would you suggest? "

Jim ›› The first thing is are you sure we're talking about oxidation? Because oxidation's one thing. If it's contamination, dirt, soils or something else, then any good cleaning product, aqueous-based or solvent-based should remove it. If it's truly oxidation, then we have to talk about the particular surface finish. If it's OSP, it can be stripped off, the copper re-cleaned and you can put new OSP down. So that's a possibility. What about other surface finishes, such as immersion silver, ENIG or HASL?

Phil ›› With ENIG, I don't think you have to worry too much about oxidation. It's one of the beauties of paying for gold, but the others including immersion silver are different. I remember years ago a number of the solder companies used to have chemicals for exactly that, for cleaning up the boards prior to assembly. Nowadays, besides consulting your solder company, I would also talk to one of the companies that makes cleaning agents, for example, Kyzen or Zestron.

Joe ›› I'd also recommended you contact your printed circuit board supplier to get their recommendations. Although it says in the question that they understand the importance of handling and storage, you have to find the root cause for this contamination.

Phil ›› As we've mentioned in other sessions, finding the root cause of any problem is where you're major effort should be.

One of the things we recommend to all customers is that in handling, whoever handles these boards, once they're out of the package, has finger protection, whether it's a glove or finger cots. That's a world-class practice. A big source of contamination on any board is from human handling. So you want to minimize it.

Jim ›› The implication of the statement here is that these boards may not have been handled correctly. If that's true, the other question you should be asking is what about moisture absorption within these boards.

Should they be baked and if you have an oxidation problem - is that going to make it even worse? Should you bake the PCB in a nitrogen atmosphere? If you have boards that have been stored improperly for too long, you have to look at the total construction before you use them.

Joe ›› And one last comment. If they're immersion tin or immersion silver, hot air solder level, whatever, you want to make sure the board was processed properly from your supplier. Is the right thickness of material on those boards? How did the supplier store them and handle them prior to shipping to you? Do you need them packaged individually?

Phil ›› You have to look at all these questions because this is one of the things that should not be a problem in any facility. It is not a common problem. Is there something specific in your supply chain up and to the point the boards are being assembled that's causing this issue? Expend some effort to find out what that is and correct it.

Demise of the Plated-Through Hole?

(components, through-hole, soldering, wave-solder, selective soldering)

Jim ›› Phil, today's question is about through hole components from J.C.. "How long do you expect the industry will continue to use through hole components? I can envision connectors being used for some time, but what about the other component types?" This comes from J.C.

Phil ›› It's the end of the via as we know it…and I feel fine.

Jim ›› If they go away do we have to play Taps at the end? We've got a bugle right here on the wall.

Phil ›› I remember the early days of surface mount there were some people who declared, "Ah, surface mount is just a fad". Of course, they're not around anymore.

Jim ›› I remember in the height of the surface mount revolution people were saying through hole components are going to be gone. I worked for a company that made insertion equipment and they were ready to pack it up. They ended up building a small modular insertion machine. They thought it was going to have a two to three year life yet they couldn't make them fast enough. They were making them till the end when company was acquired.

Phil ›› And those guys are still building. Well, the one you worked for no longer exists but the one I worked for is still building component insertion equipment.

I can also recall another story. This goes back about '82, '83, I remember talking to a designer at Apple Computer and they were building the Apple IIIC, if I recall this was pre-MAC. He said, "Not only do I foresee using a D type connector for the joystick, but I'm looking at one military grade." I said, "How come?" He said, "Because it's got to withstand the force of a 10 year old kid plugging the thing in and pulling it out." So that's the driver for through hole components, typically, is the service life that they're seeing and reliability expectations.

Jim ›› I think J.C. refers to that with his or her comment on connectors. But I want to bring up another thing and that is that we still have dip packages around. Why? A lot of it's just inertia. Companies that are building them, they make a profit, they got all the equipment, it's paid for - they're not going to stop until something breaks or somebody absolutely refuses to use it.

Phil ›› You don't think it's a conspiracy from the guys who built dip inserters, do you? Inquiring minds want to know.

Jim ›› The other thing is parts that are not surface mountable, such as electrolytic capacitors. They can't withstand re-flow temperatures, you make them in a through hole package and hand solder them.

But again, you go off and get into the mechanical issue, whether they feel that the through hole joint is needed for mechanical strength as in connectors. So, I don't know, I don't have a crystal ball. As long as you're going to have connectors, you're going to be wave or selective soldering, I don't know how much it matters.

Phil ›› By the way, do you know where I can get a good vacuum tube these days? Well, that's our philosophy for the day, the answer is through holes use is going to be around for the foreseeable future. They'll be around longer than we are.

Shelf Life Before Conformal Coating

(conformal coating, PCB handling, storage, cleaning, moisture)

Jim ›› Today we have a question for you, Mr. Conformal Coating. "Prior to conformal coating, how long can we keep a circuit board assembly in an open condition before they will be impacted by moisture absorption?"

So I assume that they're saying, "My board is completed, soldering and everything else. I want to conformal coat it. Do I have to be concerned about the circuit board or any of the materials absorbing atmospheric moisture over time?"

Phil ›› Based on my understanding, the most critical thing prior to applying conformal coating is to ensure the board is dry and that's one of the reasons we look very carefully at the drying section on cleaners. We also are concerned about storing the PCBAs before conformal coating application and prior to curing the coating in such a way as to avoid exposure to high relative humidity. But the answer to your question will come from the conformal coating supplier.

Jim ›› There may be a misconception here that the conformal coating prevents moisture absorption and that you've got to apply it while the board is dry so you get that coating on or that moisture will ultimately get into the board. With most conformal coating, that is a misconception.

Phil ›› Very few, if any, of the conformal coating processes will give you a long term, hermetic seal on a board. Yes, they will slow down moisture absorption, but you take a conformally coated board, put it out in an atmosphere and leave it there for weeks, months or a year and it is slowly going to absorb moisture as it diffuses through the coating.

Jim ›› I'm not that familiar with parylene and some of the more exotic coatings, but certainly for acrylics and silicone's, they do not prevent moisture absorption. The moisture will diffuse through the coating over time and eventually set off the electrolytic cell and produce dendrites and other things.

So if that is the question that's being asked, I think the answer is, don't worry about it, because you're ultimately going to absorb moisture over the long term anyway, even before or after coating.

Phil ›› Our conformal coating buddies will weigh in on this and label us a bunch of bozo's which a number of people do anyway.

Cleaning Re-balled BGA Components

(BGA, cleaning, no-clean, OA, water soluble, ultra-sonic, re-balling, moisture)

Jim ›› This is a question on cleaning reballed BGA components, Phil, and it comes from I.F.: "We currently clean re-balled BGA components using an ultra-sonic cleaner with hot water and a cleaning solution. The components are then baked at 100 to 120 degrees C to remove any moisture. The components appear very clean after this process. Is this an acceptable practice for cleaning re-balled BGA components?"

I'm a little confused. Seems to me that cleaning a bare package is a pretty easy job. It's not in a tight space, you have access to all the surfaces. They're using a full immersion cleaning process. I'm wondering what the concern is. But let's review the issues.

First, the cleaning solution - in this case water and cleaning agent - need to be matched to the flux that you're using. If you're using a water soluble flux for this process, you shouldn't have to use any cleaning agent. Hot water should be more than adequate. Now if you have a no clean or a rosin based flux, you're going to have to use something else that is appropriate for the chemicals you're trying to remove.

Phil ›› That explains the chemical side. As far as the mechanical energy, you're using an ultrasonic cleaner.

Jim ›› Phil, aren't there some concerns with IC packages and ultra-sonics?

Phil ›› It is one of the great debates of our industry. The whole thing about it was the legend, if you will, is that the ultra-sonics can destroy the wire bonds within an IC. There was a lot of work that basically disproved this theory. Most notably, there were projects done for HP and Delphi, and a few of the others. In our experience, Fixed Frequency ultrasonics are a problem – Sweep Frequency ultra-sonics seem to be okay.

But obviously, the real test is your particular components. If they've been retested and they're not failing, then apparently there is no damage done. It's good to have mechanical energy when cleaning, but a very important thing, as Jim mentioned, is the chemical component. I hope they're not using the same solution you clean jewelry with, you know, ammonia or something like that.

Jim ›› Two other things. One is the idea of drying. If you're going through a reballing process, that means that the package is going through at least one re-flow step. Therefore, it should have been dried before the re-balling operation to make sure there's no moisture in it so you don't get moisture sensitive damage - delamination, pop-corning or whatever - during the re-balling process.

Phil ›› If that's true, then there should be no need to re-dry the package after a cleaning process. Packages absorb moisture, atmospheric moisture - humidity in the air - over long periods of time - hours and hours and hours. They don't get saturated with moisture because of a five or ten minute immersion in an aqueous cleaning process.

Jim ›› The other thing is, they look clean. Well, there are standard techniques for measuring cleanliness. Two of them are the rose test, or the ionograph, and the other is ion chromatography. Your eyes are not a real good indicator of the cleanliness of the surfaces of BGA or any surfaces.

Phil ›› And there are new tests being developed that are in preliminary stages. So we hope that answered I.F.'s question. We are still waiting for Myth Busters to call us about doing a joint project (bad pun intended) as to whether ultra-sonics kill wire bonds.

Problems With Starved "J" Lead Joints

(soldering, components, PLCC, reflow, solder paste, stencils, apertures, step-stencil, Pin-in-Paste, over-print, insufficients)

Phil ›› What kind of question do you have there today, Jim?

Jim ›› This question comes from M.M.: "We have insufficient solder joint heel fillets with a PLCC J-lead component. The aperture on the solder paste stencil is one to one or 30 by 100 mils." Pretty big aperture. "Visually, the solder fillet appears okay, but testing indicates that we need additional solder at the heel joint. We cannot increase the stencil thickness due to the presence of TSOPs and QFP packages. What do you advise?"

Phil ›› We don't know what the stencil thickness is, but apparently it's a little on the shy side for those poor little hungry little J-leads.

Jim ›› The world has come to fine pitch components dominating everything because of hand-held devices.

You know, even in cell phones they still have the same conflict because they have all those fine pitch components and then they solder an RF shield down which needs huge volumes of paste. So, what we have here, ladies and gentlemen, is a classic case of different solder volume requirements sometimes called mixed mode printing, broadband printing and so forth. And the answer is a step stencil.

Phil ›› The most robust solution is, indeed, a step stencil. Where the questioner here indicates, "I'd like to make the stencil thicker, but I have fine pitch component so I can't." So, you step up the stencil at your J lead locations, or you step down the other ones using a thicker stencil, whichever is more economical based upon the distribution and the number of the different styles of components. Of course we're assuming you have ample clearance between where you have to step down to accommodate step down. If not, another alternative would be double printing.

Jim ›› Yes, double printing, where you print a thin stencil first, then print with a thick stencil which is etched out, relieved for the other ones, but you really need about three mils of difference in order to do that.

Phil ›› And another printer, too.

Jim ›› The next option would be staying with a thinner stencil and over printing.

And people go, "Oh, but won't I get solder balls and stuff off the pad?" and of course that's a risk, but I'd like to point out that overprinting beyond the pads has been a very common practice in intrusive soldering or pin-in-paste for many years and it can be done with a minimal risk of solder balls and bridges. Particularly, remember, you're dealing with a 50 ml pitch part so the chances of bridging are pretty small.

Phil ›› Of course we have the options of using a preform - adding a preform via your placement system. You print your paste and then during your placement operation, one of your feeders has a reel of these solder preforms and your placement machines simply picks it up and places it in the wet paste out beyond the edge of your J lead heel where you want that extra solder. The pick and place machine just sees these "solder slugs" as rectangular components about 0402 size. Then when you reflow, it melts and combines with the solder paste and gives you the extra solder you need.

Max Interval Between Reflow for OSP Boards

(reflow, OSP, PCB surface finishes, soldering, nitrogen, wetting, oxidation, PCB fabrication, solderability)

Phil ›› Today we have a materials question about OSP.

Jim ›› It's on surface finishes. "With OSP coated circuit boards, what is the maximum allowable and recommend time interval between reflow of the first and second sides to insure proper wetting." Well, first off we must say that the subject of OSP is a very emotional and subjective issue. Some people do not believe that OSP is a good finish, even for single side reflow. They just don't like it and that's their opinion. Other people have no problems.

Phil ›› OSP materials themselves have come a long way. In the early days if you were doing double sided reflow you wanted to process to second side as soon as possible because the original OSPs dissipated in the presence of heat So those original materials required a very, very strict regimen in terms of nitrogen atmosphere. If I recall, below 100 PPM O2 .

Jim ›› But I think the question is more significant for most people who have these concerns. The question regards the un-soldered pads, second side pads. Being exposed to the first re-flow cycle, are they still solderable? I think some people believe that damage to those un-soldered pads occurs during the reflow cycle. Hence, the mitigation strategy to use nitrogen.

Phil ›› The idea here is that the material itself becomes more porous and of course, heat - which you're doing in an oven - is a catalyst for oxidation and so the pores open up a little bit. But by the same token, we see a lot of people doing OSP's without nitrogen atmosphere.

Jim ›› That's absolutely true, Phil. The more important concern is about the quality of the coating process. OSP is an organic material. It's got to be put on right. Proper thickness, proper quality controls, proper curing cycles and so forth. All of that contributing to allowing it to survive that first re-flow cycle and give you good solderability and wetting. You probably have a pretty wide window in terms of the timing to your second re-flow.

Phil ›› So if you are concerned about perhaps a longer time frame than we're talking about here, you should consult your supplier of OSP materials and get the finite answer in terms of their specs because they know their chemistry.

Going Beyond Your Solder Paste Work Life

(solder paste, flux, components, printing, soldering, oxidation)

Jim ›› An intelligent questioner has sent in a problem, proposed a solution and is asking us for validation. "We encountered cold solder joints on all of the 0603 components on the bottom side of a small batch of board assemblies, yet the larger components had good solder joints. These components are all near via holes but this does not seem to be related to the cause. We replaced the solder paste on a new batch of assemblies and the problem was eliminated."

Phil ›› What changed?

Jim ›› The solder paste used for the problem batch had exceeded the 12 hour setup usage time when we applied the solder paste in our facilities. It was exceeded it by one hour. Was the problem likely do to paste exceeding our 12-hour work life?

Phil ›› The amount of time that a paste stays on the stencil while you're printing is called work life. Obviously after a long enough time, any paste will dry out and degrade and need to be replaced.

Jim ›› Apparently this material was rated for 12 hour work life and this small batch of boards was printed after 13 hours. All pastes have solvents in them as well as other materials. So over time they're exposed to the atmosphere, sitting out on the stencil; they dry out. Also chemical reactions take place, but mostly it's drying. So you print and the paste isn't what it's supposed to be. It's lost some of its chemistry.

Phil ›› Whatever the mechanism, you see it on your smallest components because they have the smallest deposits on the board and they have the largest surface area to volume ratio. This is much more "amplified" with people doing 0201 and 01005 components where you have tiny deposits.

Jim ›› What happens? You're going through your reflow. We're assuming you're reflowing in air. You don't have as many solvents and materials in the paste. You exhaust them during the reflow process. They do their job cleaning the oxides on your 0603's and on the pads. But the chemistry of the paste is exhausted before you reach the reflow section and you get re-oxidation.

Thus, the impression that you're getting a cold solder joint. Worst case you can even get graping because you've reduced the fluxing capability, re-oxidation occurs and the individual particles don't coalesce on the surface of the paste deposit and the resulting joint.

Phil ›› I think as a sidebar, one of the things is that expiration time, or in this case the work life - you should know it and adhere to it. You can establish or re-establish the work life when you qualify your solder paste. But in lieu of that, pay very strict attention to the manufacturer's specification sheet on things like work life, pot life, shelf life, expiration dates. They tend not to be too conservative.

Jim ›› Establish your own realistic work life on your own conditions because it's obviously a function of temperature and humidity.

Solder Paste Transfer Efficiency - What/Why

(printing, solder paste, apertures, stencil, SPI, nano-coating, area ratio)

Phil ›› Welcome to Board Talk and greetings from Mount Rialto, the Board Talk recording studio where we ponder the questions on process and materials and equipment that our wonderful audience sends in. Jim, what have got for today's question?

Jim ›› Phil, today's question comes from B.Z.: "I've heard the term transfer efficiency relating to printing. What does this term refer to?"

Phil ›› Funny thing about solder paste - you have your stencil, your aperture, dimensions of the aperture, your thickness of the stencil. So, then you can calculate volume.

Yes, printing is three-dimensional. Theoretically you have a volume of solder that you are placing in the aperture and that you are transferring to the board. However solder paste does not necessarily want to go everywhere you want it to go. The bottom line is, what you're filling in the aperture with is not necessarily going onto the circuit board which is where you desire it. And there are things that can impact what we call the transfer efficiency to various degrees.

Jim ›› The transfer efficient is simply the ratio, usually expressed as a percentage, of the volume of the paste you actually get on the board divided by the actual theoretical volume of the stencil aperture.

If you're counting on the full volume of the aperture to give you enough solder to give get a good joint and your transfer efficiency is low it's going to affect the quality. Putting on my Lean Six Sigma hat, the repeatability of transfer efficiency can also effect quality. You print one time and you get 90 percent transfer efficiency and the next time you get 70 percent transfer from the same aperture. So now you have a variable volume that you're getting on the board for a particular joint and that could be really problematic and tough to debug.

Phil ›› So the question in stencil engineering over a number of years has been what we need to improve to help assure better transfer efficiency. One of the things that almost everybody's aware of is the efforts made to make sure the aperture walls are as smooth as possible.

And that's one of the things that led to changing from chemical etching of apertures to laser cutting, and finally, to electro-formed stencils.

We've gone into things like fine-grained stainless steel and high grade stainless steel materials.

Jim ›› And polishing the apertures after laser cutting. Polishing through plasma etching and micro-machining and other techniques, to make them smoother so there's less tendency of that solder paste to stick.

And this is what's happening. It's strictly a function of paste tackiness sticking to the pad and aperture walls. Thus the use of area ratio giving a prediction of transfer efficiency. But now aren't there even newer things from the fifth dimension? The magic word: nano.

Phil ›› Yes, these are coatings that come in basically two forms:

The coating can be applied by the stencil manufacturer when they're putting their stencil together for you.

Coatings that you can put on after-market. I guess they go on with something that looks like a wipe.

There have been some interesting studies. Most recently, a very extensive study by our good friend Chrys Shea. She's presented some material and she did this in conjunction with Vicor. It's a really interesting study. You'll learn a lot about transfer efficiency from this paper alone.

Moving Ovens, Moisture and Optical Inspection

Consensus for Baking Prior to Rework?

(baking, soldering, moisture, PCB, delamination, rework, hand-soldering, MSD, PCBA)

Jim ›› Today we have a rework question and comes from P.A.: "We often rework circuit board assemblies that may have disc drives, batteries, plastics, or other heat sensitive components. What is the industry consensus for baking out moisture in circuit board assemblies prior to convection rework, localized mini-wave rework, or hand soldering rework? In each case we are scrapping the removed components. So, we're not worried about baking time on those. In addition, we are masking and shielding the adjacent areas to isolate the extreme temperatures of the rework site. Should we be baking the board per IPC J-STD-033? Or can we utilize IPC 1601, Handling and Storage Guidelines, which focus on the board material?"

Phil ›› P.A. has really done their work. The simple answer is: we're concerned about the board, so you want to use IPC 1601. As you said, in your rework process, you're shielding your other components. IPC J-STD-033 refers to components. You've defined it very well. You're not worried about the components you're taking off.

Jim ›› You've got to think about the components you're putting on of course, and they should've been dried according to 033. But what you're concerned about is delamination of the PCB. Even though it's localized, if there is moisture globally in the board, you could damage it at or near the site where you are applying the (to use your term) extreme temperatures.

Phil ›› IPC 1601 gives you guidelines for exposure times and bake cycles and everything like that. Yes, you very carefully defined the issue and we agree it's the board you're concerned about in rework.

Jim ›› IPC 1601 is a good spec. The answer is that IPC 1601 and J-STD-033 are parallel. They both talk about the absorption and moisture, potential damage during reflow (or in this case rework) and J-STD-033 talks about components and 1601 talks about the PCB itself.

Tips When Moving a Reflow Oven

(reflow, soldering, maintenance)

Phil ›› Let's see, what kind of subject do we have to warm up to today Jim?

Jim ›› One near and dear to our hearts - reflow. This comes from Q.N.: "After moving a reflow oven to a different site, what steps do you need to perform on the machine and the heat exhaust in order for the machine to be certified?"

Phil ›› Certified? Is there an official reflow oven certification? Oh yeah, that's right. That's us.

Jim ›› Right, there is no known certification standard for ovens. But certainly, you do want to make sure that your oven is performing in the same manner in terms of accuracy and repeatability that it did at the former site. The most important thing that's more likely to give you problems is the conveyor system.

Phil ›› Absolutely Jim. This is what carries the board. You only have your little edge conveyors. Getting the machine leveled, getting them lined up, vibration free, parallel and so forth so that you don't drop boards or jam boards in your oven, is probably the most important step.

Jim ›› That being said, you want to get the same thermal performance. You want to get the same repeatable profiles on your board. You are very astute to ask about exhaust because proper exhausting can affect the performance of an oven. So, you want to make sure that the exhaust is set up with whatever measurements you use to set it up initially.

Once it's set up you want to take some calibration vehicle that you have history on, ideally both a profile and repeatability of that profile, and run it again. And run multiple profiles to make sure that you're getting accuracy, getting the same peak temperatures, the same time above liquidus, slopes and so forth, and that profile is repeatable over multiple profiles so that you can get the same performance and get the same quality boards that you were getting.

Phil ›› You might also check with the oven manufacturer and see if they have any other recommendations in addition to maintenance. They have some experience with the particular model and know - and just might reveal - where the vulnerable spots are.

Big Problems with HASL Finish

(surface finish, HASL, soldering, components, defects, contamination, PCB fabrication)

Jim ›› The question today comes from P.T.: "We recently needed to repair a defective PCBA. This required the removal of an SOIC. We were able to simply lift the SOIC off the PCBA using tweezers and light force and no heat. The pads on the PCB are bare copper, but the PCB was originally manufactured using tin lead HASL finish. And the SOIC was soldered with tin lead solder. What do you think happened?"

Well P.T., you've got a bad circuit board my friend. HASL (hot air solder level) coating has been one of the most robust finishes for many years, to the point where even with the problems with lack of flatness on the pads, people still hang onto it because it solders so well.

And the reason it solders so well is because during the process you actually solder the HASL finish to the copper therefore forming the copper intermetallic on the board.

Phil ›› So when you solder the HASL you're really not soldering because the intermetallic has already been formed. You are simply reflowing the solder. In fact, it was the presence of HASL finishes, or the predominance of HASL finish, that coined the term reflow. Because people said you're not really soldering, you're just reflowing solder.

Jim ›› But the point being, if you're got a board where after reflow (or whatever technique you use to attach your SOIC) all of the tin lead lifts off of the pad exposing bare copper. You had a horrible glitch in your HASL process. Because what is HASL? You take a bare board, clean the copper, coat it with flux and dump it in a solder pot and then blow out the extra solder.

Phil ›› This is a process that's been around since the mid-'70's. Can we say, "mature process"? It's pretty hard to screw up. But apparently your board fabricator probably did screw it up. At least that seems the most likely thing.

Jim ›› The only thing I can think of is a fingerprint. Before the HASL process, the first thing the fab shop will do is scrupulously clean the copper, as they do before they put on any surface finish. In fact, usually they micro-etch the surface to remove a thin layer of copper so that you get all the contaminants off. You have absolutely pristine copper to put on your finish, in this case HASL.

I'm guessing that somehow some contamination got on those pads for this SOIC. And, of course, it raises the question: you ought to check the rest of the boards.

Phil ›› Yeah and the rest of the boards of the production too. And maybe some of the stuff was shipped to customers?

Jim ›› One of the most common causes for poor soldering is contamination coming from fingerprints. Somebody puts a thumbprint on a specific board between the cleaning process and the fluxing process.

Phil ›› The flux doesn't have the capacity to clean off the oils. It goes through the process. For some reason the HASL coating stuck a little so that you didn't notice that it was bare copper. Or maybe it was bare copper, and nobody picked it up. But the point is it didn't solder right because it was contaminated under the HASL.

PCBA Cleaning with Sodium Bicarbonate

(cleaning, solvents, contamination, defects, surface finish)

Jim ›› Our question today is about cleaning. It comes from L.P. "Is there an effect on PCBA long-term reliability for assemblies cleaned with a sodium bicarbonate scrub followed by DI water rinse to remove tarnishing of silver immersion plating?"

I assume that you have checked the compatibility of all the materials on your circuit board, your components, compatibility with the sodium bicarbonate and your cleaning operation. But most important is that sodium bicarbonate to the best of my knowledge is a caustic solution, as many traditional cleaners have been, and you absolutely need to get it all off the board when you're done.

Phil ›› We would suspect that DI water probably is not quite hacking it. It depends upon the components on your board, the clearances and so forth and the mechanical action during this "scrub," whether it's forcing sodium bicarbonate under low clearance parts such as a QFNs. If you leave sodium bicarbonate on your board, you are definitely taking a risk.

Jim ›› He's talking about an assembly so I interpret that as having soldered components on the printed circuit board, or a printed wiring board if we want to be more descriptive.

Phil ›› Immersion silver finish has been around for a while now. And it's becoming really popular. This is a common problem. I would check with some of the industry cleaning companies.

Jim ›› You want to get a cleaning process that's designed to be compatible with all your electronic materials.

Phil ›› Happy scrubbing and happy cleaning.

Can Immersion Gold PCBs Oxidize?

(surface finish, ENIG, defects, rework and repair, contamination, oxidation, PCB fabrication)

Jim ›› We have a question from J.T.: "I have immersion gold PCBs that have developed oxidation. Is there a specific material/process to recover these boards?"

Phil ›› Somehow there's a disconnect here, one does not normally associate oxidation with gold finishes.

Jim ›› I think it's impossible, isn't it?

Phil ›› It'd be really, really hard to do.

Jim ›› I think it takes a nuclear accelerator to get oxygen to combine with gold. So, there's obviously something else going on.

Phil ›› There is something amiss here. I would say among other things get thee to a failure analysis lab henceforth because we don't really know what's going on.

Jim ›› I would think of historical sources first. Have these been exposed? Obviously, the thing that comes to mind is some sort of contamination. Something has grown under the surface, from handling, from an atmosphere, from some other process, from something that was or wasn't done in the initial board fabrication process where they put on the gold finish.

If you can track that down historically, it may be a little less painful than going to an analysis lab, but then that being not possible, the only way you're going to really know what it is, is to have it chemically analyzed.

Phil ›› Or you may be a victim of the dreaded plague of black pad.

Jim ›› Phil, it doesn't say that it's ENIG. It says immersion gold. Immersion gold. So that could be gold over copper. In which case it might be something else

Phil ›› It could very likely something in the plating process.

Jim ›› Let's be honest. Gold is fabulously expensive today so any manufacturer who's putting gold on is going to try to get away with absolutely the minimum amount of gold that - perhaps pushing the low end of a thickness specification.

Phil ›› So if you have a porous gold - either over nickel or over copper - now you can get oxygen diffusing through a porosity and causing some bad stuff to happen, which may change color.   And again, a failure analysis lab would be a great place to turn to determine exactly what you are seeing there.

Jim ›› They could measure the thickness of the coating and so forth. But again, going back to your supplier and getting their specifications, checking your certificate of compliance - which hopefully you have. Unless I really have forgotten that much of my chemistry, I don't think that you're chemically mixing oxygen and gold.

Phil ›› There's something amiss here and it is most likely at your board shop. But again, send it to a lab and find out what's really going on.

Solder Paste Volume for BGA Rework

(printing, solder paste, BGA, reflow, rework and repair, stencils)

Phil ›› What is today's question, Jim?

Jim ›› It comes from M.B. who asks: "When we rework BGA components we typically apply solder paste. Our BGA rework stencils match the aperture size and thickness as used on our production line. Therefore, the solder volume added during BGA rework is equal to the solder volume used during production. Since rework can never be as controlled or consistent as original assembly, should we use slightly more paste during BGA rework to compensate for irregularities or flatness, pad conditions and so forth?"

Phil ›› Well, very astute noticing the obvious inconsistencies of reworked or repair being a highly manual process. No matter how automatic the equipment is, it's only semi-automatic and there is a lot of variation in consistency compared to a nice automatically printed solder paste. So, it's a really good question.

Jim ›› Reworking BGAs has been the topic of many papers, books and articles. The range of "acceptable" procedures ranges from using a relatively large volume of solder paste to no paste at all instead using tacky flux. My personal feeling is that with all the variations associated with BGA rework such as warpage and so forth that, yeah, a little more paste volume is going to give you a more robust process and ultimately a more robust solder joint as long as you don't push it to the point where you're getting solder balls or bridging.

Phil ›› AS long as you're not down at the ultra-fine pitch BGAs, a little more paste shouldn't be an issue. We probably should say, there's one issue that's involved here and that is how carefully are you dressing or cleaning the BGA pads after you remove the initial BGA.

In most cases, you leave some solder. You do not remove all of the solder from the pads on the board after you remove the original BGA.

Jim ›› I think this is part of the reason why some people use tacky flux because they assume that there is some residual solder and that combined with a fresh new ball and a new BGA that you're putting back on the board is adequate. But again, I can't defend it from an experimental standpoint. But I'm with you, I guess, M.B., to use a little extra paste as long as it is not causing bridging or solder balls, if you can add a little more paste, it won't hurt at all and may help you.

Delay Before Cleaning Partial Assemblies

(cleaning, contamination, OA, defects, water soluble, corrosion)

Phil ›› Welcome to Board Talk, this is Phil Zarrow and Jim Hall, the Assembly Brothers, coming to you from high atop Mount Rialto. What's today's dilemma, Jim?

Jim ›› This is a cleaning question from J.C.: "We're assembling circuit boards with a water soluble flux but have run out of some parts." J.C. is the first person in electronic assembly to ever run out of parts while assembling a board. "Is it acceptable to leave these partially assembled boards for 3 to 4 days, then put on the rest of the parts and then finally wash them?"

Phil ›› In a word, NO. You have to think in terms of organically activated water soluble fluxes as basically acid fluxes. This stuff is very highly reactive. The benefit is of course you can clean it with water or with deionized water. But the idea is that they are water-soluble.

The downside is you have to clean them, and the wisdom is clean them as soon as possible. Let me give you some anecdotal information.

Years ago, there was a client we knew in the Boston area who had ENIG boards, and they were soldering with the OA flux and their inline cleaner bombed out. And so, they were waiting for the repairman to come and the boards sat over the weekend. What they found Monday morning was that in some instances the OA flux residue had actually eaten through the gold. That's how nasty this stuff is.

Another situation with another company where it was a similar type of predicament. They were assembling boards on Friday and the old quitting bell rang and there were a bunch of boards that hadn't been cleaned.

Again, with water-soluble fluxes and in this case on HASL boards, and lo and behold, come Monday, there was dendritic growth. Where did that come from? I believe the bias voltage in this case came from some testing they had done. Scary stuff.

The rule of thumb is clean as soon as possible and make sure everybody knows that they are being cleaned.

Jim ›› On a much less dramatic level, it's also easier to clean them the sooner you clean them, you leave OA fluxes, harden and dry out for another couple of days and it makes them that much more difficult to clean even if you didn't have any of the horrible effects that my brother has alluded to.

Phil ›› So the long-term solution here would be- in this case of the parts shortages is if you're going to solder those boards with the OA flux, missing a few parts, clean them as soon as possible, and then when those other parts come in, you can -- depending on whether you're wave or hand-soldering, whether you're going to use an OA flux and clean them again, or you're going to use a no-clean flux, again depending on the application, everything else and not cleaned, so, you know, be careful. But we feel your pain about missing components, welcome to the club we call electronic assembly. It's happened before, it will happen again.

Jim ›› Hopefully you weren't waiting for an answer before you got our wonderful wisdom on this but clean them as soon as possible.

Proper Exhaust Pressure for Reflow Ovens?

(reflow, soldering, maintenance, ovens)

Jim ›› This question comes from E.R.: "You had mentioned about proper exhausting of the reflow oven. At what exhaust pressure normally should the oven be measured at?"

Phil ›› Talk to us Mr. Oven.

Jim ›› Well, certainly measuring pressure in an exhaust system is one way to quantify it. You've got to have the right exhaust and it's important. The real critical parameter that most ovens will specify is a flow rate in cubic feet per minute or cubic meters per hour or some other volumetric flow rate.

Then the static pressure, if it's outside the oven, to create that flow rate is going to depend upon the geometry and dynamics of your exhaust piping. Some ovens may give you a pressure tap inside the oven within their known piping. But the bottom line is you go to the manufacturer.

If they give you a flow rate, then you go to your piping and make the conversion using standard duct flow procedures.

Phil ›› What instrument would E.R. be using to performs these tests, Jim?

Jim ›› For measuring static pressures, it's just any kind of a pressure gauge or manometer. Often you see these little red mercury or alcohol manometers that they use in duct work. The key is pressure is only an indication of flow rate. And what you're really concerned about is getting the proper volumetric flow rate and that it's stable. That it doesn't vary over time such as when the people down at the end of the exhaust duct turn on the spray booth or something and the static pressure, and therefore the flow rate, changes and your oven thermal process is upset.

Phil ›› The only thing I want to add is when you do your ducting, make sure that the ducting you're using to connect from the oven to the rest of your exhausting system is rated for the proper temperature for the reflow oven.

Jim ›› Depends upon the way the oven is ducted internally and so forth. But yes, high temperature rated and cleanable. You know, all the manufactures do their best to put filters for flux-capture inside, but always anticipate the possibility of some flux getting into the duct and condensing somewhere. Make sure that you put in provisions to take the duct apart and clean it.

We Bake, But Still Have Delamination, Why?

(PCB, handling and storage, baking, MSD, humidity, delamination, defects, moisture, thermal considerations)

Jim ›› Phil, This comes from K.R: "We baked our bare PCBs at a 100 degree C for six hours. And then dipped in our HASL machine at 250 degree C for 10 seconds with no delamination problems.

The same PCBs were then assembled and passed through our wave soldering system at minimum conveyor speed with no delamination. Finally, the PCBs had SMT components placed and the PCBs passed through our reflow system at 217 to 230 degrees C. Most of these PCBs had issues with delamination. Where should we look to solve this puzzling problem?"

Phil ›› I might start, asking about this process sequence because they're talking about sequential processing HASL exposure, followed by wave soldering, followed by SMT assembly.

What were the timing between these steps? Was it possible that between wave soldering and reflow soldering the boards were exposed long enough to an ambient moisture condition that brought enough moisture back in. Remember, your soldering cycles don't bake out moisture.

Jim ›› Assuming that they're conscious of this problem. I was just glancing at IPC 1601. I noticed that all their bake cycles call out for 105 to 120 degrees C. These boards were baked at 100 C.

I'm guessing that maybe the baking was just a little too cool. And that you got some residual moisture deep in the core of the board such that these shorter cycles and HASL and wave soldering did not pump enough heat into the board to cause the problem. But the longer 30 to 60 seconds in a typical reflow profile may cause the problem.

Phil ›› Deep penetrating moisture might be the source of the problem. An easy thing would be to bump your bake temperature up 10 or 15 degrees.

Jim ›› I'd recommend looking at IPC 1601. It's the first document that really addresses in numbers and in hard facts or hard recommendations the idea of PCB baking. This new IPC spec is a first in the industry for a universal specification and looks like KR may be a little outside of it.

Phil ›› Also, with any multiple processing, is there another source of moisture within the process that's getting in there? Did you clean after wave soldering? We recommend a bake for ½-1 hour at 65C (or what ever part limitations are present). Blowers only remove the gross moisture but not out of the mask porosity or out from under low stand off devices. *(Ed.)*

Jim ›› But again, you can't see moisture. It's sort of a mystery, out of sight.

Is There a Limit to the Step in a Step Stencil?

(printing, stencil, apertures, step-stencil)

Phil ›› Welcome to Board Talk. It's Jim Hall and Phil Zarrow, the Assembly Brothers, who by day go as ITM Consulting. So, what is today's question?

Jim ›› Today's question comes from B.B. The question is about step stencils. "I've used step stencils with one and two mil steps successfully. But recently, I've seen a problem with the 3-mil step. This is an 8-mil foil step down over most of the printed area to a 5 mil thickness.

The problem I am seeing is that the stencil tends to warp around apertures, particularly in areas like fine pitch where there are long apertures close together and the remaining material is a thin strip. The warp makes the stencil act thicker, allows more paste to be deposited leading to bridges on fine pitch QFPs. Is there a rule of thumb regarding the amount of step that can be etched into the stencil?"

Phil ›› Well, YES there is. It's been speculated for many, many years. I know back, years ago, we used to use about 2-mil step, but now I think the common wisdom is one about 1.5 mil.

Jim ›› My experience is that most everybody who does step stencils feels comfortable with the 1-mil step. A lot of people use 1.5 mil. Above that, very few people like to go more than a 1.5 mil to get repeatable printing. But this raises other questions. This is really a step-up stencil. Where most of the area of the stencil is the lower thickness and you are stepping up for a few thicker areas. I don't know that much about the specifics of the stencil fab, but this seems like a common issue that you should discuss with your stencil manufacturer.

Phil ›› Because if you're getting that problem, you're paying for the stencil and you're probably paying extra get all that extra material etched off or whatever milling process they use to reduce thickness. Perhaps it's something about the pressure, the squeegee or something that you're using that's causing the stencil to be damaged.

Jim ›› But either way, 3 mils is really pushing the envelope or in this case, pushing the aperture. Although we should say stencil manufacturers have successfully stepped 5, 7, 8 mils, but I honestly have never seen an application. The question - is this a viable robust process to put into a manufacturing operation. So, our general rule is 1.5 mils, maybe to 2 mils, but 3 mils definitely goes over rule.

Keys for Moisture Sensitive Device Control

(MSD, components, moisture, humidity, handling and storage)

Jim ›› Here is a question close to our hearts. "Our customer is requesting documentation on our MSD program. We attach travelers to every group of MSD components whenever they are taken out of the moisture barrier bag; is this good enough?"

Phil ›› Well, it's a good start. I'll elaborate by saying at least you are trying to make an effort to do an MSD program. The traveler is a good start, but so many times we see cases where the times are not filled in or they guesstimated the times they put in the dry box or back in the bag with a desiccant.

Jim ›› Is it fair to say that in 15-20 years of auditing customer facilities we have found very few facilities that had an airtight MSD program in place. Most of them had some program, it just had holes in it.

Phil ›› Usually the most common hole we see is the lack of operator diligence. MSD is important. The problem has been around as long as we've had surface mount ICs.

We see people starting to become aware of it and we see a lot of people that just don't even have programs. And very few are airtight, or vacuum-sealed in this case. What we find lacking is that they put the program in place, but nobody really understands it. They've got all kind of essential training on ESD and everybody understands what is about, they do it and follow the procedures.

One of the most important things you could do is have an MSD training program, a boot camp, if you will. Bring everybody up to speed, what is this, why they have to be diligent about filling in the travelers and do that.

And make sure the traveler is proper. I ran to this a couple weeks ago. Company had a traveler and they had it affixed properly, and they input dates on the bag.

Jim ›› What's wrong with that?

Phil ›› Let's give or take about 24 hours. No times were included, just the date.

Jim ›› At another facility they were having problems, but nobody bothered to subtract the hours and total the amount of time that the parts have been out of the bag. By their own documentation, parts exceeded the J-STD-033 limit for moisture sensitive level. So, for type 3, that means it had been out of the bag more than seven days. Type 4, out of the bag more than three days.

So if you are filling out a traveler and it's a type 3 part and it has been out of the bag more than seven days, the bag should be labeled, must be baked before reuse.

Likewise, if a type 4 part has been out of the bag more than 12 hours continuously, it must be baked.

Phil ›› There are more elaborate systems. There is bar code systems that use bar code scanning of the parts, and there is even RFID code scans system.

But regardless, it's only as good as the operators and technicians knowing what the MSD thing is all about. So, the paper travelers can be a very effective methodology, but you've got to do the due diligence. You have to bring the team up to speed, why we are doing it and how we are doing it.

Jim ›› And people have to understand it and follow it.

Will Nitrogen Reduce Wave Solder Defects?

(soldering, wave-solder, nitrogen, profiling, components, defects, dross, solder pot, pre-heat)

Phil ›› What is today's dilemma, Jim?

Jim ›› Improving DPM for wave soldering using nitrogen. This comes from A.S.: "We are wave soldering complex board with 3000-plus components using OSP finish and SAC305 alloy. Our current defective parts-per-million level for soldering is 400 to 500 and for solder voids is around 1000. To improve our DPM, we plan to install a nitrogen environment around the wave soldering tank to reduce oxidation. Is this likely to improve our DPM level?"

Phil ›› With regard to voids, that's another question. Let me say this about nitrogen before we dive into it. Anybody who has listening to this program knows we're not big fans of using nitrogen for reflow. However, wave soldering is a totally different process. With the addition of flux, addition of solder, it's a totally different beast.

We have found both from our personal experiences as well as studies that were done a long time ago by Soltec and Electrovert, that nitrogen really does help in the wave soldering process with through hole components by improving the surface tension and by reducing the oxidation, it helps the solder go in the right places. So, things like less propensity towards bridging, reduced solder balls, reduced open and skips - you can see some improvement. And the other advantage of inerting the wave is you're only inerting the wave areas. And can do that out of a gas bottle. However, with voids, well, this kind of leaves a void in the problem here.

Jim ›› I'm not totally convinced that I understand exactly what they're describing. What's the difference between DPM level for soldering and solder voids. But if they're experiencing solder voids in wave soldering that waves the flag of inadequate preheat.

Phil ›› Voids are typically caused by solvent in the flux being captured in the wave and causing bubbles and voids. The answer is to make sure you're profiling your preheat correctly, putting thermocouples on top of the board on a land adjacent to a heavy through-hole component and making sure that the top surface of the board is reaching the appropriate temperature for the flux.

Jim ›› Typical numbers are for alcohol-based flux, it's 100 degrees. For water based VOC-free fluxes it's 110 to 120. But in any case check what your manufacturer recommends because I suspect that's the principle cause of voiding. I don't know that nitrogen is going to help that very much. But I agree that it should help the other defects, particularly with insufficient solder and insufficient hole fill. The question is raised, if you are not preheating adequately, in addition to not boiling off the solvents, you may not be fully activating the flux.

I agree that nitrogen is a good idea for reduction of dross, particularly with the high tin content lead-free alloys.

Phil ›› Nitrogen can help but is not a magic bullet.

Do BGA Components Warp During Reflow?

(reflow, components, BGA, Temperature, warpage, soldering, defects, solder paste, stencil, apertures, over-print, HoP, baking, pre-heat, cooling)

Jim ›› Phil, there are common themes that show up now and then and I'm going to read three independent questions that were sent on the same topic.

This comes from B.S (I hope that's no joke because it's certainly a legitimate question.?: "We have been stumped by occasional opens at the corner balls of some BGA components after reflow. We have experimented with many minor adjustments, yet this occasional problem continues. Do you have any suggestions?"

The next is from A.S., maybe a brother or a sister: "We are having a problem with BGA components bridging. The problem is specific to one corner ball location on one BGA, but it's common to a significant number of circuit assemblies. What could be causing this consistent BGA bridging problem?"

From D.W.: "We recently reworked a BGA component and the corners all bridged. This was a new BGA component that had never been installed on a circuit board before. Can these components be removed and reused if we remove the warp? The plot gets thicker. Would you consider the component to be scrap? What causes the corners of the BGA component to warp and how do we prevent it in the future? "

Well, ladies and gentlemen, this is a news flash: BGAs warp during reflow.

Phil ›› Yes, they do.

Jim ›› Virtually all do, certainly plastic ones, I mean, maybe not ceramic; particularly the ones that have a complex internal structure and they are not thermally balanced. And as my brother, Phil, would want to say: it's a fact; don't fight it, live with it.

Phil ›› Whether you are -- and of course when you think about a BGA warping, the corners are going to have the largest displacement causing open and potentially bridges because of them either warping up and lifting above the circuit board or warping down and pushing into the solder paste therefore causing bridges.

Jim ›› The best technique to try to minimize warp is to slow down your heating and cooling processes. You ramp up during your preheat section and you cool down during your cooling section. Now of course, in cool down, you don't want to go too slow because you don't want to create a coarse-grained structure. So, it's again, as in many things with electronic manufacturing, it's a compromise, it's a trade-off.

Phil ›› Now I am going to open up another moisture barrier bag of worms. Moister sensitive devices, plastic and BGAs are big culprits. What level MSD is this component and are you adhering to the JEDEC standards on this, in terms of your exposure time, bake-out time. If you have a sloppy program, now is the time to get it together.

Jim ›› One experiment you could do with the particular components you know are bad is bake them immediately before reflow. And see if that reduces the problem.

The other things of course are getting a good solder paste that tolerates head-in pillow and other type defects that is specifically formulated to deal with these issues.

If you are seeing opens some people overprint the corner balls of their patterns, to get a little extra paste to minimize the chance of having it open

If you have seen bridges you might want to try minimizing the aperture; I haven't honestly had any experience with that. But BGA warping is a fact of life and you need to deal with it, and heating and cooling at the minimum acceptable rate is the most common strategy to deal with it.

Phil ›› But most of all fundamentally, before you start any experiments, make sure you have got an MSD program in place. If you don't, you are not alone and that's no excuse. You have to have the MSD program going. Get with it.

How to Reduce Voiding on QFN Components

(components, voids, BTC, soldering, reflow, fluxes, soldering)

Jim ›› J.R. writes, "I'm getting concerned about voiding in the central ground planes of my QFN components. What can I do about that and how concerned should I be about it?"

First of all I want to say that although many of the components we deal with technically are QFNs, the "official" IPC term is BTC, Bottom Terminated Components.

Phil ›› So on these bottoms terminated leadless components, sometimes known as QFNs, voiding issues in the large central ground plane have been around for a while. One question is how much voiding is actually permissible. That's defined by the conductivity and as well as the mechanical strength. We've seen cases where 65% voiding is permitted. But if you want to try to reduce voiding there are a number of different methods. One methodology is the use of preforms. Indium Corporation has some excellent papers on this. The flux is on the outside of the preform, as opposed to mixed in with the solder paste in normal solder paste.

Jim ›› What does a preform look like?

Phil ›› The preforms we're talking about are not the old-fashioned donuts we used to deal with years ago. These are basically solder slugs and they are introduced on tape and reel and put down by the pick and place machines.

Jim ›› So it's a rectangular square piece of solid solder about the size or slightly smaller than the pad with flux on the outside.

Phil ›› These preforms inherently have less flux in them, in some cases none. So, with reduced flux in the equation, there is less to get entrapped as it might in a similar volume of pure solder paste. That's a method worth experimenting with. Your result may vary, but it's well worth a try.

Jim ›› A common technique to reduce voids is to design a stencil using one of an infinite number of variations of the window-pane technique. Here you print solder paste on less than a 100 percent of the area using some pattern of apertures within the area of the pad. That's a whole day's work, perhaps we will talk about that another day.

Should We Invest in 3D Optical Inspection?

(soldering, solder paste, stencil, aperture, DFM, inspection, AOI, SPI, x-ray, throughput, selective soldering, Lean six-sigma, efficiency)

Phil ›› Jim, what's today's inquiry?

Jim ›› It comes from P.S.: "We are forced to correct many solder defects on the PCB bottom side - SMD glue side. The inspection and search for defects is taking too long. Our soldering waves are not new. We have tried several times to prevent these defects, but with the old equipment, we are limited. Would you suggest we investigate a 3D AOI system to save inspection time, any other suggestions?"

Phil ›› The answer to the question is YES - sure go ahead and investigate, there are lots of great end of year deals or beginning of year deals whenever you are listening to this. But that's not the real answer to your problem because as better as automated optical inspection is getting, it's not value added - you may find the errors, but why don't you do something to prevent the errors from happening in the first place. And I would say from what you described here; you're using kind of an antiquated methodology. The minute I see glue side I get the heebie-jeebies. And the fact that we're doing wave soldering here and everything else, so the first thing I'll offer is I would made an adjustment either to your designs and/or to your methodology. I would try to get away from the methodology you're using now in terms of wave soldering.

Jim ›› A 3D AOI system is not an inexpensive piece of hardware. You're going to spend significant money. Why not buy a new solder wave or selective soldering system so that you don't create defects. That would improve reliability, productivity and all those good things that should be driving your profit and the effectiveness of your enterprise. Finding defects faster so you then can fix them is really not an effective utilization of capital expenditures.

You know if you had nothing else and it was just a change in a procedure, that's one thing, but to look at a very expensive piece of gear - it will find the problem, but it's not going to rectify the problem.

It also surprises me that you feel you need 3-D AOI to find wave solder defects? I think defects when wave soldering are typically easy to find.

Phil ›› So bottom line is you need to move into the 21st century here and you really want to look into getting double sided reflow, get rid of the glue, sell that glue machine on E-bay, get the money, use it towards getting a selective soldering machine.

Or a good wave machine, again if you're stuck with surface mount on both sides, look at the pallets, but the better way is selective. Pallets are good, they can work, but it depends on your layout and they can add to your little demons.

Jim ›› If you want to spend money on inspection, spend it on an x-ray machine so that you can look into the barrels of holes or underneath components and so forth, where more and more of your joints are going to be.

Radio Frequencies and Rigid Flex

Cleaning R.F. Circuits - Aqueous or Vapor?

(cleaning, flux, solvents, aqueous, no-clean, OA, water soluble)

Jim ›› This came from B.B. It's a process question. "We are a contract house using no-clean paste and wire solder. We clean assemblies by hand dipping using solvent and want to get away from that. A third of our customers' products are R.F. Which would be better for R.F., vapor degreasing or aqueous cleaning? "

Phil ›› To be honest with you, regardless of if you're building R.F. or whatever, the basics of cleaning apply. There are three key elements you have to have here. You have to have a solvent be it in vapor form or an engineered aqueous in this case (or whatever your solvent is),\ that is suitable for the residue that you are trying to remove and that is matched to the flux residue that of the solder that you are using. Whether it's solder paste, wire solder, flux, wave or selective soldering, it's got to be matched. So that's the chemical aspect of it. The mechanical energy aspect is the other important thing and that's going to depend largely on what you have on your board in terms of clearances and board geography. You have to have ample mechanical energy to spread that chemical solvent, as well as rinse and dry, depending on what you are using. And that solvent must be heated. So regardless of whether you are doing R.F. or anything else, it's really more determined upon what you are cleaning. Try to clean, doing it right.

Jim ›› I'm no expert on R.F., but I would be more concerned with the board and solder mass materials' compatibility with whichever cleaning chemistry I'm using in terms of compatibility because you don't want to mess up the surface chemistry at all. So, you want to make sure that the solvent, be it aqueous or vapor, is compatible with your board materials and solder mass.

Phil ›› Well one of the other important things with regard to the R.F. situation and I don't know what frequencies you are going, if you are going up to the UHF spectrum, at least you are cleaning your boards. There is a lot of debate as far as using ultra-high frequencies and above, you start getting up above the 15 GHz - 20 GHz range if no-clean will suffice to stay on the board or whether it should be cleaned.

We don't know if you are getting up anywhere near there, but again, it's good to keep track of what papers are coming out and work is being done with clean versus no-clean, but in your case, you are cleaning it so almost becomes a non-issue now.

But you've got to have proper cleaning and that's the most important thing. As Jim is saying you don't want to do anything detrimental to anything else on the board and we've seen that happen a lot too.

Jim ›› And since it is a no-clean that you are trying to clean, you have to make absolutely certain that whatever solvent again, aqueous or vapor, is compatible with the specific paste formulation that you are dealing with.

Phil ›› So hopefully that answers your question and doesn't provide you with further confusion.

Sticky Residue Under Low Clearance Parts

(components, cleaning, residue, no-clean, flux, soldering, entrapment)

Jim ›› And welcome to Board Talk with Jim Hall and Phil Zarrow, the Assembly Brothers pick and place.

Phil ›› This comes from G.F. and it's a really well defined question, giving us lots of data to dig our teeth into.

Jim ›› In other words the question is going to take longer than the answer.

Phil ›› "Our contract manufacturer is producing power supplies for us with no-clean leaded solder paste, it's a large component, it's half inch square, sit flush on the board. We're having failures after only a few days of operation that looked to be the result of an electrical short. When we mechanically remove these large parts, we find a tacky substance, the consistency of rubber cement underneath. Our initial thought is that this is uncured no-clean flux from the solder paste that cannot escape from under the component during reflow. The no-clean paste manufacturer said that it's impossible for the flux not to be cured after reflow. However, in its uncured state, it would be tacky and would break down under voltage, these parts see 300 volts DC.

So, that's the situation. Is this uncured residue common when no-clean leaded solder paste is used with large, no clearance parts? What causes this? Can we bake the completed assemblies to ensure the material is fully cured? Does the part need to be changed to one with a clearance gap?" If you have some paste under there, I assume you're creating some sort of solder joint, so you have to have some clearance at least equal to the height of the joint?

Jim ›› So I assume it's a QFN of some sort, or BTC Bottom Terminated Component (IPC spec 7093). But first the idea of a large part, there is a very good article that was published several years ago when BTCs first came on the market by one of the cleaning and contamination gurus of our industry, Terry Munson. He (mechanically) pulled off a part after it was soldered at the proper reflow profile and it wasn't even that big, it was a relatively small, bottom terminated component. He found sticky residues underneath and analyzed them, and they were in fact uncured no-clean flux from the solder paste. His analysis stated that the flux around the perimeter of the part exposed directly to your heating environment cured and hardened more quickly than the paste under the center of the component. Creating a barrier, a relatively solid barrier around sealing off the perimeter, preventing the escape of volatiles from the paste remaining under the part.

Phil ›› Remember, no-clean starts out active, if it is properly heated it should be deactivated. Three mechanisms are used by most no-clean formulations. The first is chemical reaction. Take active chemicals and react them into something that is no longer an active chemistry. Encapsulation by the resins of any residual active chemistry, and evaporation. And Terry theorized that this barrier around the perimeter prevented evaporation which creates this uncured, sticky residue that you are seeing.

Jim ›› This is a common problem dealing with low clearance parts assuming this is more of a BTC which will have a very minimal clearance, 2 or 3 mils. There are solder paste formulations that can help with this. Printing modifications may also help, if you have a large ground plane you're printing a lot of paste under there, some sort of window-paning is a common technique that is used.

Phil ›› There's some other venting methodologies as well.

Jim ›› Modifying your reflow profile is another possible solution -- some tests have shown that a long soak section before reflow can minimize these problems.

Phil ›› Another approach has been using solder preforms which have a lower flux content -- Indium has been experimenting with that and it's worth looking into.

Jim ›› A number of solder companies have published new information on that. Certainly, it would help if you could have a part that provides a larger gap under there by whatever mechanism. But I don't know how you would do that if this is a true BTC. But again, we're speculating because as good as your definition is here, we could be more specific if you had described the part a little bit better.

Phil ›› This is for all you future questioners. So those are basically the tools that you have available, but certainly if you can use parts better with a higher gap underneath, you can minimize the possibility of corrosion, entrapment, cleaning problems and so forth, whether you are using a no-clean or not.

What is Causing Dimples in Blind Via Pads?

(DFM, via-in-pad, blind via, soldering, reflow, defects, PCB fabrication, voids)

Jim ›› The question comes from J.J. : "Recently we encountered defects on some bare boards we received from our supplier. The defect is a small dimple on some of the VGA pads.

These pads have blind vias. What might be the cause of this defect?"

Phil ›› Blind vias are definitely a handicap.

Jim ›› Particularly via in pad. You have got to deal with them, before you try to solder them because if you just leave a blind via, you've got this little cylinder of gas, you put solder paste on top of it, the gas is going to do you no good. It's going to cause voids, bubbles, or some of this gas may get out and some of the solder may wick down the resulting hole giving you an insufficient.

Phil ›› When you're dealing via pad, you have to fill them, so I'm assuming that these are being filled and capped in some way and that it's just not being done properly. Think about a PCB fabricator trying to fill these and cap them so that you have a nice, flat undimpled surface to solder on. They've got the same problem with whatever they used to fill it - they've got to get all the air out as they put the filler in.

Jim ›› If you just try to tent it, you've now got this little expansion chamber of trapped gas in there that's going to expand or contract depending on temperature.

So that's not a very good plan either. You've just got a tough thing designing boards with blind via. Via in a pad is bad enough, even when it is a through via, so that you have some hope of and confirmation that you filled it and you get all the gas out by filling from one side, the gas goes out the other end. But, blind via, to deal with it in pad is going to be problematic.

Phil ›› I think you need to have a long talk with your PCB supplier about whether they can really repeatably deal with these and maybe you have to change your design to go to through vias will allow them to be filled properly and reliably.

Solder Paste Inspection - When and Why

(SPI, inspection, BGA, BTC, inspection, solder paste, calibration)

Jim ›› Today's question comes from P.P.: "Some folks at our facility are pushing us to purchase a 3D solder paste inspection machine or system, better known as SPI. Are these systems common and under what condition should we consider buying one of these new-fangled machines or systems?"

Phil ›› There are a plethora of these machines available these days and you picked one of our favorite soap boxes. I don't know what else is going on in your facility, but as far as equipment goes, I can't think of a better investment going forward. Especially with the component technologies and everything else that we have today. Solder paste inspection is a process development tool, but an in-process tool as well.

Jim ›› Whether you are choosing a solder paste, or evaluating/optimizing your print parameters, how do you judge between what's a better quality or more repeatable print if you can't quantify the process. There is no better way to quantify the printing process than to measure the volumes of the individual solder deposits under comparable conditions or repeatability conditions. To be specific, if I'm looking at two solder pastes, I want to say which one gives me more reliable printing. Well, you're going to print some tough boards, but how do you compare them? With a solder paste inspection system, you measure the volumes, see how consistent they are, see what the transfer efficiency is, and you can make a much, much more accurate comparison and use statistical analysis to make a choice.

Phil ›› And as far as an in-process tool, look at the number of components we have today where you cannot use visual inspection of the reflowed joint. In some cases, you can make a partial inspection, but not a thorough inspection of bottom terminated leadless components. But with others including area arrays... I can tell you that in our consulting business, since we do a lot of process failure analysis, that in many cases the problem has been inadequate solder particularly on area arrays. When you do the root cause analysis, basically this could have been averted with properly implemented solder paste inspection.

Jim ›› Properly implemented means, establishing realistic spec limits for your rejections coming out of the system. It's nice to have these systems, but if you don't use them correctly, use them effectively, based upon real feedback from quality results -- Garbage In Garbage Out.

Phil ›› We've seen a lot of that, these things have become very, very expensive pass through conveyors and that is like a sin against the nature of electronic assembly. But there are a number of these things available, whether you are doing it on an AQL basis offline with a really rudimentary per se, table top solder paste height inspection, if you got some inline volume inspection, anywhere in between, you are better off than not doing it.

Jim ›› There are some very good quality bench-top systems, granted they do one point at a time, but for an AQL level, for process development, at least to get your feet wet. To get a feel for it, and to help you make a decision investing in an in-line system, I think it's really worthwhile, rent one, borrow one, check it out, go have a demo, but remember, at least 50 percent of the defects in all assembly come from solder paste printing.

Phil ›› Most test show more like 70 or 80 percent of the defects. So that's where you want to put your process development, that's where you want to put your inspection, after printing. And 3D SPI, where you get height and volume, have shown to be, in my opinion, hands-down the best way to do that. Basically, it's a fantastic investment, so it's going to work and it's going to be one of the things you look back with and wonder how you got along without it.

Jim ›› And if I might say this about the commercial market today, it's another one of those capitalistic successes. You've got a number of companies out there, competing for an ever expanding market, giving you a lot of features, a lot of capability, data outputs allowing feedback to your printer, feed-forward to your other inspections machines, etc. There's all kinds of exciting things that you can do in overall process improvement, process control, and process optimization with your SPI system as a building block.

Phil ›› So take a look what's out there and find the one that is best suited for you.

What is the Life Span of a Profile Board?

(soldering, reflow, profiling, thermocouples, Calibration, Ovens)

Jim ›› The question today comes from PV.: "What is the life span of a profile board? How many times can I use one test board to profile our reflow oven before throwing it away and why? "

Phil ›› Now, are you talking about a normal person or me? I remember this one board - it was an old ugly looking one. It originally was an Alcatel board. We were at Vitronics, and it was properly instrumented: thermocouples were properly applied using conductive epoxy. I later used that PCBA to benchmark oven performance for a number of oven manufacturer clients of ours. As a result, ultimately that had seen over a hundred thermal reflow profiles; some rather extreme, as we were testing that included the old radiant machines. The board itself, which due to its size and complex surface geometry we named "Boardzilla" – though long retired from service, all the thermocouples were intact. On the other hand, most of the components were gone, parts of the board were charred, crumbling into dust. So, the answer to your question is, "long before it turns to dust." The reality is that if it's going to be ongoing program where you are going to want to profile and then audit the profile from time to time, there are tools for doing that.

Jim ›› Most of the people who manufacture profile data loggers, also will supply you with what they call a calibration vehicle which is a large board-shaped piece of usually Delmat®, or other high temperature material with some variety of thermocouples attached to it, suspended from it, giving you a high mass, low mass and so forth. These are used for a calibration; it's a very durable piece of hardware, very repeatable. And you can get a new one that is calibrated.

Phil ›› So, in the ideal, or the theoretical, or the best case world what is the best practice we like? You sacrifice a real assembly to the profile gods. You take a fully loaded board with all the components on it, attach thermocouples to the key locations using light gauge thermocouples with tiny amounts of either high temperature solder or high temperature epoxy, so that you don't add too much thermal mass to what you are trying to measure. And that is very important, adding too much mass would really throw off your readings.

Jim ›› And then you use this "profile board" to develop your profile and hopefully when you do that, you are using software predictors, and so forth, so that it doesn't take you too many runs. Maybe your profile board has gone through two or three or four runs and that is certainly safe. Then you have that recipe established in the oven, then you run your calibration vehicle through the oven using the same recipe. You now have a calibration profile which may not be the same temperatures as you got in the profile board, but it's directly correlated to it up front.   Now you can use your calibration vehicle for set up confirmation whenever you run that board again. You reenter that profile recipe in the oven and want to confirm that you are getting the same thermal processing, so you run your calibration vehicle. This allows you to keep that golden actual profile board carefully stored in a closet, so it doesn't get destroyed. So, if you really have a critical issue, maybe you have some defects, you want to change the recipe to create a slightly different profile board. You can then pull that out, but you don't use it over and over again daily or weekly or whatever your calibration/validation protocol is, and you don't get like Phil's board where components have fallen off and it's so charred and burned and there's been so much juice cooked out it.

Phil ›› Yes, but the bottom line is that you avoid the question of whether the profile board is responding thermally to the oven in the same way that the original board when it was virgin. So, there is a solution in hand and that's our free advice today, money back guarantee on that.

Solder Pallets With Titanium Inserts - Yes/No?

(wave-solder, pallets, selective soldering, soldering, flux, components, DFM, hole-fill)

Jim ›› It comes from H.Z.: "We use selective wave soldering with aperture pallet. Our new designs have tighter spacing which are causing problems with hole fill. Our pallet manufacturer recommends titanium inserts to allow larger apertures near the closely spaced SMDs. They are expensive. Are they worth it?"

Phil ›› Let's just put it this way; wave solder has been around for over 60years now. And it worked great in the through-hole days.

Jim ›› With 100mil lead pitch with no surface mount parts obstructing the bottom of the board.

Phil ›› Ever since surface mount appeared on the screen here basically we've been trying to adapt it in every way, duct tape, spit, scotch tape, peanut oil, spitting in the flux, air knives, nitrogen, vibrating nozzles. So obviously one of the more, I would say, successful adaptations has been the use of the pallets, the masking or "aperture" pallet fixtures for adapting your wave solder for doing, if you will, a variation of selective soldering. And that's what H.Z. is talking about where you are masking off the previously reflowed surface mount components and trying to solder just through-hole remaining areas in mixed technology.

Jim ›› Surface mount parts on the bottom (wave solder) side of the board that such as QFNs or QFPs and things like, that you can't glue and wave solder.

Phil ›› It does work, but it is fraught with problems and defect generation potential. A lot of people try to build their own aperture pallets. There is a lot of engineering involved in terms how close the edge you can locate these things: What kind of aperture you can have, the density of the leads, the bevel on the aperture edges, and so on. It is not as simple as it might appear, and it is not as fool-proof as it might appear.

Jim ›› But underlying it all is basic physics. It's just like stencil printing. If you've got a big stencil aperture, it's easy to get paste to flow in and out of it, to fill and release.

If you got a big aperture around your through-hole joints it's easy for the wave solder to get the flux, the preheat and the flow from the wave up into the aperture.

But as the aperture gets smaller, it becomes more difficult and more error prone as my brother has indicated. What drives that? Well, the close spacing of your SMDs relative to your through-holes. In the old days when things were spread out, your apertures were big, you have plenty of room.

Phil ›› So now you got a surface mount part that's really close, you still have to have the mask cover the surface mount part. You have limitations in the Delrin high temperature plastic materials that they're using for the pallet. So, the answer is, make the wall around these tight tolerances out of a little piece of titanium and set it into the fixture, so we can make that that wall between the aperture for the through-hole and the covered up surface mount part as thin as possible. And that's the strategy. And the answer is, yeah, it can work up to a limit. You know, you can buy yourself a little more aperture opening and for some things it might be successful, but -- don't fight a fact, deal with it, you're basically doing an adaptation of an adaptation.

Jim ›› Consider using a process better designed to deal with this problem. We are talking about point to point, multi wave, or fountain selective soldering.

Phil ›› And that's assuming you can't do pin-in-paste. A selective soldering system allows you to customize the process on a point-to-point level down to a solder joint. And what's the ultimate fallback? Solder it by hand, you get a real pro in there with a tiny little soldering iron and they can get the heat and the soldering flux from the cored wire in a tight space without damaging the adjacent surface mount.

Jim ›› Well, that's what the selective soldering system is designed to do and it's why it is the fastest growing technology in our industry because things are getting tighter, spacings are getting closer and closer. And it's putting more and more strains on wave. So yes, maybe for HZ, maybe for your application you might be able to get away with titanium inserts depending on the ultimate spacing, all the characteristics of the joints, how difficult it is to get the flux, preheat and solder into that aperture.

But, long term things aren't getting better, spacings are getting tighter. We feel that most assemblers should be considering moving to some form of controllable selective soldering to give you a much greater process window.

Phil ›› So look to the future, H.Z. – and that future is now!

Can a CTE Mismatch Cause Reliability Problems?

(CTE, TCE, reliability, PCB, soldering, reflow, BTC, DFM)

Phil ›› What's our question today?

Jim ›› Okay, it comes from D.H.: "Silicone coating a board has been a standardized process whenever a customer wants protection from moisture or dust. Lately we have heard it could be detrimental to reliability of solder joints due to CTE mismatch with other materials FR4. Does usage of BGA, bottom terminated parts QFNs or SONs have increased risk? These packages are low profile and likely to have less seepage of silicone under them compared to the channel and caps of discrete parts.

Phil ›› Well, the first thing being really technical is that the CTE mismatch that the concern is about is between the coating material, your silicone or whatever other conformal coating and the solder joints of your balls or your terminations on your bottom terminated components. And the general answer is that, YES, we have seen problems particularly with bottom terminated components. QFNs and so forth where there is enough seepage flow of the coating material under the parts so that when it goes through heating environment, the material which is now under-filled, at least the edges of the part expands, puts a vertical tensile stress on the solder joints and cracks them. We've particularly seen this on BTCs.

Jim ›› So yes, there is always a potential of some seepage. And yes, it can be a problem of course. As you were saying the thermal environment is going to be the biggest driver. What is the thermal temperature excursion that your finished product is going to see? As Phil said the most important thing is that expansion in the z-axis that will be out to get you. We actually saw one example where the customer was using a bottom terminated component and was not soldering the center plane, it didn't call for that, you know, in terms of heat transfer or everything else. And yes, the conformal coating seeped under there and, yes, they had a terrible problem with regard to cracked and open solder joints. I guess you can say. that CTE is powerful stuff.

Phil ›› It is a concern. And certainly, the first thing is to understand well, the thermal environment that you are going to be subjected to.

Is There a Spacing Spec for SMD Components?

(components, DFM, pick-and -place, micro-passives, reflow, soldering, profiling)

Phil ›› What is the question today?

Jim ›› Well, it's in the area of pick and place. It comes from P.R.: "Is there a general minimum spacing requirement or should we apply SMD components to comply with the majority of the SMT pick and place systems on the market? And are there different minimum spacing requirements for small chip caps such as 0204s or 0805s versus larger components such as QFPs?"

Phil ›› Well, to the best of our knowledge there is no specification per se, you know, some governing really you can go by.

It's basically driven by the capabilities of the pick and place machine, particularly the tooling they are using for pick up and placement and so that's going to basically run it.

Jim ›› Obviously you have to have enough clearance to allow for placement repeatability variations of plus or minus 50 microns or 40 microns or 70 microns whatever it is. And you probably want to give a little more space because those are typically done at 3-Sigma.

Phil ›› Usually I think of the clearance issues as being driven more by the other processes rather than the pick and place. For instance if you are talking about ultra-small chip component such as 0201s and 01005s, a number of issues have been raised about spacing relative to the ability to print repeatably in very tight arrays has been shown to be somewhat of a problem.

That is you go with spacing those very ultra-small chips closer and closer together. You start to have printing problems, primarily bridging, resulting from stencil issues and so forth.

Jim ›› Another one, on bigger components is rework. If you are talking about QFPs or certainly area array parts. You need to think about the clearance you need in order to remove the parts. To get your hot air tools down in there to avoid partial reflow of adjacent components and so forth.

So I guess I agree with my brother for once that there are no specs beyond the individual repeatability of your placement machines, but you should look at your other processes such as printing, with your stencil design and the ability to repeatedly print at tight spacings and rework.

There may be others that I am not thinking of.

Phil ›› Yeah but I totally agree with my brother. I know the planets are aligning here but I think you will find that the common denominator, - the lowest common denominator is repair and that's probably going to basically drive it. So, taking a look at what kind of components you are dealing with and what kind of equipment you are using there.

Jim ›› Smaller is a mantra of SMT, smaller components located closer and closer together. But inevitably the pads gets closer and closer and you have to say, "am I creating too many bridging opportunities?"

Phil ›› A lot of times we go to the shows and we'll see them demonstrating pick and place machines by putting components side by and side and drawing little pictures and portraits and spelling out things. But you know, from a practical standpoint, for those of us actually building working circuits, as opposed to pretty pictures, these are some of the things you would want to consider.

Long Term Component Storage

(components, storage, handling, MSD, humidity, soldering)

Phil ›› What's our question today, brother Jim?

Jim ›› It comes from listener R.A.: "We need to store a variety of electronic SMD components for at least 10 years. What do you recommend for a humidity and temperature settings? Would these settings be different from typical short-term storage? "

Phil ›› You don't make life easy on yourself, do you RA?

Jim ›› We know these people Phil. We have dealt with them. These are people who want to get lifetime buys of components that are going out of stock or becoming obsolete and you have to deal with them. Of course, the most critical concerns are if these components are moisture sensitive and you receive them in their nicely sealed moisture barrier bags which have their desiccant inside and the temperature humidity indicator card. But if we read IPC/JEDEC standards 033.we see the moisture barrier bag is technically only guaranteed for a year. Most people have not had problems storing longer than a year, but the question they certainly raised, do you want to keep them in a moisture barrier bag for 10 years?

Phil ›› One alternative that we have known people to use to address this issue with moisture sensitive parts is to immediately remove them from the moisture barrier bag and put them in a dry cabinet with humidity less than 5% which is the standard storage conditions. Then monitor the humidity level in the storage cabinet continuously so that if anything should ever fail you have a record of it.

With other components which are not moisture sensitive you have to be concerned about the solderability of the terminations. And in that case having a relative low humidity, perhaps not 5% but and a reasonable temperature would seem to make sense.

Jim ›› Remember every time you re-bake these components, if you indeed indulge in that, you are going to probably have an effect on the solderability of leads, depending on the finish. Another strategy, a much cheaper strategy, with MSD components is just store them in normal temperature, humidity and bake them before you use them.

Phil ›› As my brother wisely points out, baking them always raises issues with the solderability. And certainly, in any case protect your components from any kind of atmosphere contaminants. Temperature and humidity are probably somewhat contributory although especially humidity for moisture sensitive components.

Printing vs. Dispensing

(solder paste, soldering, printing, stencil, dispensing, step-stencil, apertures, DFM)

Phil ›› What's today's input Jim?

Jim ›› Phil, this is a rare treat. We have had a listener who has come back and actually suggested an alternative or further refinement of something that we taught.

If you remember way back when we talked about the problem of printing different sized components such that some big components need a lot of paste and we would like to use a thicker stencil. Micro components need less paste and we like to use a thinner stencil.

What we talked about principally was the ideal solution, which is step stencil, but there are limitations. But this listener says, "Do you know any people who size their stencil for the larger components, then use a needle dispenser for the smaller components.?" Yes, it might be slower, but it seems more flexible than step stencils.

Now, this is unique. We have certainly heard of people using dispensing to augment stencil printing. Probably the first time we saw it was way back in the beginning with pin-in-paste, or intrusive reflow, or reflow of through hole, where people would add additional paste with a dispenser because they didn't feel that they could print enough paste to get good hole fill on the through hole components.

Phil ›› I will invoke the wisdom of the revered Dr. Hemsley J. Zapfardt who said that the only absolute is that there are no absolutes. So yeah, you could probably do it this way. Have we run into anybody recently doing it... Not in the convention sense. There is Solder Jetting – but that's a subject for another day…

Jim ›› The most common procedure is to print the entire board with a thinner stencil and that means print for both the large components and the small components with a thinner stencil and then augment the volume of paste for your larger components with the dispenser. What I am assuming in this comment is that they don't have any apertures at all for their smaller components.

They have a thick stencil, they print only the large components and then they dispense the entire volume of paste for the smaller components with a dispenser and no, I haven't heard of anybody doing it.

Phil ›› It sounds awfully cumbersome adding a whole another process and tools.

Jim ›› Well, what other choices? Let's review. We said step stencil is the best way to do it. It has its definite and limitations, spacing and the maximum amount of step you can put in. The next most common is to stay with a thick stencil but reduce the apertures for your smaller components.

We run into limitations with tall and narrow apertures if they get to the ultra-miniature components. Less than 0.5 millimeter area raise and 0201s and 01005s.

Phil ›› Another alternative is to use the thinner stencil but overprint your larger components. I am again still staying with one process one stencil. Therefore, you don't have any stencil design, area ratio issues on your stencil. Then we get to the one we just described. Another augmentation process is to use solid solder slugs... preforms.

Jim ›› You use a thin stencil; you print the entire board but you add additional paste volume for the larger components with the solid solder slugs which are on tape and reel and placed by your place machine. The belt and suspenders is to use two completely different stencils and two printing machines. With the thin one first and then have a second thicker stencil that's etched out on the bottom over the thinner deposits. But since most don't want to invest in two stencil printing machines in one line that's probably the most complex. I don't see any reason why you shouldn't use the procedure described, but dispensing is slowing down the process. Dealing with solder paste in cartridges has its own set of problems, but people do dispense solder paste to augment screen printing and stencil printing.

Phil ›› Although we have never seen this exact application, we have seen it for pin and paste, reflow of through hole and augmentation of the larger components in printing with a thinner stencil.

Reflow For Rigid Flex

(PCB, rigid-flex, reflow, soldering, solder paste, PCB handling and storage, humidity, baking)

Jim ›› Today we have a question from S.J.: " We have a new PCB assembly that includes a section of flex cable and FR4 circuit board. What are the reflow rules I need to consider while processing a mix, FR4 and flex cable assembly through the reflow process?"

Phil ›› Well, first of all I believe that's known in the vernacular of our industry as rigid flex, clever name don't you think? That's an interesting question with regard to reflow. Reflow is reflow. You follow all the other rules that you need driven by the specs of solder paste and of course your most vulnerable component on the board.

Jim ›› Your flex cable might become your most vulnerable component.

Phil ›› You may be fixturing so remember when you do profiling to use the fixture.

Jim ›› I want to go over my brother's head and say you should be fixturing. You really should very carefully look at fixturing, keeping that thing level, particular if there are surface mount parts on the flex section of your assembly. You want to make sure that's not moving around and flexing during reflow and moving your components.

Phil ›› Generally most people build the entire assembly, either flex or rigid flex in a fixture, right through printing, pick and place, and reflow. So, they avoid disturbing stuff through handling.

But with regard to the reflow question I think that's straightforward, but the thought I am wondering about is with regard to more important issue particularly with rigid flex is storage and handling.

Jim ›› And why would you worry about storage and handling?

Phil ›› Because rigid flex boards tend to have an interesting moisture absorption aspect and we get involved with bake out.

Jim ›› Flex materials tend to absorb moisture much more quickly and so proper storage and perhaps baking before reflows is a significant consideration.

Phil ›› So that would probably be the main concern. There are some pieces of wisdom coming out of IPC on handling flex and rigid flex, I believe it's included in 1601 - the circuit board handling and storage specification.

Best Method for Repairing Underfill Arrays?

(BGA, chip-scale, flip-chip, soldering, rework and repair, underfill, materials, DFM, soldering)

Phil ›› What interesting, provocative question do we have today Jim?

Jim ›› A topic about rework. It comes from E.C.: "What is the best method for removing an SMT array package that has been under-filled and cured. Mechanically, thermally, chemically, a combination of these methods. Is there an industry approved method?"

Phil ›› One thing you could do is trash the board, but that's probably not an option here. That would be the easiest.

Jim ›› I think the reality is a lot of boards get trashed because this is not an easy process.

Phil ›› The answer to the question really depends on the nature of the under-fill itself. Whether it's thermoset or thermoplastic. You heat it up and if it's thermo-plastic if it gives ... but my thinking is you better have a chisel handy.

Jim ›› I find that most of our repair technicians say that, they use a twisting motion, gripping the component in some sort of holder and rotating as well as pulling rather than trying to pride up from the edge. But it's not an easy process, we would be kidding you. Certainly, any process that involves some mechanical energy and as my brother Phil says depending on the material some heating may help to some extent. With some materials it may not, so you really should talk to the supplier of the under-fill material if that knowledge is available.

Phil ›› Therein lies the real solution. Sadly, the reality is a lot of boards are going to be torn up and probably damaged beyond repair. Such is the nature of the beast. You might have a little bit of reprieve if you have only done the corner bonding of the under-fill which people do on flip-chip. That's one of the limitations of the flip-chip or under-filling anything.

Jim ›› I know of no chemical methods for aiding in the removal of under-filled parts.

Fluxes, Feeders and Failures

Wave-soldering Contamination

(wave-solder, contamination, solder pot, dross, maintenance)

Jim ›› Today's question comes from K.U.: "We are wave soldering using 63/37 tin lead solder. After wave we are finding solder dross particles sticking to the printed circuit board surface. We cleaned the dross from the solder bath and yet have the same problem. Do we likely have a contamination problem with the solder bath, what else could cause dross particles to stick to our PWBs?"

Phil ›› One thing that immediately comes to mind is how often are you cleaning the dross from your solder pot? Are you doing it like once a week, once a month, once a year, because at the very least you should be doing it once per shift.

Jim ›› What my brother is saying is that if you don't clean the dross regularly, dross particles can build up within the bath and cause your problems even though you now start to skim to clean it. You really need to keep on top of it.

Phil ›› Question: When was the last time you had the contents of your solder pot evaluated? Because, as my brother will tell you, contamination will definitely have an effect on dross.

Jim ›› If you get bad enough contamination in the pot, metallics that have dissolved from the different metals, and if you build up high enough concentrations of these other metallics, they actually become particles in the wave and some of them don't float. Some of them are not lighter than the tin lead and so they will not be skimmed off with the dross but will circulate continuously in the pot.

Phil ›› What you are describing as dross might be other metallic contaminants other than tin and lead oxides that are not floating and are re-circulating in the pot but again, you have the core of it. You should have your pot analyzed.

Jim ›› Check that the chemicals that they analyze your pot for are within the specifications because yes, they can definitely cause other particles that can stick to your board and look like dross.

Why Should We Consider Smart Feeders?

(pick-and-place, feeders, set-up, optimization, efficiency)

Phil ›› What serious question do we have today, Jim?

Jim ›› Well this question comes from T.R.: "In selecting a new pick and place line, why should we consider smart feeders? How can the added cost be justified?" Good question.

Phil ›› Let me answer a question with a question, T.R.

On your previous and existing pick and place line, have your operators ever put the wrong component feeder in the wrong location, and how many times has that happened? And as a result, how many wrong components have you put down in the wrong locations as a result of that? And finally, what did it cost to repair them? There's your justification. That's putting it in profound terms. When we look at any of the assembly equipment in the line and we look at pick and place, statistically one of the most frequent errors attributed to the pick and place operation is the wrong component and the wrong place, and it's usually attributed to the operator putting the wrong feeder in the wrong place. Human error.

Jim ›› Oh brother of little statistical knowledge. What my brother means to say is that the most significant number of defects generated by placement machines result from putting the wrong feeder in the wrong slot. The most frequent errors in placement machines are probably feeder jams, but they typically don't create a defect, they just shut the machine down.

Phil ›› Sometimes that's because the operator's so frustrated because they put the feeder in the wrong location somewhere else, and he's jamming it in, you know, and their breaking those feeders. I see that all the time you know. You ever heard of road rage? Here's pick and place rage. Hey, it's a tough world we live in you know.

Jim ›› Although I hate to do it, I absolutely agree with my brother. I think that is the most important reason for smart feeders, but I have to admit that avoiding mistakes is sometimes hard to justify in monetary dollar terms. So, I would offer another advantage of smart feeders, and that is increased productivity. This new pick and place line that you're going to spend a lot of money on regardless of whether you buy smart feeders or not can only make money for you when it's placing parts. It can't make money for you when you're setting it up, changing it over, installing feeders, and so forth.

Phil ›› Spoken like a true lean six sigma master black belt, which you indeed are. And smart feeders may give you, depending on your environment, a significant reduction in setup time by streamlining it, certainly by allowing you to do all your feeder setup and confirmation offline. So that if your smart feeders are loaded with a barcode or whatever other mechanism they use, you've loaded the component part number into the feeder so that then when you plug it into the machine the machine knows exactly what part is in what feeder location and you can't have the mistakes that my brother just enumerated in great glowing detail.

Jim ›› So the biggest factor in terms of dollars is just to keep those placement machines running, get them up and running fast because that's what's controlling your line. You're not building anything on your surface mount line if your placement machines aren't running. So, by streamlining setup and doing more your setup offline while the previous job is still running, when you have to actually stop the line, stop building boards, stop making money, you can throw those smart feeders right in there very quickly without any additional crosschecking or anything else. The machine can read them, know exactly where what parts are and start building boards with minimum downtime, increasing productivity, and that can definitely be cost justified. All you have to do is check the numbers out.

Phil ›› You know it's interesting because both Jim and I have been involved in pick and place for what seems like all eternity. Hey, we are "Pick and Place", and you know actually the conception of smart feeders was one of the first innovations that was applied to pick and place. We're going back over 25 years and we've seen the technology evolve. You know originally there was like a RAM memory, and then we went to - I think the most common right now is barcode verification, and in the last few years we've seen a number of machines out there offering RFID verification (which is very cool).

Jim ›› Yes, I agree. But the reality of the marketplace though, Phil, is that you do pay extra for smart feeders in most cases.

Phil ›› "Pay me now or pay me later…"

Jim ›› So I can understand looking at that big price tag for new surface mount line, new pick and place line, that you know justifying extra feeders, justifying smart feeders is a big chunk of money, but think of productivity. And remember that that machine is only going to make you money when you're placing parts.

Phil ›› And by the way, we still advocate that even if you have smart feeders, with the latest greatest technology, we feel it's still a very good idea and a best practice to have the buddy check system. You know have a manual check by a second person going through with the BOM and again verifying everything's in the right place.

Jim ›› Right, but you can do that at a feeder level offline. As long as you've got it right, if you barcoded the right part number into that feeder, and that can be buddy checked, and that can be done offline, and again it doesn't have to slow you down and lose your productivity. Okay, I think we have beat this proverbial horse to within an inch of its life, Phil.

Top Side Reflow Causing Solder Balls

(reflow, soldering, solder balls, defects, wave-solder, pre-heat, profiling, selective soldering)

Jim ›› What kind of question do we have today?

Phil ›› It comes from C.W.: "When selective soldering the secondary side, we are producing solder balls on the primary side. We are also reflowing surface mount components and it's on the primary side. What can be done to prevent this from happening?"

Jim ›› Stop - my button has been pushed!

Phil ›› Uh-oh – Soapbox alert!

Jim ›› You've got to define what we mean by primary side and secondary side. I'm assuming that this board is double-sided reflow, and that the primary side was soldered first, and the secondary side was soldered second. And now we are selective soldering this board from the bottom side where the primary side is now on top. Actually, Phil, it really doesn't matter in what order they were reflowed. The assumption I have to make is that the primary side is the side that is facing up while we're doing the selective soldering from the bottom. You see how easy it is to get confused about the physical situation we're talking about when we don't have standard terminology?   But everybody's heard me rant about this. I think, Phil, that the pertinent question here is are you reflowing surface mount components on the primary side. And I'm assuming that that means re-reflowing. These are parts that have been reflowed once and now are reflowing again during the selective soldering process.

Phil ›› Kind of like refried beans, except in this case, this is not a good thing. This just screams of a process out of control. Why are those top side components reflowing? It's funny that C.W. asked about the solder balls first and oh, by the way, topside's re-reflowing. Oh, man. This is a mess.

Jim ›› Well, obviously you're getting too much heat to the top side.   Whatever combination of pre-heating and immersion in your molten solder, nozzle, or wave or whatever form of selective soldering you're using, you're getting too much heat into the top side of the board. It's just like in wave soldering, you can't reflow the parts on the top side.

Phil ›› Actually, what's the worst thing that you can do is to partially reflow. And if you're getting reflow on some parts, you're probably getting partial reflow, and it's usually the partial reflow that will cause damage.

Jim ›› But the point is you're getting too much heat. You've got to go back to profiling your selective soldering process, putting thermocouples on the top and bottom side and adjusting those heating parameters so that you don't take the top side up above reflow temperatures. And I think that I agree with my brother - can you believe that, ladies and gentlemen - that the solder balls are just a secondary occurrence because of this overheating and reflow on the top side.

Phil ›› What are the advantages of selective soldering? And I say this in the broadest sense of the term selective soldering. When I think of selective soldering I immediately think of using a selective soldering machine. But C.W. is likely wave soldering using aperture pallets, which is also termed as selective soldering.

Jim ›› So, if C.W. is using a palletized wave soldering process, that pallet is covering the parts on the secondary side. The reflow is occurring on the primary side, the top side. The combination of preheating and wave exposure or preheating and nozzle exposure in the point to point soldering, is getting too much heat to the top of the board, and you're going to have to adjust those parameters and profile the board properly.

Phil ›› What do you think this board looks like?   Does he have a surface mount component so close to a through hole that he's soldering on the bottom side? It's transferring that much heat to reflow them. But Jim, what if C.W. is using a selective soldering machine?

Jim ›› Remember, Phil, top-side preheating in selective is something that's only become available recently. It may be that on certain machines, it isn't understood or controlled well enough. People are improving and releasing new things about selective soldering machines every day. I can't pretend to keep up and be knowledgeable about all of it.

Phil ›› Yeah, but I'm going add that the old standard still applies. C.W., hook up your profiling device (data recorder) and find out what you're preheating that top side to, because it sounds like it's way too much. You need to sit back and take a look at that process. If you need help, reach out to your selective manufacturer.

What Rate is World Class for SMT Machines?

(pick-and-place, de-rating, efficiency, set-up, feeders, standards, micro-passives, 01005)

Jim ›› We're going to have to figure this out pretty quick, because this question is about pick performance, it's not pick and place performance. And it comes from R.W. The question is: "What rate (in percentage) is considered world class when it comes to pick performance for SMT placement machines? Also, can you define pick performance?"

Phil ›› I don't know that I've ever seen it broken down that way. And going back to our mutual pick and place days, we used to do things like cycle time, and we would do so by picking from the same feeder location. I think in terms of performance R.W. was alluding to accuracy as opposed to speed, the actual accuracy picking the component out of its respective pocket?

Jim ›› Let's assume we're only concerned about the performance of the machine in picking parts out of the pockets of tapes and feeders. So, at what percentage are you successful when you go to pick up a part? And why is this now becoming a question and not one that was asked 30 years or 40 years ago when you and I were working with the prehistoric placement machines?

Phil ›› Let's see if I can answer that.

1. We don't have enough specs to worry about, and the salesmen need something else to talk about.

2. R.W. is dropping a lot of components.

3. R.W. is not getting components out of his feeders.

Jim ›› I'm guessing, Phil, that the reason is that R.W. is having to deal with very small components - 0201s, maybe 01005s. Having worked with 01005s, you know that picking them up becomes a big issue, because they're so small.

Phil ›› Seeing them is an issue, let alone picking them up. Plus, we all know the other issues attributed to picking them up, getting good release from the pick-up tooling.

Jim ›› Yes, but this is confusing. I'm shooting from the hip here, ladies and gentlemen, because pick performance can be affected by the machine. It can also be affected by the accuracy of the part within the pocket of the tape. And again, if we're talking about these real small chips, you can get bill boarding or parts flipped upside down parts. If the machine fails to pick it up because it's bill boarded in the pocket before it even attempted to pick it up, is that the machine's fault? Should that be included in the percentage of failures?

Phil ›› My brother's made a very good point. It doesn't all come down to the equipment itself. We're equipment guys, and we've always had a bone to pick with component guys. How good is the actual tape and the way it's being fed? But to answer the question directly, I don't know of any metric per se. Certainly, you suggested some good ones, Jim, but I don't know of anybody - we're probably giving the component placement machine guys some ideas, as in "Hot damn, here's a new one we can out spec 'em on." We know how that works.

Jim ›› I don't know. I just know that many people have talked about the issues about picking these really small parts with perchance the need to use vision to find the part before you pick it up in some extreme cases. What is world class? I honestly do not know. I would assume you'd have to rate it for a given size and style of part. I know a 0201 or an 01005 - I would assume that your success rate, if we say it's the success rate of the pick-up tools to be able to pick parts up from a feeder pocket, then I would assume it would be lower for an 01005, because it's simply harder.

You're bound to get more mistakes. But in terms of world class, I don't have any numbers.

Phil ›› But, putting on my six-sigma curmudgeon hat here, this is definitely an opportunity for specmanship on the part of the component placement machine manufacturers.

Jim ›› And everybody understands the difference between placement accuracy at three sigma and placement accuracy at four-sigma. We will not go there today...In the meantime, when you get those components placed, don't solder them like my brother.

Phil ›› And don't solder them like my brother.

What is Ideal Humidity for Final Assembly?

(soldering, components, humidity, ESD, moisture, MSD)

Phil ›› I believe today, Jim, we have a climate question.

Jim ›› This question comes from C.J. The question is: "What is ideal humidity for final assembly? No soldering."

Phil ›› We're basically talking about box build. I'm interpreting that as saying not attaching components.

Not attaching components, not putting on conformal coating, everything's done. It's time to go in the box.

Jim ›› What is the ideal humidity, Phil?

Phil ›› As we know at this point, we're not really material-sensitive, per se. What's done is done. So, essentially, our biggest concern at this point in time is electrostatic discharge, ESD.

Jim ›› Isn't generally 50% relative humidity a desired norm, minimum for ESD protection?

I almost committed you to living here in New England - but you don't live here anymore, Phil. But here in the Northeast, where us rugged men live, often when the heat comes on in the winter, like it is now, the air gets very dry. You get static electricity walking across the carpet, touch the doorknob - classic examples. The materials, once they're done soldering they are in their lifetime ambient environment and are going to get saturated with ambient moisture anyway, so there's no concern about that in final assembly.

Phil ›› But anybody who has listened to us before knows, if you are going to solder them again, as in rework, repair, field repair or something like that, the books are open again. And what do we always recommend? We always recommend baking out the board before you rework it to take care of the MSD situations and accumulated moisture in the circuit board. If you are going to solder again, yes, everything is back to zero in that respect, and you have to be aware of the humidity. But from final assembly, the ESD is the big question. I don't think there's any confusion here - 50% is the target. And always take the proper precautions, too. Don't leave anything for granted. Everybody should be properly grounded.

Jim ›› You spent all that good time not soldering like my brother, so don't mess it up now. And you sure wasted enough time listening us tackle this very easy question, didn't you?

Acceptable Rate for Head-in-Pillow?

(soldering, reflow, solder paste, profile, defects, HoP, flux, warpage, BGA)

Phil ›› I see we have a solder defect question from A.B.. The question is: "We have rejects that look like Head in Pillow. We see rejects in 2-3 per 15,000 PCBs. Should we tinker with the reflow process, or would you consider this reject rate acceptable?"

Jim ›› Head-In-Pillow is a real issue. First up, I want to say before you think about tinkering with anything, are you using an up-to-date solder paste, because solder paste manufacturers have done significant work to try to minimize this with newer formulations. As to what is an acceptable rate, it's very hard to say with the numbers quoted, 2 or 3 rejects per 15,000 printed circuit boards. So, worse case, that would be about 1 in 5,000 circuit boards. That's 3,000 parts per million. That's not too bad. That's a three sigma process.

Phil ›› But that's not really the way we would define defects, because if we're talking head-in-pillow occurring on BGA parts, all of which have multiple balls, any one of which could have the defect.

Jim ›› So, the proper way to do this would be to define it not per number of PCBs, but for parts per million opportunities, so you would have to count all of the BGA balls on those 15,000 PCBs.

Since that's probably greater than 100, that would drop that down to about 30 parts per million, and that is certainly a very low defect level to try to go optimize just using general optimization strategies.

Phil ›› So, congratulations, A.B. The answer is probably not to tinker with the reflow process. Movement towards continuous improvement is good and trying to fix the defect rate would be good, but it may be things beyond your immediate control.

Jim ›› If you really want to address a defect such as head and pillow, which is going to become more common, because there's going to be more and more BGA parts, thinner BGA parts, which are going to warp more - seriously look at getting an up-to-date solder paste.

That's true for all of the newer types of defects, such as graping, and so forth. Solder paste technology is evolving daily or at least monthly, and you may be making your life a lot harder than you have to by not evaluating a modern, up-to-date paste that could significantly reduce your defects such as head and pillow right out of the box.

Step Stencil Setup

(printing, step-stencil, apertures, squeegee, stencil, solder paste)

Jim ›› Today's question is from M.K.: "When shifting from standard solder paste stencils to step stencils, should we change the pressure or attack angle?" I assume that would mean squeegee angle.

Phil ›› So, some shifty guy's stepping on somebody's stencils. That's not a very good best practice, is it? Well the answer is maybe YES, maybe NO. As in the case of anything you're going to be basically setting up, you have to do a design of experiment to ascertain the optimum settings on your printer.

And whether that's going to be any different or not depends. That sounds like somebody who's not doing their DOE properly. Doesn't it, Jim? One setup does all types of thing…

Jim ›› Phil, I think it's somebody else looking for the silver bullet, which in this situation would be: when using step stencil, just do this, and everything will be perfect. Wouldn't it be wonderful if the world was like that, but unfortunately, it ain't. You should be checking pressure and attack angle, speed, and all other printing parameters with every different stencil you use. Few people do that because their stencils are very similar in terms of geometries and size of apertures and so forth, but technically, you should optimize the printing by adjusting those parameters for every stencil and certainly, when you make a significant change, as M.K. is indicating, going from standard one thickness stencils to step stencils.

Phil ›› Usually attack angle is fixed, depending upon the manufacturer of machine you're using. But everything else, including your squeegee speed, pressure are all part of the proper setup. Do your due diligence.

Jim ›› And with all due diligence, Phil, there are newer printer machines that do advocate using adjustment of squeegee angle, and some of them, I believe, at one point, would actually allow you to adjust it in the middle of the stroke. I have not yet worked with one, but I believe that I have heard a claim and maybe a tech paper advocating the desirability for changing squeegee angle, and dynamic squeegee.

Phil ›› Good luck and optimize your stencil printing processes as much as you can. And whatever you do, don't solder like my brother.

Jim ›› And don't solder like my brother.

Is No-Clean the Trend for QFN Components?

(no-clean, soldering, reflow, OA, water soluble, flux, cleaning, solvents, BTC, QFN, residue)

Phil ›› Jim, what's today's question?

Jim ›› The question: "I recently switched businesses from simple single boards to complex double sided boards which are water cleaned. I had previously been using no-clean processes at all our contract assemblers. That is what I have training and experience on with resolving issues. Since moving to this new job, I have been pushing to reduce cost by moving and testing no-clean processes at our current contract assemblers. I recently had an issue of residue left under a QFN package, that's a form of BTC bottom terminated components, after cleaning. The resolution was a series of design experiments at the contract assembler to determine the best line speed, water temperature, pressure to run the boards and which saponifier to use. My question, is there a continuing trend to move to no-clean or is industry in agreement that certain technology will have to remain in a cleaning process?"

Phil ›› Sounds like an oxymoron: clean a no-clean. The use of a no-clean process is application driven. In this case, the decision whether to go to no-clean or clean is depending on the actual residue that you have there and the service environment that the application is going to see. Beyond that, the decision to clean a no-clean residue is also application driven. Do you agree with that my brother?

Jim ›› Obviously almost everybody would love to go to no-clean if they could. It's cheaper, you eliminate the process and so forth. Yet, for high rel applications, long service lives, people have concerns.

And with certain technologies, in this case we're talking bottom terminated components, QFNs and other related packages, there are serious issues. As we've spoken of before, there are questions even about the safety and long-term reliability of no-cleans with the BTC package. The idea that flux residues and flux chemistry gets trapped under the package, because a low stand-off, high volume of solder paste, and flux in the central pad; can you guarantee that you fully deactivate that flux under a BGA package? Even if you put the whole package through the appropriate temperature cycle during reflow. Yes, I do agree. It's application specific.

Phil ›› If you decide you have to clean the bottom terminated components, what you're seeing in the experience with your CEMs is absolutely correct and it is not trivial. Even with a good water cleaning process and engineered cleaning agents, it is difficult to get everything right to ensure that you actually clean all of the residue whether it is supposed to be cleanable or a no-clean residue, simply because, mainly the geometry. You've got low clearance and very little open space to get fluids to flow under there and flow back out again to carry the potential contaminants away. I think you're on the right path and you're dealing with the reality that exists in the marketplace and you're going to have to make your own decision of whether no clean is worth it with your specific product.

Component Moisture Question?

(humidity, MSD, component, delamination, cracking, defects, storage, reflow, moisture, baking, dry cabinet)

Phil ›› I believe today Jim, we have a component procedure related question.

Jim ›› Yes this is from M.M.: "We mistakenly assembled circuit boards using BGA components that were not properly stored. The BGA components had moisture tags that show indication of moisture exposure. All the assemblies passed testing. Can we now re-bake the assemblies to ensure that they will not have moisture related failures on these devices, or should we remove and replace the suspect BGA components?"

Phil ›› I think this is a case of closing the barn door after the horse is out, or the BGA is out. Am I correct?

Jim ›› Absolutely Phil. This is a classic example of MSD potential damage. A part was not stored properly. It was exposed to moisture. We didn't realize it. We reflowed it. The answer to your first question is NO. Re-baking at this point will do nothing to help that part. The damage occurs during reflow. If there's too much moisture in there it can crack, delaminate and all the other bad things we know that can happen to the internal structure of moisture sensitive components. So, no.

Phil ›› M.M. says all the assemblies passed testing so there's no "dead in the water" failures. Was there any damage inside the parts? The best way to look for the most common types of moisture sensitive damage, which is cracking and delamination, is using scanning acoustic microscopy. Better known as C-SAM. It's a non-destructive test. If you have it available, it's not real expensive or time consuming and again if you do the parts that are suspect you can see a lot of the typical kinds of damage.

Jim ›› You may want to x-ray them to look for potential cracks in wire bonds that may not have been caught during your quality testing, be it in-circuit or functional. But, otherwise yeah, pull off all the parts and replace them. Good luck and you've learned, as my brother said, you've got to follow these procedures.

Phil ›› I just want to add that a lot of people feel that if they didn't get corner lifting on the corner joints of the component is that they're free and clear. We want to point out that the popcorn effect doesn't always occur. That sometimes you don't get enough belly bulge during the reflow expansion to actually lift the corner leads. So just because you haven't lifted the corner leads doesn't mean those symptoms my brother Jim has mentioned aren't there.

Jim ›› Yes, the scariest thing about moisture sensitivity damage is that we have no idea how big the problem is. Because if, as Phil just illuminated, if you don't get this catastrophic pop-corning during reflow that lifts the corner, that cracks the packages, or we've seen actually parts being blown right off the surface of the circuit board, you can get situations where they look okay, they test okay but you've got some latent damage inside that has reduced the reliability of the product and you get failure in start-up, burn-in, early infant mortality, or worst of all intermittent. Because you've got some delamination that's not a failure, but the part overheats, or you get some connections that aren't reliable, and you get intermittent performance.

Typically if they've gotten out of the factory very few people try to fault analyze to the internal component level. So, think about all the intermittent problems that are out in the field. Some percentage of those are probably due to moisture sensitivity damage during reflow in assembly.

Phil ›› But we have no idea how much or how big the problem is. So, keep those moisture sensitive parts in their moisture barrier bags or in their dry cabinets. Keep track of them and don't put them on a board if you're not sure. Bake the parts before you reflow them. Baking them after reflow does no good whatsoever.

Assembling Boards with BGAs on Both Sides

(soldering, reflow, BGA, cracking, warpage)

Phil ›› I do believe we have a soldering design question today - is that correct Jim?

Jim ›› I think it's actually a PCB layout thing, but the issues relate to soldering. This is from D.S. and it's simply, "what are the pros and cons of processing BGAs single sided or double sided? First or second?" Well first off, let me say that this raises the wonderful question of how do we describe a double-sided assembly. First side, second side, top side, bottom side, side A, side B. Bottom, top.

Phil ›› Soap-box alert!

Jim ›› I use the term bottom and top to describe its final configuration. The bottom side is the side that is soldered first and is therefore reflowed a second time when the top side is reflowed. It doesn't matter what you call them as long as we all understand. So that's the terminology that we will use today.

Phil ›› A lot of people look at the mass of the component and think they would definitely want to solder it on the second pass because of the weight of the component and the integrity of the joints when it is re-reflowed that second time. We have found in our experience that's usually is not the real problem. There are other more intrinsic things, including exposure to a second thermal extrusion and other reliability questions.

Jim ›› In general, people like to put only simple components on the bottom side to minimize all the problems that my brother alluded to. But it's generally felt that if you do a good job and the parts don't fall off it should be okay. But there have just been some very good technical papers published that bring this into question for large complex BGAs on the bottom side, which see a second reflow cycle. The potential problem is cracked solder joints, brittle fractures at the component solder ball interface during that second reflow cycle. The analysis seems to indicate that for larger packages, if too much warpage occurs before this bottom side reflows a second time, it can crack that solder joint before it melts.

Phil ›› And because there's no flux present, those cracked surfaces will not re=solder and come back together again, and you can have an intermittent, a very weak solder joint, or a total failure.

Jim ›› The conclusion of these authors was application specific and probably only works for certain large BGAs that warp a lot. It's much safer to put BGAs on the top side to eliminate the possibility of this failure mode occurring.

BGA Components and Coplanarity

(BGA, coplanarity, soldering, reflow, thermal considerations, surface finish, HASL, PCB)

Phil ›› Today's question I believe has to do with surface finish.

Jim ›› It comes from T.Y.: "We are an EMS contractor. We have a customer that has requested a PCB with a HASL that's hot air surface leveled, surface finish. The assembly includes a 256 ball BGA, the component balls are .6 mm. Should we be concerned with coplanarity? Are there any other concerns?"

Phil ›› YES! We do not like HASL because of the coplanarity issue - right off the bat. You have to understand that hot air solder leveling or hot air leveling, whatever you want to call it, HASL, it originates back to the through hole days. With through hole we didn't really care about the coplanarity or topography of the surface of the board. With surface mount we care about it a lot. So, it's very important that we have a very coplanar surface. We start taking about things like bottom terminated components and ball grid arrays and area arrays, it becomes extremely paramount that we have a nice level surface. Because of the nature of it, the fact that you're using hot air as essentially a squeegee on the surface of the board it's anything but coplanar. There's a lot of variation in it. I don't care if you're talking about leaded or lead-free HASL. It's still an issue. It's not a great methodology to use for surface mount. There's even a question about what it's doing to the integrity of the surface of the circuit board.

Jim ›› Another general issue that's raised is the ability to screen print reliably on surfaces that are not flat. Since most people, particularly with larger pitches as this indicated here with the .6 mm ball probably indicating a one mm or 40 mil pitch part, that would allow you to use area reduction on your stencil apertures to assure good gasketing. Gasketing between a rectangular aperture and a domed surface on the pad is going to be problematic in any case, so that's another issue independent of components. If you don't get good gasketing, solder paste can squeeze out under the pads and give you bridges and solder balls.

Phil ›› My question is why is this informed customer requesting the HASL surface finish? We think HASL's a bad idea anytime surface mount is involved. There's your answer.

Simple Test for Flux Penetration

(soldering, flux, wave-soldering, hole-fill, through-hole)

Phil ›› Jim, what's today's question.

Jim ›› Well Phil, it actually isn't surface mount, it is that "old" technology, wave soldering. It is a pretty straight-forward question and comes from J.V.: "What is a good test for flux penetration through the plated hole barrels?"

Phil ›› Good question, and I'm glad J.V. is checking it out. So many people neglect their wave solder machine and the proper setup. It is kind of refreshing to hear. There are some procedures that are used. You can buy some fancy tools. But we like to do the old board sandwich. One way of doing that is, essentially, you take your through-hole board that you are wanting to test penetration on (with no components inserted) and you put a piece of thermal style fax paper and then another like board on top of it. You clamp them together forming a sandwich. If you don't have any thermal fax paper you can use ...

Jim ›› Well, technically any paper, but to really make the dots show up, if you have alcohol based flux, thermal fax paper is the best. If you are using a water-based flux litmus paper will give you a better reaction. Any paper will work but it won't turn color, and it will be more problematic to see the dots.

Phil ›› You make that sandwich and you run it through your fluxer as you would normally operate it. When it comes out you look at the paper and look at the dots. You will be able to determine if your flux has penetrated with the current settings through the holes on the board. Pretty straight-forward.

Jim ›› Do not run the board through full pre-heat or the wave with paper in it. You take severe risks to the well-being of your factory.

Larger Stencil Apertures and Type 4 Paste

(printing, soldering, reflow, solder paste, apertures, stencil, 5-ball rule, powder)

Phil ›› Jim, what's our question for today?

Jim ›› Well it's a materials question, Phil. It comes from J.V.: "What is your experience with larger size apertures and type four solder paste and how does it affect solder joints for non-collapsible BGA and CGA type solder joints?"

Phil ›› Okay, fair question. I'll start off by saying that from an economic aspect, of course, you don't want to use a type four paste unless you have to - if there are apertures on the stencil that require it, per the 5 Ball Rule. Type four does have a little bit more propensity to oxidize because of the small particles than say a type three and it costs more money. But aside from that, Jim, it's becoming more and more common, isn't it?

Jim ›› Absolutely and with a propensity of smaller components, 0.5 millimeter, 0.4 millimeter area array packages, type four is becoming almost the standard. Actually, Phil, I think many of the oxidation issues have been long handled in the newer type four pastes.

That certainly was a concern back, you know eons ago, when you and I were cutting our teeth in the industry. But now the advances in modern flux technologies in today's paste with the type fours being so common, I think have virtually eliminated all those problems. I don't see any issues with using them with larger apertures. I mean, think about it, most boards that are being built today are some combination of the larger apertures and the small apertures for the very fine-pitched components.

Likewise I wouldn't see it having any problem for the non-collapsible ball grid or column grid array type of solder joints. All modern pastes are being formulated with very robust fluxes today.

Phil ›› But nonetheless you should evaluate any paste you use before you put it in your process just to make absolutely certain it's compatible with what you're trying to do.

Jim ›› And you know, Phil, with the driving force of the handheld market pushing us to even 0.3 millimeter packages and chip scale packages and QFNs and what have you, people are talking more commonly about type five powders, type five pastes which were almost unheard of you know four or five years ago. Now type four is almost common and of course if you get the special variations within those of the type 4.5 or type 3.5 or 5.5 where the manufacturers have created a more limited particle distribution within the specification for those types. But, it's a good question. As you said type four is typically designed for small apertures but with modern flux formulations you shouldn't have any problem with any of your other types of solder joints. But it still is going to be more expensive because of the greater processing required to produce the smaller powders. I don't see that as ever changing.

Phil ›› Right and I would only add to that like with any solder paste and as my brother Jim alluded to earlier on, any solder paste of any size or any manufacturer, do your solder paste evaluation. There are some companies out there who do it right and there are others that leave a lot to be desired, so you have to do a thorough solder paste evaluation.

Jim ›› But there are certainly multiple suppliers who are making very good type four paste today that will print and solder under a variety of conditions.

Can Mixing Wave Solder Pallets Cause Contamination?

(soldering, wave-solder, contamination, defects, flux, residue, cleaning, solder pot, fixturing, flux-entrapment, Pb-free, SnPb)

Jim ›› Today's question comes from D.G.: "We have many assemblies moving from leaded to lead-free solder. The design change is not changing the PCB layout. Our wave solder pallets are made from material which can take the increased heat. Can we use the same wave solder pallets, or should they be replaced? Our concern is contamination from the residue on the pallets from earlier builds using leaded solder."

Phil ›› First of all, are we talking about, flux residue? Well, clean the stuff off for crying out loud. Am I missing something here, Jim?

Jim ›› I would assume that they're concerned about small deposits of tin lead solder that may be trapped in the cracks and crannies of the pallets and you know might not be entirely visible and difficult to clean. But now you get them in the higher temperature, immersed in the higher temperature solder bath going through the wave and they dissolve and now you could contaminate your pot.

Phil ›› Well, I say give the thing a damn good cleaning. The stuff is not wetting anything. It's not wetting to the fixture material. If you're using titanium inserts it's not wetting to that, either. What's the big deal here?

Jim ›› Yeah, but I'm thinking that that pallets are normally made from more than one piece. You know they got a frame on them, they're bolted together and riveted together, and you got those little cracks and crannies in there that you could stick some old tin lead solder and contaminate the pot. Of course, it would beg the question of how much - how many are you going to run, how big is your pot and what's the potential for contamination? But man, you wouldn't want to get any lead in your pot.

Phil ›› No, I agree there but I just wonder the propensity for that happening. Jim, I bet you probably floss after every meal, don't you? Instead of once a week like I do.

I see what's up here and if it's a real concern then perhaps try our latest invention(that I just invented about five nanoseconds ago). If you go over to the Board Talk shameless commerce division, you'll find our latest product, "Fixture Floss" for cleaning out those little fixture nooks and crannies.

Jim ›› How about an alternative, Phil? Even I can be re-conciliatory. You take one of your worst pallets that potentially has the most nooks and crannies and you tear one apart. You tear the fixture apart, crack it open anywhere that you think it might be contaminated, because you're going to throw it away. Otherwise, if you're not going to use it, then clean it. And see if there is any appreciable volume of solder stuck in those crannies and nooks and crevices and cracks and what have you.

Phil ›› Well, I can be re-conciliatory too, Jim. At least D.G. is thinking, and we appreciate that. He's looking to be right on top of it and not contaminate any tin lead and lead-free pots and to that I give him a pat on the back. My thinking is a good thorough cleaning of the fixture and then combine the two. Do a really thorough cleaning - even possibly running it through a batch cleaner as well and then, as Jim said, do an autopsy and see what shows up. And even if it does require a very, very thorough cleaning, even if you have to use fixture floss or whatever, the idea that since you're converting over to lead-free it's going to be a one-time thing. Bite the bullet, get them clean and forever dedicate them to lead-free. That was a good question. Thank you, D.G.

Jim ›› Phil, don't you floss all your pallets every time you use them?

Phil ›› My pallets, yeah. My teeth, no.

Can Water Contamination Cause Failure?

(contamination, moisture, corrosion)

Phil ›› And what exactly are we talking about today, Jim?

Jim ›› Well it comes from H.M.: "We have an operational circuit board that was accidentally exposed to rainwater for a few hours. The circuit board was subsequently dried and has now been operational for 14 months. Is there a greater likelihood of failure at this stage compared to other circuit boards?" I assume they mean other circuit boards that haven't been exposed to rain.

Phil ›› I guess my first impression is that the key operative thing here is properly dried. We don't know the details, but we'll take H.M.'s word that it was an appropriate procedure and it seems to have been effective.

Jim ›› I can't think of anything that could be a failure mode resulting from water exposure that wouldn't have showed up in 14 months. Assuming there's some regular operation and this isn't an emergency device that sits on the shelf for most of its time. The main thing is that it was dried and if it wasn't dried properly it would have failed pretty quickly I would suspect. The other thing would be contamination. Whatever is going to happen, dendrites or corrosion, it should have happened by now.

Phil ›› Let's be honest. Most circuit boards are perfectly able to be water washed. It's very common so there really aren't any problems with water and circuit boards as long as they're clean. But extended exposure, again, you have to dry them out so that when you first turn the things on you don't boil or expand that water too quickly and crack or delaminate something.

Jim ›› The 14 months to me is the indicator. If it hasn't failed by now, it's probably just as good - maybe better. Maybe the rain-water dissolved off some bad stuff that had been there before and now it's actually cleaner and less susceptible to corrosive attack.

Phil ›› Who knows, maybe H.M. was an area where they have de-ionized rainwater. You never know about these things.

Why Do Our Boards Warp During Reflow?

(reflow, soldering, warpage, thermal considerations, PCB, calibration, profiling, ovens)

Phil ›› Jim, what's today's exciting question?

Jim ›› Well, we, the Assembly Brothers, Pick and Place are going to answer a question sent to us by A.M.: "Board flexing has recently started to occur on one of our circuit board assemblies. The assembly has a 40 millimeter package-on-package BGA component. The BGA has an integrated heat sink. We are using a three-zone reflow oven. The profile worked without issue for at least six months. The problem with boards bowing or curving upwards towards the middle of the board has just started recently. Yet our process has remained the same and there have been no changes. Any help is appreciated."

Phil ›› First you have to take your dish of derision - a three-zone oven! Obviously you bought it out of a catalog. Second, last time I saw a three-zone oven used was when it was to make toast at the hotel buffet. And thirdly - something changed. If it's not your process, it's probably your application because that's a pretty sophisticated application. To basically be using process equipment you bought at a restaurant supply place is not a good idea. Let's talk about the mechanics.

**Jim ›› ** I agree, a three-zone reflow, assuming they are three equally sized zones, is really not very flexible in controlling the time temperature profile. So, most people use at least four or five zones for tin-lead, and preferably six or seven if you're doing lead-free.

The idea of something changing, though as you said, Phil, in your infinite wisdom, is true. There's two things. You say the process hasn't changed but all of a sudden you're getting warping. Is this warping on an assembly that you have been building with this big PoP component for all this time, or is this assembly a new one that you're trying to run in the same "process", i.e. the same recipe on your reflow oven, which could obviously be a source of the problem where a reflow recipe was adequate for one board and along comes a heavier board and you have to change the process to achieve acceptable soldering. The other thing is that unbeknownst to you something could have changed in the oven. And getting back to my brother's comment, three-zone ovens tend not to be of the highest sophistication and quality, so there may have been a degradation in the oven, fan degradation, heaters, temperature sensors getting off balance. Or something that's beyond the internal control system of the oven to diagnose. So, you think you're getting the same thermal profile on the board and you're not. Have you run a confirmation profile with a good calibrated profiler and a dedicated test board which we always recommend? thermocouples on the board permanently mounted, hooked up to a reliable calibrated data logger, run it through the oven, are you sure you're getting the same process you were getting six months ago, assuming it's the same board.

**Phil ›› ** You know I just hate to see people skimp on equipment and just going below bare minimum like in this situation and going on the assumption that reflow is commoditized. But that's even below commoditization. A 40 millimeter PoP, that's almost over an inch and a half square. A package-on-package with a heatsink.

**Jim ›› ** Most people I know wouldn't attempt that without a 10 or 12 zone oven to make sure they had the heating capacity to heat that assembly uniformly and avoid warping and all the other bad things that can happen. Maybe you can do it with this oven but wow, I'd be really surprised if you get consistent results over a long period of time. I think your interpretation that the assembly has changed, that the other boards were simpler and now this is a heavier one, that isn't hacking it with this process that they have set up.

**Phil ›› ** It brings to mind what the rest of the line looks like. I don't even want to think what they're using for printing and pick and place, but I'll bet you a dollar that they're using a paper slicer for singulation. We beat up on this poor guy enough. We feel your pain and you're just going to have to hunker down and get some real equipment. It's probably not what you wanted to hear. I've always said that "the only absolute is that there are no absolutes". We've seen people reflow in a toaster oven which is pretty close to what you're doing. But in reflow there is a requirement for consistency, repeatability, and practicality. Caveat emptor!

What Is the Recommended Component Storage Environment?

(components, MSD, storage, humidity, oxidation, corrosion, moisture)

Jim ›› This comes from G.H.: "What do you recommend as an environment for component storage to prohibit oxidation, relative humidity, nitrogen atmosphere, temperature, etc.? Is there a standard storage environment scenario considered as good practice?"

Phil ›› With moisture sensitive devices, there are specifications:

JEDEC J-STD-020C Moisture/Reflow Sensitivity Classification for Non-hermetic Solid State Surface Mount Devices

JEDEC J-STD-033C Standard for Handling, Packaging, Shipping, and Use of Moisture/Reflow Sensitive Surface-Mount Devices

You definitely want to abide by those and that's absolutely a best practice. We say that but not everybody does due diligence on those so take care of those MSD's and we've covered that on some other Board Talks. But looking at run of the mill components, if they came in bags leave them sealed in the bags they came in until you're really ready to use them. Minimal exposure to ambient conditions. Obviously you can repackage them. As far as in your storage area, relative humidity, temperature, nothing really special is needed.

Jim ›› You have to be conscious of any contaminants that are in the atmosphere that are going to affect solderability over the long term. I think the most important thing is to put them back in packages and seal them up reasonably well to prevent them from interacting with the environment. I want to point out that the standard against which exposure of all MSD components are measured against is 30 C, 60% relative humidity. You wouldn't want to go above that. Again, you should be worried about contamination, any sulfur or other stuff that's in the air and avoid big swings in your storage condition so that you won't get condensation. Put them back in the storage containers and seal them up. It's not necessary to vacuum seal like you do for MSD components, but reasonably well sealed when you're not using them.

Phil ›› For best practices monitor and control relative humidity and temperature in your storage area. Beyond that, no, you normally don't necessarily have to put them in a dry box, though that would be advantageous.

Jim ›› The long-term solderability of any part at the highest level is determined by the quality of the surface finish that's on the leads. They should be ok if they're good and well coated with whatever kind of plating they have. Most parts are coming in today with tin over nickel. Make sure that the tin is put on properly because if it's not you're going to have problems long term no matter how you store them unless you go to the extreme of a nitrogen environment.

Issues With BGA Rework Residue

(reflow, rework and repair, BGA, residue, flux, soldering, contamination, cleaning, saponifier, solvent, PCB, IPA)

Phil ›› Jim, what's today's question?

Jim ›› One of our favorite topics, BGA rework. The question comes from J.C.: "After a BGA has been removed for rework, there is an outline of residue on the laminate around the pads. It does not come off easily but has to be carefully scraped away with a knife. Is it necessary to be removing this residue to reinstall a BGA, or is it fine to leave it?" No, it is probably not fine, or at least risky, to leave that residue. Think about what that residue is. It came from the original solder paste when the BGA was reflowed onto the board the first time and that residue has gone through whatever thermal cycle was required to remove that BGA. So those residues are baked. Perhaps polymerized depending on the temperature and how carefully the rework was controlled.

Scraping with a knife on any PCB is not fun and it's risky. Removing residues with a cleaner and a solvent and some sort of chemistry is a much better way.

Phil ›› And we emphasize using the right solvent - the right chemistry. Don't go necessarily reaching for that bottle of IPA. It may not be the appropriate solvent. You may be making more of a mess than you intend. You want to find out to the best of your knowledge what that original residue is or as our cleaning friends call the soil, and you want to find the right solvent chemistry to adequately treat and remove that particular residue. If you have trouble identifying what that original flux was, like for example it wasn't done by your process or something along those lines, consult some of your chemistry companies like Kyzen and Zestron and they can probably help you out finding the right solvent. The other thing of course is the question selective cleaning. In other words, are you going to clean in that area only or are you going to attempt to clean the whole board. There are lot of people out there and I certainly follow the logic, that don't believe in selective cleaning because you're disturbing other things. So, you might want to consider using the proper solvent and clean the entire board assuming the assembly can go through a cleaning cycle. So, it does get a little bit more complicated. I know, now you're thinking about going back and using that knife and scrape it. But you know we're here to tell you what we think best practices are based on what you described to us.

Jim ›› If you know what the original paste formulation was and it truly was a no-clean, then you might have some more confidence in leaving that residue on there. But if you don't, now you're going to introduce perhaps a different flux chemistry in your rework process, either a paste flux or another form of paste and now you get the residue from the first paste chemistry mixing with the residue from the second repair operation again, could be quite risky.

Phil ›› So we hope we've suggested a better alternative than scraping it off. Again, as Jim said, depending on what that residue is you might be okay leaving it on, but our experience and logic dictates that you probably do want to remove it and as we're emphasizing, remove it properly.

Fillets, Fiducials and Vias

Incoming Circuit Boards - How Clean Is Clean?

(cleaning, contamination, PCB, handling, PCB fabrication)

Jim ›› This question comes from A.S.: "We're having cleanliness issues on our finished circuits. We feel that our assembly processes are not introducing contaminants. Could it be the result of incoming PCB cleanliness?"

Phil ›› The answer to that is YES - it is possible. Of course, we're glad you have good competence in your internal process but just make sure you look under every stone and every fixture. But addressing incoming - yes that could be a big problem. We don't know where your boards are being fabricated, but one critical aspect of fab is, of course, is the final rinse. We've heard the circuit board depicted as a contamination soup. A lot of these contaminants are added during our assembly process including ionic and weak acids, as well as non-ionic contaminants from the handling. But bear in mind that there's a lot of chemical processes going on in the fab operation. In general, you're only as good as your final rinse. And certainly, from a fabrication standpoint, you are only as good as the fabricator's final rinse. So, the question I would ask, short of auditing your fab facility, is what is the cleanliness of the final rinse water that they're using before the boards are shipped off to you? We've run into a number of cases where the fabricators were using tap water and these are in places you wouldn't want to drink the tap water, let alone put it on your circuit boards.

Jim ›› Phil, I put myself above circuit boards.

Phil ›› I try to treat circuit boards as I treat myself. That's probably not very good but let's put it this way. I don't know what the FDA recommends as far as cleanliness of drinking water, but I know for circuit boards, certainly from a cleanliness spec, in the vicinity of 200K ohms resistivity, which of course is an indication of the cleanliness of the water, is probably what you want as a spec. Depending on how wonderful the water is coming in, wherever in the world you're using it, is the degree that you're going to have to filter it, or use a system with reverse osmosis, and what level of purification and distillation the deionization is going to require. So again, the spec that we understand is a good one for cleanliness of boards coming from the fab shop is again 200K ohms. The cleanliness of the boards coming out of your assembly process, of course, have to be a lot higher, a lot cleaner. Typically, a minimum of two meg ohms. But from the fab shop that's what we're looking at. Of course, the cleaner the better, but I would use that as a basic minimum.

A number of PCB assemblers we have worked with, particularly those doing high-reliability applications, are resorting to routinely washing the PCBs coming from the fabricator prior to submitting them to the assembly process. I would recommend that you at least "qualify" your fabricator by submitting samples for ROSE and Ionic Chromatography testing.

Let's face it, we've been in parts of the world where you wouldn't even drink the water, let along rinse your PCBs with it.

What Causes Solder Balls During Hand Soldering?

(defects, solder balls, hand-soldering, flux, wire-core solder, oxidation, contamination)

Phil ›› So what question is drifting our way today Jim?

Jim ›› This comes from C.P.: "We have experienced solder balls during automated reflow and tweaked the process to eliminate them. Now we are finding solder balls during the hand soldering of some eight-lead SMT components. Any idea what causes solder balls during hand soldering?"

Phil ›› Everything and anything - just like what causes solder balls in reflow and wave-soldering. I guess the first question we would probably ask is what's different thermally or chemically?

Jim ›› The first thing Phil is to say are you using the same solder paste in doing your hand soldering which you used in reflow where you found that adjusting the thermal profile eliminated solder balls; or what I think is more likely is that you're using some sort of cored wire. So, the parameters are much different. Solder balls are typically caused by incomplete fluxing because the flux does not clean all the solder surfaces, so that when the solder metal becomes molten, it does not coalesce into one single mass and you get these little guys floating off on their own as balls with their own little oxide coating around them preventing them from coming back together. So, do you have adequate flux in your hand soldering operation and also I think as you indicated Phil, the thermal profile. Are your operators trained? Are they using the proper tip size and tip temperatures and IPC specified soldering techniques?

Phil ›› As Jim said, do you have the right tips? Do you have the right heat range for what you're doing? Have the irons been calibrated? That's another prerequisite. And again, how well trained are your operators? Are they soldering with the right end of the soldering iron?

Jim ›› I feel that my experience is that solder balls are not common in hand soldering. One other thing that you could think of, would be contamination of the leads of the parts that you're soldering. But if they work in reflow with paste, I would think that that would not be the issue. But you can never be sure.

01005 Component Challenges and Bugs

(micro-passives, components, 01005, printing, reflow, pick-and-place, soldering, apertures, stencil, tombstoning, feeders, AOI, inspection, step-stencil)

Phil ›› Welcome to Board Talk with Jim Hall and Phil Zarrow of ITM Consulting, the Assembly brothers. We're here to talk about electronic assembly; materials, equipment, components, practices and procedure, and who knows what else. Who does know what else? Jim does because he's got the question of the day.

**Jim ›› ** It's sent by T.G.: "We are going forward with assemblies that use 01005 components. We're wondering if you would have some input as to what the most important challenges we are going to face." Well, your whole world's about to change and maybe come crashing down. Everything that you do just got harder from loading a feeder to picking up a component, inspecting it, handling it, printing the solder paste for it, everything in the line. Reflowing gets easier because, believe it or not, 01005s have a lower tendency to tombstone than 0201s. That is the one redeeming grace that I have ever heard about processing 01005s.

**Phil ›› ** But first you have to surmount all of the hurdles Jim mentioned on the path to the reflow machine. A lot of people think that pick and place is the toughest, and there are a lot of pick and place issues. As Jim mentioned; feeding - how the component's sitting in the pocket on the tape, how it's being picked up, and also how it's being released. There's been modified pick and place tooling, so the buggers don't get caught in the pockets and also for releasing from the pick-up tooling.

**Jim ›› ** I want to elaborate on placement a bit more, Phil. Think about putting a reel of these into a feeder. The operator is manually loading them, stripping back the tape to get a pocket with a component, your operators can barely see that there's a component in the pocket. That's the reality of dealing with these without magnification. If you're splicing tapes on the fly just the simple thing as loading a feeder can become an issue. Finding the part in the pocket; tolerance is so small sometimes some people find they have to use their vision system to find the parts in the pockets. Hopefully you don't have to go that way but I'm just emphasizing how every process step has now become more critical.

**Phil ›› ** I think that printing is far and away the biggest problem.

**Jim ›› ** Agreed!

**Phil ›› ** Basically, you're dealing with very small apertures. If you were printing a cellphone PCB where everything is ultra-miniaturized, and you can you use a 3 mil stencil then the problem isn't so bad. But most people have other larger components where they would like to use a 5 mil stencil or at least a 4 mil stencil.

**Jim ›› ** The apertures get really small and you begin to get, as I call them, too tall and narrow apertures when you make them small enough for your 01005 pads. So, you're faced with the situations of step stencils, enhanced stencil materials such as e-fab or nano-coatings and things like that. Bottom line - getting consistent, complete fill and repeatable release of solder paste from these tiny apertures becomes a bigger and bigger challenge.

**Phil ›› ** Make sure that, if you're using AOI, it has the resolution to identify these parts. With older systems, the camera pixels were not really small enough to give you good repeatable inspection of these even though they're just a simple resistor or a capacitor component. As Jim said at the outset your whole world is changing and there are so many implications. But it is do-able, lots of other people are doing them. Master 01005s and then see what your designers throw in something that's even smaller. They're out there.

How Effective Is Nano Coating On Stencils?

(nano-coating, printing, stencil, apertures, solder paste, SPI)

Jim ›› This question comes from R.W.: "With nano coatings on stencils evolving over the past few years, what is the best method to measure the nano coating thickness and how to determine if it degrades over time?" You just get out your nano ruler that has nanometers on it and you just stick it down on the edge of the board... nano coatings may be single molecules thick. There is no practical way short of a very, very exotic materials lab to measure the thickness of a nano coating. Nano implies 10-9 meters. It's tiny as in really, really thin. And it degrades over time. Also, the types of coatings are still evolving. New improvements are coming out almost monthly.

Phil ›› You have to, at this point, rely on the manufacturers to tell you things like how long it's going to last, how to determine if it degrades. The obvious criteria is do you start to get the printing defects that you were trying to eliminate when you applied the nano coating. You're trying to get better release, more consistent deposits, less smearing on the bottom so this can reduce your cleaning. That is why you're doing it and so if it's degrading you should see the effects. You should be monitoring your solder paste printing in some way and you're using your SPC chart.

Jim ›› You should see the variation in height or volume as the nano coating degrades. Talk to the vendors, hopefully they can give you some references about other people's experience because it's new, it's evolving. There is not a long track record and I'm sure with the different materials, the working life is going to vary, but definitely the performance of your printing should be the best indicator.

Is HASL a Good Choice for Surface Finish?

(surface finish, HASL, soldering, components, printing, OSP, ENIG, hole-fill, BTC)

Phil ›› Jim, what's today's question?

Jim ›› It comes to us from D.S.: "We are using lead free HASL (Hot Air Solder Leveling.) Is this the best choice for a surface finish? We have several bottom-terminated components on our board and our production is low volume and the PCB's are often stored for a year or more."

Phil ›› Once you mention surface mount specifically, bottom terminated components (BTC), the answer is NO - it's not. HASL was originally invented back in the days of through-hole in the mid '70s and it was a welcome change from methodologies we were using before like IR fusing and hydro squeegee and all those other fun methodologies of putting a tin-lead coating on. But once surface mount came around what we found is unlike through-hole we are concerned about the topography and the smoothness of the board, especially after we started to get finer and finer pitches. Look how much we critique solder paste deposition and solder paste height - how important that is. So, if you're starting off with a lumpy, bumpy finish you're going to have problems. And that was even before the advent of bottom terminated components, well before they became so popular in area arrays. So, it becomes even more critical. Even with the lead-free versions, some of the mythology out there is that lead-free HASL is smoother than tin-lead HASL and Jim and I have attended enough seminars and propaganda sessions and stuff like that to say NO it's not. If they're still using the vertical methodology for a hot air solder leveling, whether using an SN100 alloy or tin copper, it's basically from what we've seen not going to be any smoother than tin-lead HASL. So, we believe that HASL is not the way to go.

What are some of the alternatives? Well there's OSP (Organic Solder Preservative.) Jim, what are some limitations with OSP?

Jim ›› What jumps right out, shelf life. Nobody recommends that you store OSP coated boards over a year so based upon the data given here in the question, eliminate OSP. OSP works great for single soldering applications but most people don't like to store to for more than six months or so. It's very inexpensive. It's the least expensive. We don't know if their cost is an issue here. The other question that people will raise, are there multiple soldering operations? Does it maintain solderability through multiple heat cycles? Most specifically, if you have a board where you have to reflow both sides and then do a wave soldering or selective soldering operation, can you get reliable hole fill after the barrels of those holes have gone through two reflow cycles.

Phil ›› You want the advantages of OSP, and it's come a long way in that it is the cheapest surface finish, but as I said there's a lot of caveats. Then we get into some of the immersion finishes - immersion tin, immersion silver. The jury's still out on those and with regard to some of the pros and cons. There is shelf life concern with immersion silver. Certainly, it's a lot more forgiving and it's longer duration than OSP, but it also I would say from an assembly standpoint, you better have your act together as far as handling. There's still oxidation issues and there's tarnishing issues.

Jim ›› I feel that immersion tin is not an acceptable finish. It just doesn't solder well. It suffers many of the problems that OSP does with multiple heat cycles. It's used a lot in Europe but most people in the U.S. don't like it and most people I've heard that have tested it say it doesn't solder well which is surprising for tin. I feel that although the limitations that my brother outlined with immersion silver are true, many people feel comfortable for specific applications. Certainly not if you're going into a high sulfur atmosphere because it is the most prone to creep corrosion of all the surfaces. But some of the server people and other high rel people use immersion silver and they are comfortable with it so I feel that it is a valid choice depending upon your application.

Phil ›› I would tend to lean to tried and trusty ENIG (Electroless Nickel Immersion Gold) surfaces. Been around awhile, it's time tested. Certainly, storage concerns are most nominal because oxidation's not really that much of an issue. But again, the only caveat with ENIG is make sure you got a good fab shop. We've talked about black pad and some of the other concerns. Make sure they've got the process under control and particularly as it pertains to things like gold thicknesses and nickel thicknesses, all should be in conformance with the IPC specifications. So, I tend to favor ENIG (and ENIPIG) but again it's your choice. But I think my brother and I definitely concur with regard to HASL: run away, run away! HASL is not the way to go for surface mount with bottom-terminated components, area arrays and certainly any pitch below 20 mil and below.

What Causes Board Delamination?

(PCB, delamination, moisture, humidity, storage, PCB handling, PCB fabrication)

Phil ›› Jim what's our question of the day?

Jim ›› We actually have a similar question submitted by two listeners; the first one is from D.H.: "We are experiencing delamination on our printed circuit boards causing scrap, is there a way to definitively determine that the delamination is being caused by moisture or some other type of defect? Is it possible to repair printed circuit assemblies with delamination?" F.P. has basically the same question but notes that they are processing their boards, reflowing them, very soon after receiving them so that they're not hanging around his shop. But he, basically had the same question; should he bake them and so forth.

Phil ›› There are a lot of aspects that come into play here, but in our allotted five minutes let's hit on the key ones. First, make sure that your fabricator is using laminates that conforms to the current specification. We've run into a number of people who are still fabricating to the IPC 1399 spec. That went out quite a few years ago. Per our good friend Gary Ferrari, "Dr. Design", basically any material being used these days, particularly for lead-free, should be conforming to IPC 4101/126 or /129 and this is basically high performance material with very high Tg and TD decomposition temperatures and tolerances. Make sure you're using the right material. Then, once we get into your shop, you should be following IPC 1601 that covers the handling and care, and storage of circuit boards. Make sure that you've done the proper due diligence and your design of experiments for your reflow profiles or your wave solder or selective soldering profiles and certainly confirm that your hand soldering is under control. Jim, there is a way, I believe, of measuring whether you have absorbed moisture.

Jim ›› I know that some people have determined that there is moisture in the board by weighing the board first then baking it per IPC 1601. That's the nice thing about 1601, it defines specific baking time cycles which has been a question throughout the industry for a long time until that came out. I know that some people have weighed the board and then baked it and weighed it afterwards and the difference was the amount of moisture. In terms of determining whether there was moisture and whether it was causing your problem that would be one thing to do. I'm not sure if that procedure is described in 1601 but you just need a very accurate scale.

Phil ›› In terms of repair, it'd be nice if, perhaps, the more sophisticated circuit board repair shops that repair damaged boards can repair a certain amount of delamination. I can't, off-hand imagine how that would be done. Delamination is really destroying the basic structure of the board.

Jim ›› I can't imagine that a badly delaminated board could be repaired. But it's something you can check with a professional circuit board repair service.

Phil ›› Like Circuit Technology Center or B.E.S.T. as well as a number of others out there. Make sure that your supplier is handling the boards properly and drying them and following the procedure so that they're not getting to you wet and that they are coming in the properly sealed packages.

Jim ›› Most boards are coming from overseas and there are transport times depending on whether your shipping by boat or by plane; but in all cases, IPC 1601 will guide you about how to seal them and you should keep them sealed until you're ready to use them.

Phil ›› Yes, been there, done that; I own a delaminated t-shirt.

Suggested Stencil Wipe Frequency?

(printing, solder paste, stencil, apertures, cleaning, solvents)

Phil ›› Jim. what's the question du jour?

Jim ›› "How do we determine what is the best under stencil wipe frequency?"

Phil ›› Wiping the underside of the stencil, we're talking about in process, and the answer is 'it depends'. It's application driven.

Some of the factors include:

solder paste

how it's reacting to ambient conditions

aperture size

the range of aperture sizes

But the best way to actually determine it is to do a design-of-experiment, just like with every other printer parameter. So rather than guessing and doing it hit and miss, bring on the data.

Jim ›› Get back to basics is always my tendency. Obviously we don't want to wipe the stencil any more frequently than we have to because it typically costs us money in terms of paper and solvent and consumables.

Phil ›› And cycle time. If you're in a high volume high-speed line where stencil printing could become the limiting gate in the line, stencil wiping typically adds to the overall cycle time, so you don't want to do it any more frequently than you have to.

Jim ›› But on the other side obviously if you don't do it enough you start to get solder defects, due to the factors my brother was alluding to.

Phil ›› It's interesting to note is that a lot of the more modern printers can be equipped where they're utilizing a vision system to actually do an inspection of the underside of the stencil. These systems are good. Of course, it depends how they're applied and what apertures you're actually checking. We still recommend the best thing is direct knowledge. Do a DOE (design-of-experiments) to actually determine for that given application, stencil, materials etc. You determine what the frequency should be along with the materials and the methodology; whether using a dry wipe only with vacuum or whether you're using wet followed by a dry.

Jim ›› One other factor is that if you choose to use a solvent as part of your under stencil wiping, make sure it's an appropriate solvent for the paste you're using.

IPA is not a universal solvent for all solder paste, and you can get into trouble by using IPA or any solvent that isn't compatible with a specific paste you're using. And that's true of all cleaning operations.

A Review of Industry Terminology and Acronyms

(BTC, BGA, QFN, components)

Phil ›› I believe today, Jim, we have a component issue.

Jim ›› I would call it more about the terminology issue Phil. It comes from C.F. and it says: "What does the term BTC refer to? Is it the same as QFN?"

Phil ›› I know it's different than a BLT because that's what I was thinking of earlier today.

Let's talk about uniformity of terminology and how this industry is so good at making acronyms and using various terminology for the same thing. This is one of Jim's favorite soapboxes so I will step over and hand the microphone over to him.

Jim ›› We work in a wonderfully exciting industry where new stuff and new materials, components are appearing all the time and that's great. But we suffer from the lack of standard terminology. Different people want to put their own brand name or terminology to get some brand recognition or personal recognition and as my brother said, we get into a situation where people are calling the same thing by different names or using the same name to refer to two different things. But here we have an example of a new family of component types that have evolved and the big standards industry in our world, the IPC exerted its clout and said we are going to take all these things and we are going to call them bottom terminated components. What they're referring to are parts that have no leads protruding out or no balls or bumps on the bottom but just have pads on the bottom. To answer C.F.'s specific question, a QFN is a Bottom Terminated Component or a BTC. But also, an LGA, a Land Grid Array or an SON, a Small Outline No-lead. Or the most infamous one that I've heard is the MLFP, the Micro Lead Frame Plastic Package. All these are BTC's and IPC has produced a wonderful specification to help us along with this and it is spec 7093, Bottom Terminated Components. There's a tremendous amount of information and you should use it.

Phil ›› I know in our work, we're not perfect but we try to use the generic term BTC whenever we discuss this type of component so that we avoid confusion and promote universal communication. But yes, it's an excellent spec. We don't usually rave about specifications as our audience well knows but this one is well worth downloading.

Issues With Fillets on Via Holes?

(soldering, ICT, wave-soldering, through-hole, hole-fill)

Phil ›› Jim, what is today's question?

Jim ›› The question is about concave via fillets causing problems. "When we wave solder our circuit boards, some of the vias have concave fillets giving them a dimple effect. The boards function fine, but we are having problems when we test using our flying probe system. What can we do to create flatter fillets on via holes?" And this is sent in by G.F. The first thing is there are no flat soldered surfaces. Solder is formed by surface tension and wetting forces which are always going to give you a curved surface. Now you can try to minimize that. First, let's make sure we agree upon what our questioner is asking. He's talking about filling via holes. These I'm assuming are plated through holes which do not have leads in them. So, they go over the wave and they just fill up with solder. He's talking about a concave fillet on the top surface which means that the surfaces of solder in the middle of the via hole is lower than the surface of the board. That's my assumption.

Phil ›› Jim, I'm kind of surprised and a little puzzled as to the problem he's actually having with this flying probe. To my knowledge, flying probe generally can compensate in the Z axis for varying topography of the board and, of course, the test points it's going after. So, I'm not sure why it's a problem but he might want to confer with the manufacturer of the flying probe system or reexamine the programs. Let's address the other issue, how our friend might be able to attain somewhat flatter vias, or shall we say better filled vias.

Jim ›› If you think about the situation we have this concave fillet. That means we haven't completely filled the through-hole. So, we're up against a classic question of how do I get better hole-fill in a wave soldering process? In most cases we're looking for the Holy Grail which is positive top side fillets when I have a lead in the hole. Even though IPC tells us that it is not necessary even on class 3, seventy-five percent hole fill is okay. Many of us in our heart-of-hearts want to see that top side fillet. But in general, getting better hole-fill on plated through-holes during wave soldering is a function of optimizing the process. Adequate fluxing, proper topside preheat, proper wave parameters, depth of immersion, immersion time and so forth. The idea of controlling the process to get flat vias would be a really fussy optimization process. If you increased the hole wetting you might get a convex fillet where you have a bump sticking up that might also cause problems with the flying probe.

Phil ›› It's going to be really fussy to try to fine-tune the wave soldering machine to get exactly the level hole fill in via holes across a circuit board. I see it as being probably nearly impossible to achieve. Check with an expert at the flying probe manufacturer. They can probably make some recommendations on compensating for the varying topography that you're dealing with.

Beyond that we wish you the best and when you are playing around with your soldering machine and trying to make those adjustments, try not to inhale too deeply when you're over the flux pot.

What is the Best Way to Clean Solder Stencils?

(stencils, cleaning, no-clean, solder paste, solvents, IPA, ultrasonics)

Phil ›› Today our question deals with stencil printing.

Jim ›› Stencil cleaning is indeed the topic and we're actually going to try to cover two questions. The first one is from P.M.: "Once every four hours we remove each solder paste stencil from the stencil printer and wipe both sides using IPA saturated lint free wipes then follow by blow drying using air pressure. Is this the proper procedure for cleaning solder paste stencils?" The other question comes from M.K.: "We are in the market for a stencil cleaning system. What are the advantages and disadvantages of standard spray cleaning or ultrasonic cleaning for the job? Are there cleaning solutions specifically designed for stencil cleaning?"

Phil ›› Let's start with the second question first because we like to do things in reverse order.

There's a number of different stencil cleaning systems and certainly best practices are that you should always clean the stencil before putting it away in storage. Never put away a dirty stencil. While you're at it, inspect it for any damage. Never continue using a damaged stencil and cleaning is a good time to look at it when you take it off the machine and send it over for cleaning. As far as spray versus ultrasonic, they both work and Jim will talk a little bit about that solution but as far as the mechanical action they both work. I have had personally more experience with the ultrasonic. It seems to work well particularly as we get into finer apertures.

Jim ›› This refers back to the first question - IPA is not a universal solvent for all solder pastes and flux systems. Whatever method you're cleaning you should be using the proper solvent for the paste that was on that stencil. IPA will work for some pastes, but it's not going to work for everything. Make sure in all cases you're using the proper solvent. I personally feel from my experience that either spray or ultrasonic is superior to hand-wiping. You get a better flushing action and it's a more comprehensive system that you know the whole surface is being mechanically cleaned, more uniformly than if somebody's doing it by hand with wipes. Cleaning systems are available, and I think they are superior to hand wiping. Always inspect a stencil when you put it back on the machine to use again because it could have been damaged between the cleaning cycle and the time it got back to the machine.

Phil ›› The same principle applies to the squeegee. You want to clean the squeegee, store it, make sure it's clean before you put it on the printer and always inspect it before and after you use it. Well, you've been listening to Board Talk with Phil and Jim, the Assembly Brothers and remember Board Talk has not been FDA approved and possible side effects may range from enlightenment to bewilderment.

Solder Paste Beyond The Shelf Life?

(solder paste, storage, handling, defects)

Phil ›› I think today we have a material question, is that correct Jim?

Jim ›› It comes from G.H.: "We have some solder paste that has been in a sealed box at 4 degree Celsius for more than 8 months. The shelf life is 6 months. Can it be used? What adverse effect might we expect, if any, using solder paste slightly over the shelf life?" Well my brother Phil has very intimate knowledge of the answer to this question. Don't you, Brother Phil?

Phil ›› NO - don't use it! There's a limit, they have expiration dates for crying out loud! And that means it doesn't keep up anymore! If you want to do that with your medications, I know I do with mine go beyond the expiration date, go ahead, take your chances and suffer the consequences. There's a reason there's an expiration date. Having been involved in a lot of solder paste evaluations, I've seen paste that even in a short time beyond its expiration date just turn to crap - for lack of a better word. So, it might look like it's working but you're really rolling the dice as far as additional defects. We recommend actually going the other way. We try to look at putting almost a half-life onto solder paste. The manufacturer recommends an expiration date of 6 months, we try to make sure we're going through our inventory within 3 months. People wave their finger at you and say, "it costs more buy it in smaller quantities." What a lot of solder paste companies will allow you to do is to make a blanket purchase order, spread out the actual deliveries of the paste so that you're getting the price of the quantity, but yet you're basically getting fairly fresh solder paste in whatever quarterly, monthly basis. I think most solder paste companies will accommodate you. I think they want it because it's a very, very, competitive industry and they want your business.

Jim ›› Just to re-emphasize, it's the most critical material that you've got in your assembly. It's doing a lot for you. It's going to stencil print well, it's going to be tacky to hold your parts in place, it's going to solder in reflow, it's either going to have a safe no-clean residue or you're going to be able to clean it - it's a lot that you're asking from that paste and there's a lot that goes into that formulation. As Phil said, there's a reason they put a shelf life on it because there's a very delicate chemical formulation and you don't want to take any risks. Because it could affect virtually every joint on the board.

Phil ›› We like to equate solder paste as being what blood is to your body - your solder paste is to your circuit board and as Jim has said, it's pretty important stuff.

How Frequently Should We Recheck Profiles?

(reflow, soldering, ovens, defects, profiling, convection dominant, calibration, IR, thermocouples)

Phil ›› Welcome to Board Talk with Phil Zarrow and Jim Hall of ITM Consulting. We're the Assembly Brothers coming to you today from atop Mount Rialto at ITM Consulting's Failure Analysis Cave. So, today's question is?

Jim ›› It's about reflow. It comes from H.A.: "Is it necessary to replicate the thermal profiling process during long-term mass production?"

As a reflow expert, I would say it is not necessary to replicate the thermal profiling process, but it is a good idea to recheck the accuracy of the recipe to create the profile on the board and how frequently? Most modern ovens today are very reliable, and they have a lot of self-checks. Many people have the practice, whenever they change an oven, after it's stabilized, they will run the profile board again. Another really important thing is to save a permanent profile board with permanently attached thermocouples so you can always validate it. That's a really good practice. Or some people use a calibration device such as an oven rider. Run it through the oven to make sure that you are getting the profile on the board that recipe is supposed to generate. In long-term mass production where you're not changing recipes, if you never turn the oven off, maybe not. If you shut down daily or weekends it might be a good idea to validate the profile using your test board or tool. What are we looking for? The oven has temperature controls so it should be producing the same temperatures. Things can happen. Errors like a thermocouple can come loose. It's reading the temperature, but it's not reading the same temperature relative to the process gas flow. More significant is variations in gas flow because, if something happened with the fan or the diffuser plate, such that flux plugs up some nozzles or holes so the air flow pattern changes, you don't get the same heating effect on the board. They're very difficult to monitor within the oven control system. There also are a number of third party tools that you can use. Some of them consist of an array of additional thermocouples that permanently mount inside your oven and continuously monitor temperatures and heating rates. That is a belt and suspenders system that gives you a continuous validation of your profile if they're installed correctly and validated as a control tool. Yes, I think you should check it. How frequently will probably depend upon how much confidence you develop in your oven, but the general practice is, whenever you change a recipe, before you start the first board, you check the profile.

Phil ›› I would add that the operative word here is, is it necessary? Maybe yes, maybe no. As Jim said, ovens are really stable these days. We've come a long way. Jim and I can remember 20 years ago when IR was a key component in the heating methodology and a combination of IR convection ovens. You would tend to drift within the hour. Things like drafts in the room could interrupt the flow because you didn't really have positive pressure inside the oven. We used to joke that if a fly farted in the room, it would affect your profile. The ovens available today from the better manufacturers are very stable, as Jim said. So "necessary", maybe, maybe not. On the other hand, best practice, absolutely.

Jim ›› Consider the risks. Let's take this scenario. Something happens to the gas flow. A fan is affected, or you get some nozzles plugged up and you're not getting the same level of heating and it results in inadequate reflow on the center balls of a BGA. How quickly are you going to determine that that's happening through your inspection and test? And what is the risk? What is the cost to that board if that happens? So, it's a matter of potential risk.

Cause of Damage During Through-hole Component Insertion

(through-hole, components, cracking, defects, maintenance)

Phil ›› Today, we're coming to you from the executive lavatory at ITM headquarters. What's our question today, Jim?

Jim ›› This is about automatic insertion of through-hole components, it comes from M.C.: "During the automatic insertion of two pin components and after clenching the pins, we encounter a small deformation and/or sometimes a small crack in the land or the wall of the plated hole. We need to use a mechanical clenching method per customer's request. These two pin components must sit flat on the PCB with no tilt. What do we do to reduce or eliminate the plated hole damage? What is the criteria for acceptability of cracks and deformations on the plated hole wall?"

Phil ›› What occurs to me is that you're looking at treating the symptoms rather than the problem with regard to what you might be able to do with adjusting at the board level. From my perspective and looking way back several centuries ago to my experience with auto insertion (while at Universal Instruments), it sounds like you've got a problem that needs resolution on your insertion machine. Something like either worn tooling, forming tooling or tooling out of measurement, out of calibration or possibly something wrong with the program. I don't want to state the obvious, but if you haven't done this yet, you probably want to contact the manufacturer of the equipment. Even if it's older, vintage equipment that you bought used, they still might support it. I'm assuming you're buying your tooling from them or you should have been or maybe you're overdue as opposed to aftermarket tooling.

Jim ›› I completely agree. Having worked for Dynapert for several years, which manufactured insertion equipment, I could tell you that cut and clench heads are big, heavy, mechanical parts that move really fast and they make a lot of noise. The general description is basically, the heads beat themselves up a lot. They're big, heavy metal heads snapping together to cut and clench the leads and they tend to wear themselves out or get out of adjustment. They require a lot of maintenance and are very high replacement parts for the tooling. Look at the tooling, talk to somebody who's familiar with this equipment, through technical support. First adjust it correctly and then inspect the tooling to see if those heavy mechanisms might need to be replaced. It was a very significant spare parts system for us because the heads basically just wore themselves out. As far as cracks and deformation on the plated through-hole, that should really be minimal, and I would think IPC-610 could give you some guidelines. Cut and clench has been around for a very long time and was very successful and was used exclusively before surface mount entered in the 1980s. Obviously it can be done correctly, but those mechanisms do need a lot of attention.

Phil ›› The origin of axial insertion was basically a glorified stapler. An inserted, cut and clinched axial component resembled a staple. A company that was building equipment to assemble shoes, the United Shoe Machine Company ultimately became Dynapert. So, you had Dynapert and Universal. Universal (much) later acquired Dynapert. Panasonic made insertion equipment, still does, as far as I know. TDK, and believe it or not, Fuji.

V-Score and De-panel in One Step

(singulation, de-paneling, PCB, PCB handling)

Phil ›› What's today's question Jim?

Jim ›› It comes from B.S.: "I am considering scoring a PCB with a 90 degree scoring blade after SMT placement and reflow to create a card edge connector on the PCB. I would score it deep enough to bevel and de-panelize in one step. Is there a precedence for doing this and are there any horror stories of failures?"

Phil ›› This is an interesting situation because we're not just talking about scoring and singulation of boards. We're talking about where an edge connector is ultimately going. I'm trying to contemplate your board layout and figure you probably have some sort of interconnectors, either fingers or holes or pads. So, we're assuming the area is clear of components in the vicinity of the score, particularly those wonderful, very crack-able ceramic capacitors. In terms of the stress of the wheel or the pizza cutter it will probably be somewhat nominal. I would also hope that you've had these PCBS pre-scored in your fab shop to IPC specifications. However, when you actually do separate the boards, what should he look out for?

Jim ›› Certainly you don't want to flex the board in any way that would crack solder joints. The classic ones are your ceramic chip capacitors which can be near the edge or can be anywhere on the board. If they're in the area and the board gets flexed, you can crack the joints. Most panels that we've seen like this are pre-scored at the fab shop before the components are placed and the solder joints are created. Supporting the board properly so that it doesn't flex and crack your solder joints is very important. There are horror stories probably around any process in SMT or electronics assembly because, we're all human and if it can go wrong, it has gone wrong.

Phil ›› Hopefully we've answered the question and given you the proper caveats. Remember, whether you agree or disagree with Board Talk, the secretary disavows any knowledge of our actions. This recording will self-destruct in ten seconds, good luck Jim.

How Many Fiducials Per Stencil

(printing, stencil, fine-pitch, components, micro-passives)

Phil ›› Jim, I believe today we have a stencil related question. Is that correct?

Jim ›› That's correct. It comes from R.C. who manufactures solder paste stencils for a variety of customers.: "We have seen as many as 180 fiducials per stencil with a step and repeat, or what I would call a multi-up panel. Is this excessive? How many fiducials are recommended for a typical solder paste stencil?"

Phil ›› Oh, good question! And from a stencil manufacturer. Well, I guess let's start off by saying that those multiple fiducials he is seeing, and then we will qualify it, are basically what we call "localized fiducials". You are seeing those because of the propensity of high density fine pitch components on the board. And it is a good thing that the users are recognizing the use of localized fiducials for smaller pitch and high density components and things along those lines. That is a best practice. However, with regard to the stencil…

Jim ›› There is no need to put more than three or four global fiducials on a stencil. Those local fiducials for fine pitch components that Phil was talking about on the individual panels are going to be used by later processes. Pick and place primarily, but perhaps dispensing, jetting, or inspection or some other process that needs more accurate resolution of the patterns on the board. But these are totally unusable in the stencil printing operation. You cannot orient or register a stencil to a specific pattern. You have to register the whole, entire stencil to the board. So, you really for stencil printing only need the global fiducials.

Phil ›› Right, so kudos to your customers for recognizing the use of localized fiducials for fine pitch and micro-passives. That is definitely best practice. However, they are totally unnecessary for printing solder paste.

Jim ›› Right, and kudos to R.C. for realizing that. Why does he need so many fiducials on the stencil. That is a very astute observation. It is good that they're on the board, but you don't need to put them on the stencil.

Will Typical No Clean Paste Pass an SIR Test?

(soldering, no-clean, cleaning, SIR, residue, contamination, corrosion, conformal coating, reliability)

Phil ›› What is today's question, Jim?

Jim ›› The question comes from D.H.: Will a typical no clean paste pass an SIR test? Is it really clean enough for a conformal coating and 20 years of service? That is actually two questions, isn't it? Well, for the SIR test, yes. All no clean fluxes are tested for SIR per IPC spec, I think it is 650.

Phil ›› I think it actually goes back to Bellcore too, doesn't it?

Jim ›› I'm not sure, Phil. But they will pass. Although there has been some recent experimental data published that shows that the value of the SIR, although it will pass, will vary with the specific reflow profile. You may want to check that out if you have specific concerns. But the general spec is 1×10^9 Ohms during the SIR test. And they all have to pass that for a generic profile. What about cleanliness, Phil?

Phil ›› That is a good question because a lot of the wisdom being passed by the cleaning experts, particularly the guys involved with Engineered Aqueous and some of the other various cleaning agents, will tell you that if you really want to be on the absolute safe side for getting good adhesion of conformal coating that you clean first.

Now of course they are also saying it is not only for adhesion, but also you don't want to have any contaminant entrapment. So, for a Class 3 product, that might be what you need to do. However, in our experience (and this is going back quite a few years) as well as experiments done by some of the solder paste companies and things like that that we have researched, in general we have found good adhesion between most of the conformal coatings that are out there and most of the no-clean flux residues that are out there. On the other hand, to meet the challenges of higher thermal excursions experienced with lead-free, no-clean flux formulations have evolved and, thus, changed. You've got to know rather than ponder. With adhesion, you do a design of experiment with the materials that you are working with. And, of course, from a reliability standpoint you do the appropriate highly accelerated life testing and other designed for reliability testing that is apropos to the application and the service and shipping environment.

Jim ›› Well, I certainly agree with you technically Phil. But I look at this question and see 20 years of service, and the back of my mind says clean it. The idea of getting 20 years' service and if you are conformal coating you got to figure that there is something in the service environment that is not going to be too friendly. If I really want 20 years it seems like cleaning is a small price to pay to buy yourself a little extra confidence. Accelerated Life Testing and extrapolating 20 years of service - I'm no expert but it might be difficult to build a very high confidence level for a 20 year service life. And make sure that you have highly accelerated all of the possible environmental conditions and failure conditions.

Selective Solder Pot Temperatures

(wave-solder, selective soldering, solder pot, thermal considerations, pre-heat, through-hole)

Phil ›› Jim, what is our question today?

Jim ›› Our question comes from R.W.: "Can you suggest a temperature range to run the solder pot in our selective soldering machine? We use a no-clean flux with 63/37 solder and with four to ten millimeter nozzles. Our boards are FR4, 1.6 millimeter and with either an ENIG or a HASL finish. Should the temperature be any different from our wave soldering system?"

Phil ›› Basically you are talking about a tin-lead alloy and solder pot temperature, and again the molten solder the same temperature as what we are doing with wave solder.

Jim ›› Right, but one of the advantages of selective soldering is that you can tailor the process to the individual solder joints. Whereas a board going through wave soldering sees one process, one pre-heat for all of the joints, one immersion time and immersion depth in wave parameters for all the solder joints. My instinct with all soldering, Phil, is never get anything any hotter than you have to, because other than promoting wetting, high temperatures do no good to any of the materials and components on our circuit board.

Phil ›› But I think with selective soldering the more pertinent questions are: what is the configuration of your machine, specifically how much heating do you have to do with the solder immersion into the solder nozzle? Do you have initial pre-heat that brings the board up or are you relying on immersion in the nozzle to give you all of your heating? I would think that would be the most significant factor in determining what the temperature should be. If you don't have sufficient pre-heat and you're going to have to do all of the heating for each your joints from the immersion of the nozzle you are probably going to have to run at a higher temperature to get any kind of throughput. There may be copper erosion issues and other things, of course with tin-lead that shouldn't be too bad of a problem. And then there is a trade-off between higher temperature and immersion time versus hole fill.

Jim ›› The advantage that I spoke of is being able to customize the process literally on a per pin basis on your board. The simple thing is that a very thin lead in a small hole can be soldered faster than a big heavy lead in a big hole. So, you are looking at your throughput and that is going to drive your temperature decisions. It would be nice to not have to get it any hotter than a solder wave of 240-250 C, but to get reasonable timing, reasonable heating in the joint if you are doing heating by immersion, it may be desirable to take the temperature up to 260 C. I couldn't say. It has to be driven by the machine configuration and the nature of the specific joints in the board that you are trying to solder.

Phil ›› You might also want to check with the applications people at the manufacturer of your particular selective machine and see what guidelines based on their experience.

Jim ›› Having worked for a lot of equipment companies, I have a lot of faith in most of the service people because that is what they do. They just solve people's problems specific to their equipment. They hear about the bad stuff and the difficulties every day. So, they are usually a pretty good source of information.

Phil ›› Well, you have been listening to Board Talk. Note that Board Talk has not been FDA approved and possible side effects may range from enlightenment to absolute bewilderment.

Handling paste, 'Uncommonly Harsh' and Humidity

Trends for Printing Ultra Miniature Chips

(printing, solder paste, micro-passives, stencil, aperture, squeegee, area ratio)

Phil ›› Jim, what is today's question?

Jim ›› Well, it comes from B.L. He says: "What are the current trends and practices for printing ultra-miniature chips, aka 01005?"

Phil ›› Well, somebody is heading into stormy waters there. But, fortunately, there is quite a bit of work going on in this direction and it really runs a whole range of things. One direction we have seen for a while in general was a trend going to smaller particle size, with regard to the solder paste itself, typically going to a Type 4 and Type 5 paste. Type 3 paste just kinds of runs out of steam.

Of course when you look at the appropriate apertures and you apply the Five Ball Rule you can see where this kind of goes mathematically. And then the other area of course that is brought up in terms is stencil thickness. Wow, if you are still using a five mil stencil and you are trying to do these, general wisdom says you may be pushing things a bit. We've seen studies where some of the best results (and this is even going back a few years here) have been with a type 4 paste and a 3 mil stencil and for the best release and coverage. But Jim, there is a lot of "exploration" to do.

Jim ›› Well certainly from a traditional area ratio for stencil apertures of .66, the 3 mil stencil gives you a lot better chance of getting there, because it is thinner. And I think we have to realize that a lot of the published research is being driven by people who are building handheld devices. They are the principle users, the first users, and people who use these ultra-miniature chips more than anybody else. They have the reality where everything, take a smartphone, everything on the board is ultra-fine pitch. So, a 3 mil stencil is a possibility. Because you don't have issues with bigger components, where you need a thicker deposit of solder paste. On the other hand, other industries such as automotive and so forth, where they have a bigger variety of components, are looking to try to stay with their thicker stencils and still print for these ultra-miniature chips.

Phil ›› There have been some pretty interesting tests published with, I will have to admit, ultra-optimized printing equipment and processes that have successfully used a 5 mil stencil and a type 3 paste. But what capabilities you have, in terms of the age of your equipment, does it have all of the latest and greatest features on it for accuracy, squeegee control, and so forth? What is the mix on your board? Do you need to continue to use thicker stencils? Those are going to drive your decisions.

Jim ›› Obviously, using a thinner stencil and a finer pitch powder is going to make the printing job easier. Can you do it with a more difficult combination? Yes, but what is the degree of difficulty?

It is practical for you in your environment? That is something you are going to have to decide for yourselves.

Phil ›› Right and your level of expertise of your people and your environment. Because it is one thing to have a bunch of printing experts and that is all they do all day, live and breathe in a lab environment. And that is a lot different than the people you may have on your engineering staff and on your shop floor.

Jim ›› It may be different. They may have really good people.

Is Customer Approval Required for Class 3 Repair?

(rework and repair, reliability, standards)

Phil ›› Hey Jim, what is today's question?

Jim ›› Well, it comes from S.L.: "We have a case where a non-aerospace customer's board was repaired without prior authorization. It was for a class 3 assembly. The question is does it specify in an IPC document that customer approval is required for class 3 repairs?"

Phil ›› Let's go look to the "holy scriptures" of IPC for all of the answers to life and the meaning thereof. Most likely not. Because this would be the type of thing that would be somewhat contractual, and I would also say application specific in terms of how much repair should be allowed. But the whole idea of whether it is allowed or not that is basically between the customer and whoever is building the board and what is agreed upon. Don't keep going to the IPC or the SMTA or the IEEE or who knows what, the AFL-CIO to look for regulations for everything. This is something that would be agreed upon, based on the type of components you are dealing with, how much repair rework should be allowed for those. There may be some indication in some of the specifications or recommendations. But in general, it is basically agreed upon and is driven by the application and the service and reliability expectations of that particular application.

Jim ›› I'm not the world's greatest expert on IPC specs, but I agree that I don't believe they get into defining change of authorization and things like that. They define what you need to do, how you communicate it, how you may document it, and so forth. And I agree with you I don't think that they should. It should be decided by the parties involved.

Phil ›› Well, whether you agree or disagree with Board Talk, remember the secretary disavows any knowledge of our actions and this recording is going to self-destruct in ten seconds.

Should Apertures be Home Plate or Inverted Home Plate?

(stencil, solder paste, printing, apertures, area ratio, micro-passives, solder balls)

Phil ›› Jim, what is our question du jour?

Jim ›› The question come from S.B. regarding home plate stencil apertures: "Should the aperture be home plate or inverted home plate? You know the performance difference between the two types. Which one is better?" Well perhaps, Phil, we should define home plate to make sure we all know what we are talking about. This is an aperture for a rectangular pad, which is not rectangular, but in fact looks like a home plate, it is five-sided, two right angles, and then a pointy side on the other part.

A traditional home plate had these apertures oriented so that the pointy section pointed towards the center of the component. They were developed a long time ago to minimize solder beading or mid-chip solder balls.

Phil ›› Particularly on ceramic capacitors because they had the metal end caps and the idea by narrowing down to that point, there was less propensity for solder to be squeezed underneath the center of the component to form that so-called mid-chip solder ball. It has been pretty traditional as well. But back to the question Jim.

Jim ›› Right, and that was developed when capacitors were larger, 1206, 0805, etc. It is probably applicable down to 0603, maybe 0402s. But historically as we got to the ultra-miniature parts, 0402 may fit this but definitely 0201s, mid-chip solder balling became less of our problems, and tombstoning became a much bigger issue. And that is where some people have developed what they call inverted, or reversed, home plate, where they rotate them 180 degrees, so that the pointy part of the aperture is not under the component, but is pointing away from the component.

Phil ›› The strategy here was that by minimizing the amount of paste on the outer part of the pad, not underneath the component, when it started to melt it would take time for the solder to flow out from under the part and would and then wet up the vertical end of the chip component. That would minimize the possibility that you would get surface tension forces out of balance, which is the mechanism that creates tombstones.

Jim ›› And some people feel that was very successful, other people were not too excited about that. Obviously when you start using 0201s tombstoning is a huge problem and there are many different strategies, starting with proper pad design and modified paste, and finally the shoulder profile developed by Dr. Lee of Indium. Once you get to slow down the heating right at the melting point to minimize the possibility that the surface tension forces get out of balance and tip the component up.

Phil ›› Which one is better? It depends on why you are using home plate. Are you trying to avoid mid-chip solder balls, or are you trying to avoid tombstoning the ultra-small components. That is why you would use one or the other, in my humble opinion. And by the way, there are a number of papers out there. If you look back through the different proceedings of both SMTAI and APEX. You will even see some papers regarding where, for the same purposes Jim was discussing there are also experiments with what they call "roundies", which are basically radius edges as opposed to the straight-defined edges. It is like everything else in this industry, for every paper or study done that is pro something you will find something that is "I'm against it!", the actual opposite. So, as Jim said, understand why you are doing it in the first place and very carefully read up on whatever you can. But Jim, basics are basics here, and that is what you want to follow. Do your homework, I guess.

Jim ›› One additional comment, Phil. Realizing that we are old you-know-whats and that we have been around forever (and there are young people out there who haven't been) - If you weren't around during the transition from the miniaturization of chip components, to go down to 0402s and 0201s, the tombstoning issues were huge. People who previously had minimal number of tombstones, all of a sudden when they went to these small parts they were getting a very, very high percentage of tombstoning. Everybody was running around trying to figure out what was the best solution. And as my brother said, there were many of them proposed and different people had different opinions.

What is Solder Paste Working Life on a Stencil?

(solder paste, printing, SPI, misprint)

Phil ›› Jim, what are we talking about today?

Jim ›› Well, it is solder paste life on the stencil and it comes from S.S.:"Our solder paste has a specified life for exposure on the stencil at ten hours. We run our stencil operation continuously for forty hours, adding 250 grams of new paste every two hours. The additional paste becomes mixed with the existing paste. After the first ten hours of operation do we need to remove all of the paste on the stencil and scrap it? Currently the practice is to keep adding new paste until the end of the forty hours of continuous production." First off I want to say, S.S. thank you for giving such a clear, concise description of what is really going on. That makes it much easier to give a reasonable answer.

Phil ›› Well, as reasonable as you would expect from us.

Jim ›› Well for me, putting on my lean six sigma hat, I would say "what are your defect rates?" If you are currently continuously running your process, adding your 250 grams every two hours, if there was a problem with that you should see it, in an increase in defects. The most obvious we think about when leaving paste on the stencil is that it is going to dry out or degrade in other ways and it is not going to print well. So, my question is, are you inspecting your printing post print, either 2D on the machine or 3D post print? If you are, are you seeing your defects increase, the number of boards you have to wash and redo over that forty hour period? If you are, then it may benefit you to completely change the paste and clean the stencil every ten hours, or at some other interval. Then further down at the end of the line the flux can be compromised, and you don't get as good wetting. Well, what are your results from final inspection and test over that forty hour period? Are you seeing an increase in that defect level? If not, then your current practice of adding the paste every two hours is probably adequate for, as my brother said, the conditions and the specific paste you are using, and the level of difficulty of your printing, and your soldering.

Phil ›› Right, the operation, your procedures and your materials, you've got a good solder paste. So again, that is one of the other variables. Some other solder paste might not give you as optimal results or some might give better. So that is another variable in the mix as well. Yeah, as Jim said, you've basically got to take hold of what you have there and go with that. The end result is what kind of yields are you getting?

Jim ›› Basic statistical process control, continuously measure what you are doing and look for trends. And even if you're not getting bad defects, can you see some trends in there that are indicating there is a degradation going on.

Phil ›› We know what you are looking for. You are looking for reduced printability and reducing wetting, more solder balls, maybe even bridges if you are getting slump problems.

Jim ›› But those should be measurable. You should be measuring them in your process and using them to improve your process through feedback.

Phil ›› Remember, as the saying goes "In God we trust, all others bring data."

Problem Meeting Minimum Hole Fill During Wave Soldering

(wave-solder, through-hole, flux, pre-heat, workmanship standards, components, hole-fill, OSP, oxidation, wetting, thermal considerations, soldering)

Phil ›› So Jim, what is today's question.

Jim ›› It comes from W.E.: "We are having problems achieving the minimum hole fill of 75% on electrolytic capacitors using our wave soldering. What do you suggest?"

A classic wave soldering problem - hole fill. This is a basic wave soldering issue. How do I get the solder to fill the holes adequately, in this case 75%. The answer is the whole process. This is why wave soldering is a challenge, because you are applying flux and you have to make sure that the flux has penetrate up through the entire hole. If the flux doesn't get up there, the solder won't go there. Then you have to make sure that the flux is properly activated, and all of the solvent has evaporated right up to the top of the hole. That is why when we profile or preheat we put thermocouples on top of the board, as well as the bottom, to make sure we have heated that entire hole.

Phil ›› With thick boards, our associate Bob Klenke, Wave Soldering Expert, says put a thermocouple in the middle of the board, in the middle of the hole, to make sure that even though you have top side and bottom side pre-heating, that you are getting adequate heating and flux activation all of the way to the center of the hole.

Jim ›› If not, even though if may be hot on top if it is cool in the middle the solder will come up and stop when it hits that cool section where the flux is inactivated and the barrel of the hole isn't up to wetting temperature. And then of course, adjusting your wave to the proper immersion depth, proper immersion time, so that again the heat has time to penetrate up into the hole.

Phil ›› Yeah, and make sure your rails are parallel. Take nothing for granted. Then, once you get through all of the wave solder machine parameters, as Jim mentioned there are tons of them, then possibly take a reexamination of your design in terms of that you have the proper gap between the outer diameter lead and the inner diameter of the barrel.

Jim ›› Or lead to hole ratio, as it is sometimes described.

Phil ›› It is amazing for technology that has basically been around over sixty years, we're still trying to figure it out. It is definitely not a zero defect process. But getting adequate hole fill, in spite all of these variables, is obviously what you want to do. That is what it is all about. Watch also your dwell time in the wave, your immersion depth... There are just so many factors.

Jim ›› Phil, let's not forgot the obvious: Solderability. Make sure your leads are adequately solderable and that the barrels of your holes are solderable. Particularly concern some people have if you are using and OSP and it has already been through a couple of reflow cycles. Are you controlling that and getting the proper coating so that it is still solderable when you come to that wave soldering step.

Phil ›› And of course cleanliness of the leads and of the board itself, annular rings and the inside of the barrels. Also, another thing is to make sure that you have adequate plating inside the holes. Take nothing for granted. It is a massive checklist you can go through here. But that is the wave soldering process.

Jim ›› Phil, taking a step back and seeing as how W.E. mentions specifically electrolytic capacitors, my focus initially might be on heating. These tend to be big, heavy units and they may not be heating enough. So, maybe your preheat, or time of immersion, or something like that may be the first thing to look at. But any of these things could contribute.

Phil ›› Right, make sure you have all your i's dotted and your t's crossed - the things that Jim enumerated there. It is just good wave solder practice

How To Verify Cleanliness After Rework and Prior to Re-coating?

(conformal coating, cleaning, flux, hand-soldering, rework and repair, residue, no-clean, wire-core solder, pre-heat)

Phil ›› Today we are coming to you from the ITM conformal coating closet. Fumes are bad in here because I think today we have a conformal coating related question. Don't we Jim?

Jim ›› That is correct. It comes from C.C.

Phil ›› "CC"?? Conformal coating! That was clever. Okay, fire away Jim.

Jim ›› The question is: "We use polyurethane coating. Rework on a coated assembly happens often. I know how to remove the coating and clean the work site, but how do you verify cleanliness of the rework site prior to re-coating?"

Phil ›› That is a good question.

Jim ›› That is why we have you, Phil.

Phil ›› At this point in time in this industry there is no such thing as what we call selective cleaning. You should try to do your absolute best with that particular site in minimizing the flux used to begin with. With no-clean flux the first objective is, and this is regardless of if you are going to be dealing with conformal coating or not, is to use as little flux as possible. One of the things we see is that a lot of people put a lot of flux on. Then they try to clean it off. But you're not cleaning it off, you're just making things worse. So right away whatever you do, take away the flux bottles. Don't let operators use the flux bottles.

You should be using either very, very small amount of wire cored solder. If you have trouble with wetting a particularly more "massive" lead, use a larger diameter flux cored wire. The additional flux is proportionate to the greater amount of solder you're applying, and the heat required to bring the solder to liquidus. If worse comes to worse, use either a flux-pen or a small syringe of solder paste. But get those flux bottles out of there!

Jim ›› Well, I agree. First off you have to be comfortable that the residue from your no-clean repair flux, that the residue it is leaving is compatible with your conformal coating. And that is a debate that goes on, but many people do it. It is a problem that can be dealt with, although many people don't like to do it. Then in terms of the no-clean, in addition to putting it on, make sure that all of it gets heated, that you are applying adequate heat. That is why using only cored wire is the best.

Because the flux only comes out as you are heating it, so you can be much more confident that all of that flux has been deactivated. That is the key. Remember no-clean starts out active and it is deactivated by the heating cycle and if that is a repair then it is the repair heating cycle.

Phil ›› An adequate heat cycle!

Jim ›› Oh, another thing maybe preheating the board can help ensure that all of the flux is adequately heated and deactivated. And some people use a post-bake to make sure that any no-clean flux that wasn't heated adequately by the soldering operation is deactivated, particularly if you are using an iron. There are different opinions upon what that should be. Those are the basic strategies. I strongly agree with my brother, spot cleaning, localized cleaning typically doesn't work. The best method is to run the whole board through a batch or an inline cleaner, if that is acceptable to your assembly at that point.

Phil ›› As Jim mentioned, the compatibility we are talking about, the debatable area, is the adhesion of the spot conformal coating you are putting on to the residue of the repaired joint. And that is something that you can do a very, very simple experiment with to test that out. Beyond that you might also consult your conformal coating supplier. They might be able to impart some wisdom in that direction as well. Of course, if you wanted to actually measure cleanliness at these sites, the use of C-3 and/or Ion Chromatography, but I think we pretty much covered the key concerns there.

What is the IPC Definition for Uncommonly Harsh?

(workmanship standards, thermal considerations, humidity)

Phil ›› Jim, what is our question today?

Jim ›› Well, interestingly, it is about specs and regulations. It comes from S.M.: "What is the IPC definition of uncommonly harsh? IPC 610 and other documents define class three to include products where the end use environment may be uncommonly harsh. Does anyone have guidelines for how uncommonly harsh may be defined.

What temperature ranges or ramp rates are uncommonly harsh?

What moisture, humidity, chemical types may be considered uncommonly harsh?

Is sunlight exposure uncommonly harsh?

Are particular levels of vibration uncommonly harsh?"

Phil ›› This is an interesting question about harshness coming from a guy who's initial are S&M….

Getting to S.M.'s question regarding "uncommonly harsh", to the best of our collective knowledge, which you could probably fit in a coffee cup, I do not believe that 610 calls out an actually definition of harsh. Now understand that other generalized specs in other portions or corners of the industry such as automotive, other industrial applications like downhole drilling things like that, they probably do define harsh or define the environment. But looking at the general term uncommonly harsh and looking at the items that you mentioned. Well, let's take a look at it, Jim…Temperature ranges and ramp rates potential for being uncommonly harsh. I don't think so, not with regard to 610 the actual joint. It might deal with flux residue. There you might get into something. But that's not what 610 is about. We're talking about joint integrity. So, I don't think that a temperature range or ramp rate, thermal cycling would definitely have an effect. And again, what it is going through there. Jim, what do you think?

Jim ›› Well, as you said, basically IPC-610 is defining the physical structure of the joint, what it looks like, how big the fillets are and so forth. The biggest impact that it is defining is mechanical stress. Thermal cycling is a big source of temperature stress. So yes, temperature range could be indirectly creating stresses which might be considered uncommonly harsh. The other thing that jumps out at me, Phil, is vibration levels. Yes, many of the specs that you talk about, military, automotive and so forth, define very specific levels of vibration and other mechanical stresses that they test to. I think that goes back to the idea of IPC specs. They are the starting point from which you base your specific needs for your specific product and its specific environment. What is uncommonly harsh may be different for different products.

Phil ›› There is a limit to how generic specifications can be. And we have discussed this many, many times. You can't look to them basically as "Holy Scripture" all of the time. You have to look at your own application and conditions, certainly your manufacturing situations, and things like that. So yeah, I totally agree with my brother here on this. Be very, very careful. You have to realize the application is what really defines it. You can't always have a "generic definition".

Jim ›› The other bullet point is that sunlight can be uncommonly harsh. Not relative to a 610 solder joint evaluation, though. But other IPC specs that talk about solder masks might relate there, or a moisture, humidity and chemical type. Once again if we are talking about some of the IPC specs that relate to printed circuit board fabrication and its materials, those factors might be considered uncommonly harsh relative to the materials once again of laminates, coatings and so forth.

Calculating Failure Rate During Rework

(rework and repair, soldering, workmanship standards, defects, component, hand-soldering, IC, reliability)

Phil ›› Today we are coming to you from the ITM Consulting Failure Analysis Cave. I do believe we have a reliability question, don't we Jim?

Jim ›› That is true my brother of infinite wisdom. This comes from A.F.: "Is there a way to estimate the potential failure rate introduced by hand rework on one SMT part? The process involves de-soldering and soldering a new part using solder iron tweezers. We are trying to understand the benefit of rework versus the potential defects induced." Very good question. A.F., you are asking the right questions. In my opinion, the answer is any rework potentially reduces the ultimate reliability of the assembly. Quantifying that, estimating the failure rate, or reduced reliability would be very difficult in my opinion. The potential of overheating something, damaging some material, damaging adjacent components, creating too thick an intermetallic and so forth all are real possibilities, real risks. Estimating them is very difficult to put a number on, in my opinion. What do you think, Phil?

Phil ›› I agree. And, of course, one of the other things is probably to a certain degree the nature of the component itself. Something like a passive. Just looking at the integrity of the component electrically is probably going to be a lot less vulnerable than some IC. In fact, the IC manufacturer might have a recommendation. Most likely not, because they don't pay much attention to the process. But some of the better ones might. Beyond that, it is a very good question to be thinking that way. I would think that perhaps people like DFR Solutions might have done some homework on that type of thing. They might have some ideas or guidelines. But, Jim, I think it is what you said, it is going to be germane to the nature of the component.

Jim ›› Phil, I am looking at the last specific question. We are trying to understand the benefit of the rework versus potential defects induced. If it is not required, do not rework or touch up a joint unless you are sure there is a defect. You will probably create more of a problem.

This has been very common in traditional wave soldering. They touch up everything to make shiny joints. It is generally agreed you are probably doing more damage than you are doing any good. If the joint looks good by IPC 610 standards, even if it is a little on the low side as long as it falls within those criteria, it is better not to touch it.

Phil ›› Absolutely. One of the ITM deadly sins of SMT is touching up for cosmetic reasons. That is one of the biggest no-nos. What you want to do is if it a dull joint rather than just touching it up with a solder iron and make it nice and shiny, determine the root cause? Why is it dull? Is your cooling sufficient coming out of reflow or whatever process your soldering, that is one thing? The key thing is actually discerning what is a symptom? What is a defect? And of course, one of the favorite areas of that is voids. If you start to see a certain degree of voids with the BGA balls you automatically say oh it's over the limit we better rework it. And risk reworking a BGA, not only the costs but the risks. Where are those voids located? Near the interfacing surfaces? What is the quantification? How does that comply with the IPC recommendations and things like that. That is one of the eternal questions on voids anyway - defect or symptom? And you've got to really analyze it. Avoid doing things for cosmetic reasons!

Processing Circuit Boards with BGAs On Both Sides

(reflow, soldering, BGA, backside components, profile, thermal considerations, PCB, warpage, ENIG, profiling)

Phil ›› Jim, what is today's questions.

Jim ›› It comes from S.N.: "What is the best way to process a 30 mil FR406 circuit board assembly that has micro BGAs that need to be soldered to both sides?" I can honestly say FR406 doesn't mean anything specific to me with regard to "406". But I am assuming that it is a variation of FR4. A 30 mil board is quite thin for most standards, but not for cell phones. And putting components on both sides, advanced components such as micro BGAs, is getting more and more common. Ideally putting on our DFM hats, it would be better if they were all on one side. But we know for circuit reasons that is not always possible. The proper way of course it to go through sequential reflow on both sides. Because the components are light and multi-leaded, they have many bumps and balls on the bottom, there will probably not be an issue of ones on the bottom-side, the ones that are reflowed first, and then reflowed a second time upside down. Probably little chance that they will fall off, although you could check them out with a weight pad area ratio if you want to. Typically, they are light components, they have a lot of surface area on the pads, so they shouldn't fall off. Being a thin board, you want to watch out for warpage. Particularly when you are doing your second side BGAs, you want to minimize warpage. Possibilities of head-in-pillow or other defects, although those are less common with the micro-BGAs. Leaning on my old sacred cow, don't make your heating cycles any longer than you have to. For a thin board, you should heat up quickly, if it has micro components. Assuming you don't have anything big and heavy on the board, a relatively short reflow cycle on both sides will minimize any possibility of damaging this thin circuit board, or any of the other components. As I always say, other than promoting solder wetting, high temperatures does no good to anything in electronic assembly. That is pretty much it. The main thing is trying to support it properly in all of your processes, keep it flat and minimize warping, particularly for the second side reflow. What about you brother?

Phil ›› Well, let's just elaborate on what my brother Jim has said here. Yeah, particularly in that first reflow excursion you want to maintain adequate support because, besides the ultimate warpage, remember you have to process that second side and you want as flat coplanar surface as possible when you go to printing, and of course pick and place. So again, if your oven has a board support system that actually works you should use it. You might look into the PCB laminate material, that version of FR4. I'm also not that familiar with that particular nomenclature on that one. Something with a decent TG that will support the temperatures going through. I am assuming this is lead-free, so that throws another wrench in the works. The higher temperatures, which as my brother was saying beware. Anything you can do to minimize your exposure at the higher temperatures. As Jim said, the better off you are. Because it does no good. Grammatically correct or not, but it is still thermally correct.

Jim ›› And not to mention the creation of intermetallics. Assuming you are soldering to a copper board and not an ENIG board every time you go through that reflow cycle you are building that copper tin intermetallic. We don't want it to get too thick because it becomes brittle and has other bad effects on the solder joints. So again, don't get it any hotter any longer than you have to.

Phil ›› I think that answers the question, a right decent question at that. Good luck. I know we threw all of those factors at you, but it is do-able. And there are a lot of people out there doing a lot more challenging stuff, if that makes you feel any better.

Beyond that, please be aware that Board Talk has not been FDA approved. Possible side effects may range from enlightenment to bewilderment, to possible derangement.

Questions About Handling Solder Paste

(solder paste, handling, storage, contamination, moisture, oxidation)

Phil ›› So, what have we got today Jim?

Jim ›› Phil, we have a question that is hard to believe that we haven't dealt with completely before, a fundamental question. It is about paste handling and the printing operation. We have had several questions about this. I think we have talked about various aspects, but never covered it completely. So, we'll do that today. One question that comes in called solder paste prep before use. It come from S.S.: "We use lead-free solder and store it at a temperature of 4 to 5 degrees Celsius. After removal from the refrigerator we let the jar sit at room temperature for one and a half to two hours. We then stir the paste with a chemically resistive plastic spatula for 1.5 minutes by hand. Is this good practice? How often should we clean the stencil printer? We now clean it every two hours. Another question similar comes from E.R.: "We purchase our lead-free solder paste in 500 gram jars and store them in the refrigerator, similar to above. After removal from cold storage we let the jars sit at room temperature for four hours. Then we place the jars in a centrifuge machine horizontally for five minutes prior to use. Is this a good practice? Would you suggest any alternative mixing practices?"

Phil ›› Looking at our first question from S.S.- with regard to 1.5 hours, I don't know what size container that is at. How did he derive that? Or, where did he read that? Where on the internet did he see that? A little fairytale or something. Basically, the same thing applies to E.R's inquiry - 4.5 hours, it is very arbitrary. The thing is, you have to do this scientifically. It isn't rocket science. It is solder paste science. Basically, you do a very simple design of experiment to find out the true time that you need in your environment to get the solder paste up to ambient temperature. What you do is you take a container or whatever you are using, a jar or cartridge, out of the refrigerator and you insert into it a thermocouple and hook it up to your data recorder or whatever you are using. Basically, track how long it actually takes to come up to ambient temperature. Unless it is a really small container, I really doubt that it is an hour and a half. Four hours, hey maybe it is. It depends on the ambient temperature of your place. I have seen other people go eight hours. And we see a lot of people doing it overnight. (But keep that container closed and sealed!)

This way you will have data. You will know that for this size container, whatever you are using 500 grams 1,000 grams, 50 grams, whatever, this is the amount of time we allot for that size container to come up to ambient for that material. So that is a starter, you actually have a real number. Now the other interesting question was the use of the centrifuge. Those things have been for sale for quite some time. They are rather interesting. I have seen them used in different parts of the world. I think they are about four or five thousand dollars. I have seen people put it in the centrifuge right out of the refrigerator (or as E.R. who has been giving it some time delay). Basically, as it spins the particles are rubbing against each other, and that is how you have your warming mechanism. Where I have seen them, they seem to be doing an adequate job. But the way to know, measure the temperature when it comes out of the centrifuge device. Is it at ambient?

Jim ›› I've never heard of the idea of using a centrifuge. And to me, it is scary. I think of centrifuging as a separation process, not as a mixing process. And you have the real heavy solder particles and the much lighter flux goo in there. Aren't you going to run the risk of separating, when the particles go to the outside of the jar because they are being affected more by centrifugal force? I don't know. I have never seen this, you obviously have the experience.

Phil ›› Most people, rather than plucking out $5,000 or whatever these things cost, would rather just stage things on a FIFO basis, which is free. I would say FIFO works for the vast majority of the industry, big and small, OEMs and CEMs. Once you know the time you need to reach ambient, you just do things on a FIFO and record the time you take it out of the fridge and how much time there is before you can safely use it. Just good discipline. And that works out well. Now Jim, mixing. What are your thoughts on that?

Jim ›› I am not a big fan of mixing. Most people I know buy their solder paste in cartridges and dispense directly from the cartridge onto the stencil, laying down the bead across the stencil.

And then maybe knead it with the motion of the squeegee. Good paste, modern paste should be designed not to settle. That is one of the reasons you keep it in the refrigerator. Although, there are now pastes that you don't even have to refrigerate. So therefore, what are you doing when you are mixing. And S.S. even raises the issue, "we stir with a chemically resistant plastic spatula". What is the implication? When you open the jar and stick something in it you are inviting contamination, or something that could possible degrade the solder paste. My recommendation is get away from jars. Buy it in cartridges, don't mix, dispense it directly onto the stencil.

Phil ›› Right, and then there is the oxidation factor when you are stirring of course. Whether it is sizable or not remains to be seen, but you are inducing oxidation of the solder paste. And the other reason we prefer cartridges over jars is because with jars you are constantly opening and closing, opening and closing, exposing it. Whereas basically that cartridge stays shut. You remove the cap, you spritz some out, and you put the cap back on. It is much better and to my knowledge most solder paste companies do not charge a premium for requiring the solder paste in cartridges, as opposed to jars.

Has My Flux Expired?

(flux, wave-soldering, contamination, storage, solvents)

Phil ›› Jim, what kind of question do we have today?

Jim ›› Well, this comes from P.H. A very caustic question.

Phil ›› You have a very acidic tongue to say that.

Jim ›› Trying to keep up with my brother…"Beyond the printed expiration date, what other criteria are used to judge whether a flux is expired or contaminated? What specific attributes occur in an expired flux? How do you know if a flux is bad and shouldn't be used? Are there any simple tests one can do to test fluxes?"

Phil ›› You better go first on this, because we are talking about PH here. And I am not talking about the person. I am talking about what I might say. So, go ahead Jim.

Jim ›› Well certainly, always respect the expiration date on any material you buy. My general feeling is, if you have any question don't use it. We are talking about creating electronics. We are talking about making the solder interconnections, which are very critical. Lots of things can go wrong as people will point out. Flux is one of the three things you need to make a solder joint. You need heat, metal and flux. Don't take any chances. If it is expired, don't use it. Well, one thing we know that can happen with flux is the solvent can evaporate. You would typically see an increase in viscosity. Maybe a change in color, change in aroma. I don't know. Simple tests? I don't know about simple.

Phil ›› You can certainly do wetting tests, wetting balance, copper mirror. Things like that. The standard tests they use to qualify fluxes. I don't know how simple you perceive them as. Wetting balance, of course, would be the best. That is what its basic job is to do, is to promote wetting, clean oxidation from the surfaces to be soldered.

Jim ›› Other than that, keep your fluxes from getting contaminated. Keep them covered so that they can't evaporate. Keep them in properly sealed containers so that contamination can't get into it. I can imagine that there are things that can go undetected until you get bad soldering and poor quality solder joints, and all the other things resulting from degraded properties of your flux.

Phil ›› Well, I think the bottom line is, as you said in the first place Jim, follow the expiration date. There is a reason the flux manufacturers put it on there. They know their chemistry. They tested it extensively. They're not putting it on there "Let's put it up a few months earlier so that we can con these bozos into buying more flux." You know, it is not an evil conspiracy here. On the other hand, I have heard of people selling their flux to third world countries. Geez, just go by the expiration date. The only other thing I'll add, hey P.H. clean out your refrigerator and clean out you medicine cabinet too.

PCBA Inspection Concerns

(ESD, inspection components, contaminates, fixturing)

Phil ›› Jim, what is today's question?

Jim ›› Well it comes from T.S.: "We inspect PCBAs on a relatively hard ESD mat. QA claims that during inspection moving the PCBs on the mat will scratch and stress the soldered components, bottom-side. Are there studies on this matter? Are there any dedicated tools on the market designed for this purpose."

Phil ›› Well, that is different, I have to say. "A relatively hard ESD surface"? Well, I don't know of any particular studies. Perhaps the ESD people might. As far as tools, there are other methodologies to be used. Jim, I remember when we were talking about different types of ESD mat surfaces. There were some that are foam and much gentler with regard to any kind of propensity toward scratching or otherwise damaging the components or the board surfaces. That would be one aspect of it. There are a number of other systems where the board is actually held by the hands of the operator and moved under a scope or a mantis, or something along those lines. But there are softer surfaces if that is a genuine concern. Of course, my question is has anything been observed or is this the QA people crabbing about things. Has this actually been observed? Is there a real problem in this situation or not? Jim, what are your thoughts?

Jim ›› Well, I guess I'm leaning toward the QC. I don't like the idea of physically touching soldered surface mount parts on either side of the board, much less lying the assembly down on top of them. Yes, if it is stationary, certainly using a foam would be better. But if you need to move it, it shouldn't be sliding on any surface. It should be either held by the operator or in a frame. You asked about tools. So, there are lots of XY sliding fixtures that grip boards on the edge that are used for rework and inspection, and other manual operations. That typically have "V" grooves that grip the board on the edge and allow you to move it under a microscope, or other inspection tool, without touching it. The other issue of cleanliness. What about that mat? What about dust?

Phil ›› What about that operator?

Jim ›› Whatever is on that mat is getting picked up on the next board that is being touched. Think about a populated board going down on a hard surface. It is going to touch on some points, some corners of things, and the taller components. What is taller? Well a switch, and LED or something like that. Yes, these things could be damaged by sliding them, or even touching them. If you are just going to be stationary, going down on foam, as you suggested Phil that is okay. But in general, I do not like to touch the surfaces of the board or the components any more than absolutely necessary.

Phil ›› Right, I agree. And again, I think the cleanliness issue is major. If everybody in QA is going to be so finicky, don't neglect the cleanliness. In fact, we believe that best practice is that anybody handling the circuit board anywhere in the procedures, certainly prior to soldering, and this might have been after soldering, you really don't want to add any contaminations anywhere ideally. If the board is being handled, it should be handled by a person wearing gloves or finger cots. That is the absolute best practice. Think broadly on this whole thing,

When To Use Adhesive To Bond SMT Components

(adhesives, components, reflow, BGA)

Phil ›› I think we have an interesting question today. Don't we, Jim?

Jim ›› Yes, we do. All of our questions are interesting. Because we are interesting guys. This comes from D.M.: "When should we use adhesive to bond SMT components to the bottom-side of a double-sided PWA before going through reflow soldering, component size, weight, etc.?"

First off, I want to acknowledge that D.M. uses the same terminology as I do. He describes the bottom side of this double-sided assembly as the one that ends up on the bottom during the second reflow. The one which is reflowed first. We all know there is no standard terminology, unfortunately. So, we have to be really careful how we describe this. But Phil, you are the world's expert in components falling off.

Phil ›› What do you mean by that, Jim? You know, it is interesting that a number of us over the years have done process development work with intrusive reflow. Somehow part of that led into reflowing parts and how it is related. A number of us did various experiments over the years. What kind of component will fall off when it is being re-reflowed on the other side.

Bob Willis has done work. I have done it as has Joe Belmonte, and a few other people.

Regarding whether a previously reflow soldered part will remain in place when inverted and subjected to a thermal excursion (during the reflow of the second side), a formula was derived quite some time ago. Basically, we calculate the surface area of the lead of the component that is in contact with the solder paste. In the case of a ball, as in BGA, CSP or Flip-Chip, we use the area of the collapsed portion of the ball that is tangent to the solder paste. While we haven't personally tested a BTC, being a low-mass component along with that ground-plane – I don't think these babies are going to fall off. But you should experiment and test with your own application.

The idea is that you calculate (and you may need the help of your design or component people with this) for each of the interconnects what the actual contact area, the surface area, is. You multiply that by the number of interconnects that you actually have. Then you divide that into the weight of the component. Now the way I recall it, if you have anything less than or equal to 44 grams per square inch the part will not fall off. In case you just want to take a shortcut and not bother. That is almost every component these days unless you have something really heavy duty ceramic, like a big ceramic BGA or some leaded ceramic part, like a big heavy-duty ceramic capacitor. I would do the calculations. By the way, on that capacitor you have two surface areas, one for each of the connections. Generally, we found most parts won't fall off; again fine-pitch, even more so the ones with many leads where of course there is more interface area. The other thing to be sure of is that you're not interrupting the process with any external forces. For example, make sure that your reflow oven conveyor is well-maintained. It is smooth and lubricated and that there is no rumble or vibration introduced. Vibration or rumble in the conveyor could help coax a part hanging on there on the bottom-side. Jim, anything to add to that.

Jim ›› Well, I sort of disagree with you a little bit on your ceramic BGA. Ceramic BGAs tend to have a lot of balls on them. Although the component is heavy, you typically have a lot of area to hold them on. My way thinking is, big components with only a couple of leads. And you hit the biggest one, capacitors. They tend to be big and heavy, and only have two leads on them.

Switches, connectors, other things that have heavy bodies but not too many leads. Those are the things to look for. Because you don't want to put on any more glue than you have to. If you have to repair something glue increases the degree of difficulty of removing the defective component.

Phil ›› Right. Plus, the whole gluing is another process step and material. You want to streamline as much as possible.

Jim ›› But, I am under the impression that there are reliable adhesives that you can put on and cure during your reflow cycle of your first side, of your bottom-side when you are doing the first reflow. Would you agree with that, my brother?

Phil ›› Yes, I would. We are in agreement.

Issues With Solder Paste Transfer Efficiency

(printing, solder paste, stencil, apertures, SPI)

Phil ›› I believe today we have an equipment question.

Jim ›› Phil. It comes from A.L. who asks: "While I understand the concept of transfer efficiency and its relationship to solder paste volume, is it possible to produce a transfer efficiency greater than 100% of the theoretical volume? Can the volume we are measuring with our solder paste inspection system be believed, or is this measurement an anomaly of the inspection measurement process?" What is between the lines here, A.L. is getting values greater than 100 for transfer efficiencies as measured by his SPI system.

Phil ›› SPI, Solder Paste Inspection, has finally really come into its own after 20 to 25 years. It is finally being implemented into all different levels. Of course, more of us are becoming familiar with the equipment and the methodologies and techniques being used by them, learning what it is all about. I'll start by saying that SPI assures accuracy and repeatability. So, to start off with, make sure your machine is properly calibrated per the manufacturer's specifications. Secondly you should do a Gage R and R. In fact, that should be part of your evaluation procedure when you are evaluating various SPI machines. Then we get into some of the variables that we see at board level.

Jim ›› Right. Just to finish up on the equipment, because of its tremendous growth, SPI equipment is improving dramatically, almost day by day. It seems like every time you open a trade periodical somebody has a newer machine, supposedly better accuracy and everything. The implication is that if you have an older machine, it may not have the greatest accuracy or repeatability.

You need to understand where you are with the piece of equipment that you have and what its capabilities are, as my brother said. Putting on my Lean Six-Sigma Hat, variability in a measurement system is one of the Six M's of your fishbone diagram. You need to determine using Gage R and R, what is the variability in your measurement system, in this case SPI. What about the variability in the process? Well, let's start real basic. You start with your stencil. How accurate is your stencil? In terms of the volume, how does your SPI make that calculation? It starts with a theoretical volume. How does it calculate the theoretical volume? Typically, it takes the Gerber data from the stencil drawing and takes the length, width times the thickness of the stencil and calculates the volume. Now you have a stencil that you had manufactured for you. How accurately was that made? Suppose you had a 5 mil thick stencil and the aperture was supposed to be 10 mils by 20 mils. That is the volume that Gerber data says and that is the value that the SPI is taking as theoretical. What was actually manufactured when it was cut with a laser, electroformed or whatever? There have been some published data where people have actually measured the dimensions of apertures in incoming stencils. And guess what, they are not perfect. One source of possibility is that yes, the aperture was a little bit bigger than the theoretical volume calculated from the Gerber. So yes, you get more paste than you wanted.

Phil ›› Another phenomenon is with the dynamics of the printing process. As the squeegee moves across an aperture (if you see some of these slow-motion cut-away videos) you will observe that sometimes depending upon the speed and the angles and all of the other print parameters there is some dynamic elasticity in the paste, Such that as the squeegee goes across the aperture, the paste depresses and then actually bulges up. If you look at the top surface of the aperture after the squeegee has gone over it the paste is actually bulging up. So once again you would have a larger volume of paste than the theoretical and give you a greater than 100% transfer ratio.

Jim ›› But probably the most common one that equipment has been dealing with is how your machine measures and calculates the zero plane. No matter what technology you are using in your SPI, it is measuring the top surface. To calculate a volume, it has to define where zero is, where the bottom of that deposit is. And if you think about a PCB, ideally you want to calculate that volume from the top of the pad, the copper pad, or whatever the surface finish is on the board. But now as your SPI system is going over and doing its measurement technique with cameras, lasers, or whatever it is using, is it actually identifying where the top of that copper is? You have two other potential surfaces, the laminate on the PCB which is below the level of the copper and you have the solder mask, which could be above or below.

So, a classic example is, for whatever reason, the paste is sitting on top of the pad, but the SPI machine is measuring zero down at the board level. So, it is adding the thickness of the copper pad to the volume of solder. That could also give your greater than 100%

transfer efficiency. I don't know if we made A.L.'s life easier. Yes, there is variability and if you look at most specs they allow for transfer efficiencies greater than 100% for some combination of all of these reasons. Ideally we would like to make that go away, but in reality we are probably only going to be able to reduce it to an acceptable level. We can never make variation go away, we can only minimize it.

Phil ›› I think the only thing that I will add to that is hooray for A.L. for using SPI and for asking these questions. We can't emphasize enough how important it is that you and your techs who are working the SPI equipment understand what the process is, how the equipment works, the entire procedure. We can't tell you how many times we've gone on process audits and here is this really nice, beautiful, state-of-the-art SPI in-line and it is being used as a pass through conveyor because no one knows how to use it. It breaks my heart every time we see it. It is so important that you understand. If the machine has been passed down, if the original operator has gone on to another job, or they got a different assignment, or got hit by a bus, it is very important that whoever is operating be properly trained. You have made a major investment, and a very wise one, use it to the optimum. On that note, I think we, not only answered A.L.'s question, but hopefully a lot of other people's. If you don't understand any of the areas we discussed, please learn more about it.

Jim ›› Talk to the people who manufacture the SPI if you are looking at or if you own one, talk to the people about these issues. I am sure they have dealt with them all before.

Tenting Via In Pad - Yes or No?

(via-in-pad, solder paste, reflow, BTC, defects, voids, stencil, PCB, PCB fabrication)

Phil ›› And welcome to Board Talk with Jim Hall and Phil Zarrow of ITM Consulting, the Assembly Brothers. We are coming to you from high atop Mount Rialto at ITM headquarters.

We are here to talk about electronic assembly, materials, equipment, components, practices, procedures, and who knows what else. So, Jim, what else? What are we talking about today?

Jim ›› Okay, this comes from N.P. Should the thermal vias on the bottom terminated components be tented on both sides to prevent flux trapping and solder wicking or is it sufficient to tent on the top side only or should the vias just be plugged?

Phil ›› Good question.

Jim ›› This is a well talked about topic. Under all circumstances you have to prevent solder wicking. We are talking about the large ground plane or thermal plane at the center of a bottom terminated component and the pad for it on the printed circuit board. Because most of these are used as thermal pads, to get the heat away from the top surface we put vias into the pad to conduct the heat down into the PCB.

Thus keeping the IC in the BTC package cooler and operating correctly. Okay, so now we are going to go solder this. We are going to put a lot of solder paste on there.

We have these holes, plated through holes right in this large ground plane. What do we do? We cannot allow solder to wick into those holes because bad things will happen. Phil

One of the worst things is that whatever is going to happen is not going to be consistent. Sometimes maybe no solder will wick into a hole. Other times a lot of solder. Sometimes it will create a big void. Sometimes it won't create any void.

If we look at published data with cross sections and x-rays you will see the same part with an array of vias, some of them are wicked and some of them aren't. So, you need to prevent that. Now, how to deal with via in pad.

The IPC specs talk about six or seven different ways. Some of them are capping, top capping on the bottom, or tenting I think is the term, or filling.

Jim ›› The "belt and suspenders" way is to fill the entire through hole and actually plate over it with copper on the top. So, if you look at the top surface of the pad, you don't even know the vias are there. Then you have no issues, you are just soldering to a flat copper surface.

Some PCB fabricators will actually fill the whole barrel. But that is the most expensive. There are a limited number of shops that will do that. Others will actually fill the whole barrel with copper to improve the thermal conduction. Then there are tenting and so forth, or solder masks or other materials filling. Different people have had success with just about all of them, but with tenting there have been problems where they don't maintain the seal and stuff still get in there and bad things still happens. You need to be concerned. You have to prevent that solder wicking. How you do it is a process you have to work out with PCB suppliers and your cost considerations. One thing that is being looked at a lot now is to not tent the via but to just put an annular ring of solder mask around it and when you design the stencil do not print paste on the hole so you don't get any wicking there. You don't worry about actually filling the via. You just prevent the solder from wicking down there through solder mask a ring around the hole. There is a lot of published literature; I could spend hours talking about all of the different things that have been investigated. Whatever you do you have to come up with a system. Work with your printed circuit board suppliers to come up with a process that prevents wicking and still meets your cost targets.

Phil ›› Very well put, my brother. And I think you sufficiently answered that question.

You have been listening to Board Talk with Jim Hall and Phil Zarrow. We appreciate your listening and hope you learned from it. One thing you should definitely learn is whatever you are doing with your vias, tented or otherwise don't solder like my brother.

Jim ›› Don't solder like my brother.

Issues Mixing Silicone and Acrylic Conformal Coatings

(conformal coating, rework and repair, reliability)

Phil ›› And welcome to Board Talk with Phil Zarrow and Jim Hall of ITM Consulting, the Assembly Brothers. Today we are coming to you from the ITM conformal coatings closet. Jim, what is today's question.

Jim ›› Well, today's question comes from B.H. It is about conformal coating.

Phil ›› I knew there was a reason we were in this room today.

Jim ›› "We do a lot of repair work on assembled PWAs. These assemblies have a silicone based conformal coating. During repair some of the coating is removed. After repair our tech uses an acrylic base conformal coat to touch up the area. Could there be a compatibility problem, particularly with adhesion, when we mix these two coatings?"

Phil ›› I would say there is more of a fundamental problem than just the physical and chemical dynamics of it. The question is why was silicone used in that application in the first place? With that in mind, is acrylic sufficient, appropriate or ample based on the application? They are very different materials, for very different applications.

Jim ›› The fundamental thing is that all conformal coatings are different and have different properties. And we all know that silicones are typically more expensive and more difficult to apply.

If it came with silicone, it was there for a reason. Somebody spent some extra money to put silicone on there. And the one that jumps out of course, is higher temperature reasons. This is one of the things that silicones excel at. Although yes, there could be a compatibility issue, I think it is much more fundamental concern than that. Even if the acrylic coating doesn't have adhesion or compatibility problems, is it going to protect that circuit in its expected functioning life?

Phil ›› Service environment temperature range is one thing, but there is chemical resistance, and other things that are different between these materials.

Jim ›› Particularly when you have a higher priced material, you know that was put on there for a reason. Somebody spent some extra money to put silicone on that board.

Phil ›› Yeah, it couldn't be just because they liked the salesman. Absolutely check that it is application appropriate. As my brother said, there was a reason they went with the expensive stuff.

Jim ›› And then your compatibility questions go away.

Phil ›› Right. So, I believe we answered your question. Not exactly what you wanted to hear because we threw a major red flag down.

Jim ›› But that is important, not all conformal coatings were created equal.

Phil ›› No, like a lot of other things. So great, you have been listening to Board Talk with Jim Hall and Phil Zarrow of ITM Consulting. Board Talk melts in your mind, not in your ears. And whatever you are doing underneath that conformal coating, however you have soldered those joints, whatever you do please don't solder like my brother.

Jim ›› And please, don't solder like my brother.

Questions About Humidity Indicator Cards and Baking Components?

(components, humidity, MSD, baking, moisture, moisture barrier bag, storage)

Phil ›› We are here to talk to you about electronic assembly, materials, equipment, components, practices and procedures, among other things. Jim, what is the question du jour?

Jim ›› Okay. This is from M.B.: "We run small jobs so a reel of MSD components could be open and closed a number of times. Each time we put a new desiccant pack and a new humidity indicator card in the MSD bag and seal it. If we total all of the times we open the bag it exceeds 168 hours. For example, eight hours open then seal for one or more days, then we open the bag for ten hours and seal, etc. If the humidity indicator cards are not pink, do we still have to bake the components?

Phil ›› Interesting question. I will weigh in first by saying that humidity indicator cards are very helpful and useful. But in terms of finite accuracy, I think they are up there with the old temperature sensing labels.

They get you in the ballpark. Would I want to hitch my wagon to that? Put it this way, do you feel lucky? The procedure calls for logging strictly in and when you exceed the exposure duration with the remaining components, you do the bake out. My answer to that is I wouldn't trust a humidity card; I would trust the time honored JEDEC-020 and 033.

Jim ›› I agree with you 100%. First off, for those of you not familiar, M.B. is talking about 168 hours. That is the floor exposure limit for a type 3 moisture sensitive device. The MSL of level 3 is 168 hours. It is probably the most common level that we deal with. MB says that the total exposure is greater than that. The thing that I would point out is that the humidity indicator card is really only telling you about the integrity of the bag, the atmosphere in the bag. It is not really telling you what is going on in the heart of your little components.

Phil ›› Think about it, your part is out for eight hours, to use the example that M.B. provided. During those eight hours, the plastic package has absorbed moisture. That moisture is inside that package. So now you put it back in the bag and seal it up with desiccant. There is no moisture in the bag, and no moisture can get into it. But it doesn't really tell you what is going on with that moisture inside.

Jim ›› I would point out that for all components if they are out for short exposure, this is clearly defined in J-Standard-033, which you should have in your possession. Somebody in your organization should have that spec and be intimately familiar with it so that you can plan how best to deal with these things. It is not a big spec; it is only about 25 or 30 pages. A couple hours you can understand it pretty well. There is something in there called short-term exposure. I don't know the exact numbers, but the numbers 8 and 12 stick in my mind. So, let's say it is 8. It says that if your part is not exposed for more than eight hours. If you put it back in the moisture sensitive bag, desiccant and seal it up, that part will reset to 0 in some long time interval. Which I think is the number ten time the exposure. Don't hold me on these numbers, read the spec. Okay, you're out for 7 hours, that's less than eight. You close the bag up. If you keep that bag closed for 10 times 7, or 70 hours, then the clock will be reset to 0. The idea being that this really dry air and desiccant does remove that little bit of moisture that you got into the bag. So that is for these multiple jobs. You may want to read that spec and see if you can take advantage of that if your storage in between runs is long enough. You may be resetting your clock to 0 on some of these things. But in all cases get that Standard 033. It is not big. Have somebody read it and really understand it. Then define a strategy that works for you in your environment with the frequency at which you open and close these bags.

Phil ›› My brother brings up a very good point.

Jim ›› I usually do.

Phil ›› Yeah, usually. The point is, you really need to have somebody who understands the whole MSD story, as Jim was saying, in terms of 020 and 033 and understanding what it is all about. It is very important that your operators and tech understand it too so that they are diligent about replacing the bag and logging the time. We recommend, as Jim mentioned, somebody that is actually responsible. For lack of a better word, an MSD guru. Most facilities have somebody who is the go to person for ESD. You want to have it for MSD as well. You don't have to pay that person a lot of money extra, if anything. It would look good on their resume. We highly recommend that.

Jim ›› This is one of the most important topics that we see problems with when we audit facilities. We talk to our customers; we often see lack of clarity on their handling of their moisture sensitive parts. So M.B. the fact that you understand it to this level is laudable.

Help With Lead-to-Hole Ratio

(through-hole, components, wave-soldering, selective soldering, hole-fill, DFM, defects, workmanship standards)

Phil ›› Jim, what is today's question?

Jim ›› Well, today I am actually going to combine three questions from three different people that all lead to a fundamental design issue in electronic assembly. Here is the first one that comes from D.P.: "What is the recommended lead-to-hole ratio? What is the proper minimum gap between a round conductor lead and the PCB hole that will allow proper solder fill? Our circuit board is 062" thick, double-sided." The next question comes from P.N.: "Our bare boards are typically 065" thick. How do we calculate the hole diameter for connector pins if the board thickness increases to .150"?" The final one is a process issue. The last question comes from C.M.: "We are seeing insufficient barrel hole with one through hole component during reflow. We suspect the problem could be the hole ratio being too small. Can you point us to a guideline with the recommended through hole component to hole diameter ratio? What can be do to improve barrel fill? "

Phil ›› Hey, a trifecta. The information that we are going to discuss applies to whether you are doing selective soldering or wave soldering because from a design guideline standpoint the requirements are the same for both. I believe, Jim, there is an IPC spec that covers this.

Jim ›› Actually Phil, my feeling is that this is some of the foundation technology that the IPC developed when they first started putting out specs. The most direct one is IPC 2222, sectional design standard for rigid organic printed circuit boards. They talk about it in terms of the difference in diameter between the pin and the lead. And they give min's and max's for different levels of difficulty and so forth. My recommendation is, yes, this is really important. The ratio, or the difference in the size of pin and hole, affects hole fill, which is what we are trying to accomplish to get a good, reliable through hole joint. It is affected by a number of factors and this IPC spec and other specs that will be referenced from this give you a lot of insight into that.

Phil ›› Particularly for thicker boards, Jim. From my experience people have actually done some optimization. Obviously as the board gets thicker, the degree of difficulty of getting 75% hole fill, or 50% hole fill, or 100% hole fill becomes more difficult.

Jim ›› I felt it was important that this really is the way to design a board. Start with the size of the pin. The IPC specs point out that there are tolerances in pins and hole diameters and so forth that you should incorporate when you are actually specifying a PC board.

Phil ›› Very good. You did indeed answer all three questions on one hit. That is pretty commendable, Jim. I've got tell you, I am in awe.

Jim ›› Well, thank you. There are fundamental questions such as getting good hole fill, through hole joints and design issues. To me this is just a foundation background technology for our industry.

Phil ›› Yeah, very rarely right? I just want to add we will save this topic for another time. This of courses applies to all fundamental through hole soldering, as we said through hole can be wave, selective and hand soldering. A future topic, we will discuss some of the parameters for intrusive soldering.

Jim ›› Or pin in paste, pin in hole. Whatever you choose to call it.

Phil ›› Reflow-of-Through-hole, and an assortment of other names. But that is a subject for another day.

Solder Icicles, Selective Soldering, and the Grape Effect

What Causes Solder Icicles During Wave Soldering

(wave-soldering, defects, through-hole, components, pre-heat, flux)

Phil ›› We actually have a wave soldering question today Jim. The question is from R.J. He is asking "Why are we getting solder icicles on some leads when we run boards in our wave solder machine? Where should be look first to change our process?"

As I get close to standing atop my soap box, I guess let's answer the question with regard to process. The first thing that comes to my mind is lead protrusion. That might be a key variable you have there. In some cases you may be exceeding what may be the ideal lead protrusion considering the immersion through the wave. Then there are other questions in terms of your pot temperature, which would certainly lead to icicles.

Jim ›› If your pot was too cool the solder is too viscous and it can't fall off as it comes out of the wave.

Phil ›› And you would probably see more bridging that way too. Right Jim?

Jim ›› Either one, the solder doesn't flow properly. It can bridge, or it can stick to the leads and cause an icicle.

Phil ›› Possibly fluxing too. If you are getting it really through the holes and everything.

Jim ›› Right. You are counting on some flux being still present at the end of the wave, on the surfaces to help the solder flow and fall off of the leads, and once again bridging is another similar problem. It could be not enough flux, or you overheated the flux during pre-heat and burned it off, so there is none left when you come out of the wave and icicles are forming.

Phil ›› And you know Jim, this is something that you and I have talked quite a bit about. Wave soldering is almost considered an ancient technology as opposed to the surface mount process.

Jim ›› This is like wave soldering 101, very basic stuff.

Phil ›› Right, but I certainly don't blame R.J. A lot of the old-timers are gone now and to some it is a new technology, even though wave soldering has been around for at least seventy years now.

Jim ›› That is older than you are Phil.

Phil ›› You are right it is. That is scary, talk about fossil technology. It is interesting, there is just this void of engineers that have experience in wave soldering. A couple of us old fossils kicking around. It is kind of like new technology to a lot of people, including R.J. here. Everything old is new again and this is the epitome of it. But anyway R.J., we hope that we gave you and some other people some guidance. Good luck.

Jim ›› Yes but understand that wave soldering is a highly inter-related process with fluxing, heat and molten solder. There are lot of things that can go wrong and you really need to understand this.

Phil ›› So if you are new to a machine because the expertise is gone, search out some textbooks and articles and so forth, or someone who really knows the process to get some of these fundamental down. Make your life a lot easier.

Solder Paste Printing First Pass

(printing, solder paste, stencil, SPI, defects, set-up, throughput)

Phil ›› Welcome to Board Talk with Jim Hall and Phil Zarrow of ITM Consulting. The Assembly Brothers, Pick and Place. And if you can figure out which one is Pick and which one is Place, more power to you. But that is not really what matters today. What really matters is this question we received today. This is from S.G. He writes, "Is it recommended to print one cycle before printing the first production board? I could use a scrap board or blank plastic card for the first print."

Jim ›› Yes. This is an issue in the wonderful world of setup. Of starting up a line to produce a different product than you have been producing or the first product in the morning. The idea of being efficient and minimizing time, materials and everything. So yes, of course you could print on a scrap board or a blank plastic card but how are you going to evaluate it? What is the issue here? I want to make sure that my printer is ready. The question you could ask yourself is, why wouldn't it be ready if I properly put on the solder paste and kneaded it if I have to. Why shouldn't my first print be good? If you say "well, I really need to be sure" then how are you going to determine it? If you use a scrap board that would have fiducials then you could evaluate it using an automatic solder paste inspection, either the 2D on your machine or a 3D after the machine SPI system. If you use a blank plastic card the only way you can inspect that would be visually. That is not a really good technique for evaluating the quality of printing. But in any case, suppose you print on a scrap board or blank piece of card and the print is good. What do you do? Well then you put a real board in and print it. So, you have wasted that first print, and the time it took you to print it. Whereas if you print it on a good board and it looked good you can immediately start your production with your first board going into your first placement machine. Obviously if it wasn't good you would have to clean or correct that first board. So those are your options. I would use the first board and try to get your setup procedure so that your first print is good. You have good solder paste at the proper temperature. It is properly applied on the stencil. You have kneaded the paste with your squeegee if that is an option on your printer. So that your first print is good. You inspect it and then you immediately put that board in your placement machine and you are up and running. You have reduced your overall setup time. Got your line up running faster and increased your utilization and your productivity.

Phil ›› It is almost a matter of how much faith do you have in your initial design of experiments when you arrived at the initial settings on the printer. How much faith do you have in the maintenance of the printer for consistency? And the fact that your operator follows proper setup procedure. Then it becomes, as Jim said, an efficiency situation, best practices meet efficiency. Do you think that is the best way of putting it?

Jim ›› Yes. And the main question is, why wouldn't that first print be good? And what can I do to make sure that it is good so that I can immediately start my production and not waste any more downtime.

Review of Tin-Copper and Tin-Nickel Intermetallic Thickness

(intermetallic, ENIG, reflow, OSP, surface finish, PCB, thermal considerations, alloys, reliability, hand-soldering, liquidus dwell, reliability)

Phil ›› Today we have a reflow question. JD has a question considering soldering intermetallics: "If the formation of tin copper and tin nickel intermetallics is a function of time and temperature, then what is to be expected in the following scenarios? Components reflow solder to a pre-heated board where the solder is liquid at 215 degrees versus hand soldering the component to a board where the solder is liquid at 215 degrees for 3-5 seconds. What would you expect the different intermetallic layer thickness to be? I have read that 1 - 2.5 micron thickness of tin copper is desirable and a .4 - .8 micron thickness on tin nickel is desirable. If when hand soldering the liquid phase of the solder is so much shorter than the liquid phase inside a reflow oven how does one achieve the desirable intermetallic thickness?" Wow, they said a lot there.

Jim ›› Yes, they did! First off, I want to complement you on understanding that when you are soldering to an ENIG board or an ENEPIG board, which has a nickel coating, that your soldering is different and your primary intermetallic is different. You have a tin nickel, rather than tin copper. Many people don't realize it. There is a difference. In general with soldering to copper, and that means OSP, HASL, Immersion Tin, Immersion Silver, and all those where the finish goes away and you end up with a primary tin copper intermetallic. Those form pretty quickly.

Phil ›› With hand soldering, typically the extra heat of the iron is adequate to do that. The IPC, which trains you how to make a hand soldering joint, has analyzed that. So those intermetallics form very quickly between copper and tin and that is not a problem. Typically heating too long and letting them get too thick has been the issue. But I have to say with all of the new analysis of solder joint reliability the issues with intermetallics are much more complex.

Jim ›› Particularly with SAC alloys, Phil, where you have the secondary tin silver intermetallic distributed through the joints. Those are tending to be much more significant. So I would not be concerned. In general, you don' want to heat your tin copper solder joints any longer than you have to. I have seen multiple soldering operations without any problem. But the reality is just a lot more data so it is not just that simple as the thickness of the intermetallic. With respect to soldering to nickel such as an

ENIG board or an ENEPIG board, those form much more slowly. The length of time is not of as much of a concern, getting sufficient intermetallic.

Phil ›› The other thing I might suggest, if it is appropriate, is subjecting scenarios to reliability testing, including accelerated life testing to see if there is any indication the intermetallic is acceptable that way.

Jim ›› I have looked at a lot of published reliability tests of that nature and I have never seen anyone come up and say that the intermetallic was too thick here. I think I saw one just recently one was published where they subjected an OSP finish to seven reflow cycles. That did slightly reduce the reliability attributed to intermetallic. But that is a really extreme test. In most cases I am not seeing anybody say the intermetallic here is too thick and that is why the solder joint failed.

Phil ›› If I were subjecting something to seven thermal cycles like that I think I would have a lot of other problems to worry about before I start getting concerned about my intermetallic growth starting with what is wrong with my procedure going down to copper erosion since that was a lead-free scenario. We'll keep reading the studies, there is always more and more coming out.

Jim ›› We are sure learning more about intermetallics. We were very naive and happy when we were all just using tin lead and could rely on our forty, fifty years of experience to know that joints would be reliable.

Phil ›› But for most of us, it is a brave new lead-free world.

Should We Modify Rework Procedures for Assemblies Fabricated Using OSP?

(surface finish, OSP, rework and repair, hand-soldering)

Phil ›› Today we have a rework question. This is from J.N. who asks: "Should we modify any rework or repair procedures for circuit board assemblies fabricated using OSP, organic solderability preservatives, bare boards?"

Jim ›› First off, I want to say if you are working with a completed assembly then there should no longer be any OSP on that board because all of the surfaces covered with OSP should have been covered with solder at one step of the assembly process. They should not have finished boards that have any OSP exposed, like test points or something else. OSP is not a long term protection for copper on finished boards. It is strictly protection between the PC fab and the time you solder it. Everything should have solder on it. It should just be an ordinary board. Perhaps you are doing touch-up after the first side of a double-sided SMT assembly. So, you haven't gone through wave soldering, and you haven't gone through second side, you may have some OSP pads which are not soldered at that point. Understand that it is not a physically robust surface. It should take soldering temperature, but you don't want to expose it to any extreme temperatures. But most importantly you don't want to scratch it. OSP is not like a metallic finish that is robust.

Phil ›› When you are in there with soldering irons and solder wicks and so forth if there is an OSP through hole nearby that hasn't been soldered yet, you want to make sure that you do not scratch that OSP. You can very easily go right through that surface, expose some copper and then have a soldering problem in your next soldering step.

Reliability of Tin Lead Solder vs. Lead Free Solder

(Reliability, SnPb, Pb-free, SAC, alloys, ROHS, tin whiskers, thermal cycling)

Phil ›› Jim, today we have a question on lead-free reliability, SAC vs. tin-lead. This is from L.B. asks: "Could you please give me some further explanation of your answers regarding the tin-lead versus lead-free versus unknown leaded alloy reliability issue?"

Jim ›› What answers were they?

Phil ›› I don't know. We must have said something, which was true. We must have imparted some wisdom. L.B. goes on to say: "From all of the reliability problems that I have read about with lead-free alloys for circuit board assembly it seems like almost any amount of lead is more reliable than none."

Jim ›› I know where L.B. is coming from and I can guess what we said. This idea that any amount of lead is better than none addresses one specific reliability issue and that is tin whiskers. The presence of lead, even in a small amount 1 or 2%, is the best way to mitigate tin whiskers. So if you are building space satellites or pacemakers or any ultra-high reliability where you are concerned about shorting due to tin whiskers adding any amount of lead will significantly reduce, if not eliminate, that reliability issue of tin whiskers.

Phil ›› What I am assuming we were talking about were the many more common reliability issues such as drop shock, vibration and thermal cycling where in most cases lead-free has been found to be at least as reliable as tin-lead, except for some high-rel, high-stress environments where the jury is still out and we are still trying to understand the complete issue to be certain that we can build a pacemaker and other "mission critical" products, assuming we can mitigate the whisker issues. Thermal cycle reliability is likely the biggest issue.

Jim ›› So that's what we were concerned with. When I say "unknown lead-free reliability" that is for these ultra-high stress, high-reliability, long-life factors. Again, the more typical failure modes of thermal cycling, drop shock and vibration where we just don't understand the nature of the failure mechanism to have complete confidence in the lead-free alloys in terms of the long-term reliability. But yes, if you are worried about tin whiskers, lead is the way to go. That is why people building satellites remove all of the tin finishes on the leads and replace with tin-lead.

Phil ›› This is a question that persists. It started in the dark days prior to 2005 and the implementation of RoHS was still being debated and kicked around. More and more papers are being written to the contrary of what our participant has asked here. It is all pointing in the direction that Jim mentioned. This is the stuff we have been reading and more and more long-term data is being harvested as we go on. Thanks to scientists like

Dave Hillman (and others) who had the foresight back before RoHS became effective to understand that lead-free was going to prevail. It is now long-term data. We have been quite a few years into RoHS.

Jim ›› That's right. An article published by IBM stating that nobody is asking for an extension of the server exemption for lead-free because all of the problems have been solved. They are going to make even enterprise-level servers with lead-free because they have developed the knowledge to have confidence in their reliability.

Phil ›› This has taken a lot of work. They have just achieved this in the last couple of years. They have been working continuously since before RoHS to understand the problems to achieve the confidence in the reliability in these different server products which are of course very critical and long-life, very high reliability.

Jim ›› Yet nobody is building pacemakers with lead-free yet.

Phil ›› Well you have to ask yourself, would you want one? With what we know so far and everything else? Do you feel lucky?

Dross Contamination After Selective Soldering

(dross, wave-solder, selective soldering, flux, residue, through-hole, cleaning, residue, no-clean, pre-heat)

Phil ›› Jim, today our question is ...

Jim ›› It is about selective soldering, Phil. Perhaps we should search out some superior knowledge and wisdom.

Phil ›› Oh my, look who just walked in. It's Bob Klenke, our other brother and world-renowned guru of selective and wave soldering and all things like that. Hey Bob, how are you doing?

Bob ›› Well, I'm doing fine. How are you guys?

Jim ›› Great timing Bob. So good to see you.

Phil ›› Today's question is indeed about selective soldering. It is from M.K.: "We have discovered an extremely fine low density dross on PCBs after selective soldering. The dross is difficult to see without careful examination. Is there an effective way to clean or remove this? Out batch washing machine is unable to remove it. We are using SN 100 C alloy and a no-clean flux applied with drop jet. The dross dust appears in the vicinity of solder joints, but not immediately adjacent to them. It seems that the dross may be carried to the board via the nitrogen blanket surrounding the nozzle. We de-dross the pot once at the beginning of each eight hour shift and de-dross the pump assembly once per week. What do you guys think?"

Bob ›› Well, from what they are describing if it can't be cleaned off, I am tending to think that the residue they are talking about could perhaps be organic, rather than metallic. Dross is made up of tin-oxide, which can typically be removed, but excessive flux especially if it has been over-heated is organic in nature and that is perhaps why it can't be cleaned off in their washing machine. It is not uncommon in the field that we see people tending to put on an excessive amount of flux in selective. You don't need much flux at all. People tend to over-flux. It is sort of one of the ten deadly sins of selective. The other thing is the writer was saying that they are using a no-clean, which I like to call a less-clean because these is always some residue. The other thing is it could be excessive flux in combination with bottom-side pre-heating and not bottom and top heating. You really want to heat your flux so that you can drive the carrier vehicle, activate the solids. You want to measure top-side board temperature to make sure to activate your flux. You should also monitor the bottom-side board temperature for flux survivability.

Phil ›› Bob, do you mean that people have to understand that they have to profile your boards for selective soldering?

Bob ›› Well, funny you should ask, Phil. When I teach selective soldering workshops I always ask a show of hands of how many people profile their reflow oven. Every hand in the room goes up. I ask how many people profile their wave machine. Maybe about half the hands go up. When I ask how many people profile their selective I'm lucky if I get one or two. I don't understand because soldering is about time and temperature. What this gentlemen is describing sounds like it could be an excessive amount of no-clean flux that is staying on the board. It could be over-heated on the bottom-side and therefore it is leaving organic material. I have seen it where people are doing crazy things in their selective solder pot that they shouldn't be, like doing manual tinning as well as soldering. They will see a black dust that they think is dross but it is burnt flux. That's what I tend to think it is.

Jim ›› Yeah, when you say I can't clean it I always think of over-heated flux. That is one of the things that will inhibit cleaning.

Bob ›› Right, because of excessive amount I can't emphasize enough that whenever I am out in the field addressing a selective soldering process issue invariably people are putting more flux on than they really need to. They are not heating it properly or monitoring the heat properly. Whether you have latent heating or infrared heating or convection or convection IR, you need to profile the board. You don't have to do it every single time but a first article in process development is certainly in order. That is what I am thinking here.

Jim ›› You're the expert Bob, so I put a lot of credence in it. I hope our listeners will also.

Phil ›› I do too. The excessive flux thing - we see it in through-hole soldering only because you can't really do an excessive flux thing in reflow soldering. The old adage "If you add enough flux you can solder anything - more flux will make it right". Have mercy! Hey Bob, thanks for stopping by.

Bob ›› You're welcome.

Phil ›› You have been listening to Board Talk with Phil and Jim and our other brother, Bob. Remember, if you can't laugh at yourself, we certainly will.

What is the Suggested Humidity Level for Electronics Assembly?

(humidity, MSD, solder paste, PCB, moisture)

Phil ›› Jim, today's question is from M.S. who writes, "I am aware of the suggested humidity level for an electronics assembly facility. Do the same limits apply within a 100,000 class clean room? Besides ESD concerns to control solder paste what other operations or processes within an electronics assembly facility are sensitive to all of this humidity outside of the specified limit."

Well, good question. To start off, the answer to your question whether they apply to a class 100,000 clean room, yeah, why wouldn't they. Just because you are cleaning off the dirt particles and fuzz and stuff like that doesn't mean the rules of humidity don't apply. Yes, they absolutely do.

Jim ›› To be fair Phil, the second part of the question says besides ESD and solder paste. Perhaps this person is not doing any solder paste printing within the clean room and that is why they are thinking that the humidity only affects solder paste and ESD. So, maybe when we answer the second part of the question it will be clear. Humidity affects anything plastic that can absorb moisture, mainly your PCBs and your components.

There is a whole IPC/JEDEC specification for moisture-sensitivity of components. J Standard 033 tells us how to handle it. The new spec for PCBs which is, Phil you always remember this one.

Phil ›› It IPC-1601. This IPC Spec defines best handling and storage of PCBs and addresses the issues with moisture absorption and gives you bake out schedules and so forth.

Basically the plastic materials can absorb moisture. If they get too much moisture in them then they can be damaged during reflowing and other high temperature processes. There is a lot going on. Definitely familiarize yourself with JEDEC 033 and 020.

Jim ›› Yes, 020 is the component specification that defines the moisture sensitive levels for components.

Phil ›› And the 1601 PCB spec, and understand what best practices are for handling these.

Jim ›› Phil, one other thing any other material such as adhesives or conformal coatings and so forth may have humidity sensitivities. If you are using any of those materials you also have to be concerned. It is just a good idea to not let the humidity get too high or two low because ESD as you say is always there.

Why Uneven Conformal Coating?

(conformal coating, cleaning, humidity, contamination, moisture, residue, counterfeit)

Phil ›› Jim, today's question is with regard to conformal coating. R.H. writes: "We are experiencing an issue with our conformal coating process. We chemically wash prior to coating and spray the material in two coats. On matte finish boards the conformal coating is vibrating away from some others and building up in others. We are getting coverage, but this causing our boards to look like a topographical map with hills and valleys. We don't have an issue with adhesion just uneven finish. Any help on this would be greatly appreciated."

Jim ›› Well, fortunately my brother is a world-known expert in conformal coating. What do you think Phil?

Phil ›› Huh? - not really. And a lot of what I did know was dissipated by conformal coating fumes many years ago. However, I think there are a lot of unknowns in this particular case with regard to materials. It could be a number of things. It could be the way your equipment is set-up, the way you are spraying it. I think most likely it is the material itself, the way you are prepping the material. If it has been mixed properly, if it is stored properly, if it is within expiration date. What kind of humidity has it been exposed to? If it has been titrated properly. So, there is a lot of "gray area" here.

Jim ›› Phil, they say we chemically wash prior to coating. Could there be some residues from the washing process?

Phil ›› Yeah, depending what kind of chemicals you are using, there could be residues that way. I am assuming the boards are dry. Really the best place to defer this question is to the supplier of your material. It is their materials that is acting kind of funny. I would advise you to contact your conformal coating manufacturer and their applications people and explain what is going on. Perhaps they can give you some insight.

Jim ›› Better than us?

Phil ›› Yes! Definitely talk to the manufacturer of the conformal coating. Who knows, maybe you have a bad batch. You didn't say where you are doing this operation, and I am not just talking facility wise with humidity. That is obviously going to affect it. This may sound a bit obtuse, but we have seen it happen - make sure you have the real material. There are certain countries abroad where we have seen cases of counterfeit materials. They were packaged under the names of well-known, recognized, validated conformal coating manufacturers. Sometimes when they mix them up, in the open air, things can get contaminated, overexposed to humidity and things like that. Make sure you have good, pure material. Counterfeiting does extend to materials, as well as components. Been there, done that, and own the stained (but "authorized") t-shirt.

Moisture Barrier Bag Issues

(MSD, humidity, components, storage, moisture, baking, moisture barrier bag)

Phil ›› Jim, we have a question from E.R. who states: "Let's say we have moisture sensitive chip components that have been exposed to the atmosphere slightly beyond the specification allowed. They are then re-packaged and sealed with desiccant and a humidity indicator card.

After about a week's time would the card indicate humidity? Could the desiccant alone remove the moisture in the chips or is baking necessary? Would vacuum sealing the bag make any difference?" Well, that is interesting. If I understand this question correctly, what E.R. is asking is whether he can get away with not baking just by putting these things in a moisture barrier bag.

Jim ›› And that is why I put in a reference to J Standard 033, which is our Bible for handling components. It specifically defines short term exposure and drying within the moisture barrier bag. For a level 3 part if your exposure out of the bag is less than twelve hours you can put the parts back in the moisture barrier bag and reseal them. I want to point out to make the moisture barrier bag work you always have to vacuum seal it. That is a given any time.

If you don't vacuum seal your bag you cannot count on them maintaining a less than 10% relative humidity inside the bag, regardless of how much desiccant you put in there. You always need to vacuum seal the bag. But if you do that and a level 3 part has not been exposed to more than 12 hours then the part will dry out and will go back to zero. Reset the clock to zero, in five times the exposure. If you were right at twelve hours, you put it back in the bag for 60 hours, or about three days, staying in that sealed bag it would be reset to zero. Anything greater than twelve hours for level 3, and I think it is 8 hours for level 4 and level 5, check 033, which you should be very familiar with if you are dealing with moisture sensitive parts.

Phil ›› If you are beyond that, which is what you are implying. For this typical Level 3 part, you have 7 days, 168 hours.

Phil ›› So, let's say it is out there for 170 hours, you know you have to bake the part. Putting it back in the bag with desiccant or a dry cabinet is not going to reset it to zero. You are going to have to do a higher temperature bake for two days or more, depending on the temperature that you bake it, which is all covered in 033. After about a week's time would the card indicate humidity? This is the idea of putting parts that have moisture in them back in the bag, seal them up with a desiccant and temperature humidity card.

Jim ›› Would you ever have a situation where the humidity card would indicate that you are above 10%? I honestly don't know. I suppose if you had a lot of parts that were over-exposed, or let's say they were near their exposure.

Theoretically I got a stack of ten matrix trays that for some reason got left out for 160 hours. So they are still under the limit for a type 3 part. I quickly put them back in the bag, seal them up with some desiccant. Over time some of that moisture will come out of those parts and get absorbed by the desiccant. Is the desiccant sufficient, relative to the number of parts, and how much moisture they have experienced and how long? I could envision a situation where you could saturate the desiccant and raise the humidity above 10% and trigger the indicator card.

No idea what it would take to do that, how little desiccant and so forth, but I guess that could happen. Obviously if you have any bag of components where the moisture indicator says over 10% all bets are off and you should bake those cards just to be safe.

Trouble With Skewed DPAK Components

(components. Reflow, profile, solder paste, stencil, apertures, defects)

Phil ›› Today Jim we have a question from B.O.: "We are having trouble with surface mount DPAK components skewing during reflow. We have checked our profile and have tried a diagonal hatch aperture on our stencil. We are still having problems with skewing DPAKs. Any thoughts?"

Jim ›› Let's take this opportunity to say why do components skew? Defined correctly it happens during reflow, specifically right at the point where the solder metal in the solder paste melts and wets the surfaces of the pad and the leads on the DPAK.

Phil ›› We all know that if everything is balanced the surface tension forces will actually pull the component into correct alignment. Now skewing is when the component is not in the correct alignment so what has happened is that those same surface tension forces have somehow gotten out of balance. There are a number of reasons for that. The best way to do it is to optimize the reflow profile. Make sure that the heating of all of that pad reaches soldering temperature and all of the paste melts.

Jim ›› And all of that surface tensions around the perimeter of the big pad on the DPAK, which is what is causing you the problem, make certain all that melts together. That the surface tension forces are balanced and do not skew the part. So, you want to make sure that you have adequate pre-heat. You may want to add a soak. Perhaps the best thing would be to go to a shoulder profile, as recommended by Dr. Lee of Indium. This is where, in the profile, you use one zone just before the reflow right at the melting temperature to slow down the heating. You cool down the temperature of that zone. The profile would basically look like a straight ramp right up to just below the melting temperature. Not this typical soak temperature, 10 or 15 degrees below the melting point but rather one or two degrees below the melting temperature. And this slows the profile down just as it goes through the melting.

Phil ›› This slows down formation of surface tension, and minimizes the possibility that those nasty surface tension forces will get out of balance and skew your component. This "shoulder" duration should be less than 30 seconds, maybe ever 15 to 20 seconds.

Jim ›› You need a big oven to do that because you have to use one zone for the shoulder. In my opinion you need at least a seven zone oven or that one-zone shoulder section will become too long.

Phil ›› The way we used to control the "float phenomenon", and still do is by balancing the pads and the apertures, in other words the overall volume of solder on both sides. However, with your DPAK you are dealing with the same problem that people have with the big BTCs and the QFNs.

We have a very, very large area and it becomes much trickier to balance. As Jim said, shoulder profile can help. You should definitely experiment with some other aperture designs, some window paning. Keep abreast with whatever people are writing about these days with regard to BTCs, certainly might be applicable to your DPAK.

Jim ›› And my answer to that, having read a lot of what people have published, is that it is component specific. The diagonal cross sectioned stencil apertures you are using might work on one style of component, might not work on another one. It all depends on the geometry and the paste and the thickness of the stencil and so forth. There are lot of different window paning patterns that you can try. From my experience it is going to be a trial and error process. Much better to solve it with the reflow profile. And Phil made some good points. Be sure that your board is designed in terms of the shape of the pad, the solder mask around it, any vias adjacent to it are masked off and so forth.

So, you don't have board geometry and construction issues that are causing these surface tension forces to get out of balance.

Opens With Assembled QFN Components

(defects, QFN, BTC, reflow, solder paste, stencil, apertures, warpage, HASL)

Phil ›› Jim, today we have a question from MN. I don't know if he is in Minnesota or not. MN says: "We are experiencing opens on assembled QFN components at a rate of approximately 9%. The component has two rows of pads and the failure only appears in rows near the component center. He says usually only one or two pads have opens. Our boards are double-side reflow and this component is mounted on the first side. What is happening?" Obviously, there are gremlins in your reflow oven. That was easy, moving on to the next one. I think you would agree with me Jim, it could be a multitude of situations here.

Jim ›› Right, he said assembled components at a rate of approximately 9% and then later he or she said that only one or two pads have opens. I am wondering what the 9% is. That means that 9% of all the QFN components experience this problem, as opposed to 9% of the opportunities because that would probably be more than one or two pads. 9% of the QFNs they are putting down of this particular design are having these defects. That is still very high, that is not good. But components with two rows increases the degree of difficulty.

Phil ›› Absolutely. There is a lot of information we don't have here. The first question is, we don't know what he is doing on the big old thermal pad. We don't know if he is window paning.

Jim ›› What percentage reduction if any? If they are using a preform. I assume you are leaning toward the possibility of floating. You simply have too much volume of paste on that center pad and it lifts the whole package up and some of your pads become opens. But that raises the question of why are they in a specific location every time, the center of the component?

Phil ›› Then the other side of the coin, is what are his or her aperture design specs with regard to the opens on the actual joints themselves. Whether we are getting adequate deposits there.

Jim ›› So basically, are you getting enough paste in those areas? For some reason are you getting less paste in the area where you are seeing the opens? That would be an obvious question. Stencil would be one thing to look at. Also, the printing parameters. Board support, is there a little lack of support in the middle of that component? Is there any warpage related to the component?

Phil ›› Very good. That could be a major contributor there too.

Jim ›› Typically, QFN or BTC components are really small, under a half an inch square in many cases. Warpage is not as frequent as it is in some of the large, complex BGA packages.

Phil ›› It is still a factor and a concern.

Jim ›› The question is raised when you have it in the middle. If you think of a frown, where the center of the component is higher than the corners, that might tend to increase the spacing between the board and component causing opens in the center locations.

Phil ›› Which brings up an interesting point, there is a movement underway to more clearly define warpage, getting away from the frown and the smile. We are actually looking at measuring warpage in all eight sections of a component.

Jim ›› There have been a number of suggested analyses put forth for more detailed quantifying of warpage, the idea that it is three-dimensional. So that people are talking about things like bowls and pipes as descriptive terms. Of course, you want to be able to quantify it. Put some numbers on it.

Phil ›› Think in terms of a potato chip rather than a smile or frown. That may be coming into play here. I agree with you with regard to the relatively diminutive size of the QFN. But, on the other hand, it occurs to me that we know the situation with some QFNs is that they are very thin package to begin with, being primarily plastic

Jim ›› If you are seeing like a non-wet open where the paste stuck to the bottom of the component but didn't make good contact with the pad or the board; or it could be the other way around where the paste soldered to the pad on the board but didn't make good contact with the pad on the bottom of the BTC component. It could be contamination on the pads of the component, either one, depending on where the open is actually formed.

Phil ›› And I guess last, but certainly not least, would be the surface finish. Are you using HASL? HASL is generally bad in terms of surface coplanarity, not good.

Jim ›› Yeah, you are saying uneven pads across the component. That is possible but I wouldn't think it would be that consistent in one location, in the middle of the package. But who knows. HASL is a weird world of high pressure air.

Phil ›› The way M.N. states it though usually one or two pads have opens. MN hasn't really indicated it is the same two pads. So, we don't know how random these are as far as the location. It could be any of these things.

What are your thoughts, Jim, with regard to emphasis on the first side and going through the reflow excursion again? Do you think there is an effect there?

Jim ›› No, it either soldered the first time or it didn't. I guess if there was a marginal solderability you would get some dewetting. But that should be pretty obvious to inspect when you are digging into the problem. I think that is less likely, but possible.

Phil ›› So MN, we have given you a lot to think about.

How To Strip Tin-Lead Solder From SMT Pads for RoHS

(RoHS, SnPb, Pb-free, alloys, surface finish, copper, soldering, re-tinning, alloys)

Phil ›› Jim, today our question is from P.C.: "Is it possible to scrub the pads of a PCB to bring it back into compliance? 63-37 solder was mistakenly used to hand solder parts. I assume on a board that is supposed to be lead-free." We have seen this scenario before. You are doing primary operations, in this case reflow and maybe through-hole soldering with lead-free. Somebody put out the wrong material for the manual soldering operation. We have seen it happen with flux. We have seen it happen with wire-core solder. What P.C. is asking here is, is it possible to scrub the pads of the board to bring it back into compliance. Jim, to me scrubbed implies a physical abrasive methodology, but what pops into your mind on that?

Jim ›› That is possible, grind it down to the copper pad underneath. First of all, let's think about the technical things. You have a lead-free board. I assume you are trying to meet the RoHS and other regulations which say that every distinct solder joint and so forth has to be less than 1/10th of 1% lead. You have just created a joint and a coating on one or more pads on the board that is now approximately 37% lead. We want to be strict. Is it really practical to get that down to 1/10th of a percent lead in that specific joint? I just don't know, Phil. Maybe if you could grind it down? This is unusual. We are doing forward compatibility. We are trying to get what is now a tin-lead joint into a lead-free board .For years we have been dealing mostly with the opposite trying to get backward compatibility, getting lead-free parts into a tin-lead assembly. But the traditional things on leads and components and so forth is strip off the solder through a molten immersion dilution process. As an example if the leads on a QFN are the wrong alloy. You dip those leads several times into a pot of the desired alloy and the undesired alloy dissolves away and you are left with the proper alloy on those leads. I guess you could do that on a pad with heating it up and putting lead-free solder on it then wicking it off and putting some more lead-free solder and wicking it off. Two things, one it is a dilution effect, so you are never going to get all of the lead off but maybe you could get it down to 1/10th of a percent? I don't know. The other factor of course is reheating up that joint multiple times is going to build up the intermetallic layer on there. That is not going to lend itself to a good, long-term reliable solder joint.

Phil ›› I also have to wonder the effect of what surface finish is being used. For example, with ENIG we know it is very, very difficult to remove any of the solder from a gold finish.

Jim ›› The answer may be no, you just can't do it. And that is scary because the implication is that you have to throw the whole board away.

Phil ›› I am trying to imagine what the reader originally suggested, scrubbing. Somebody sitting there with a grinder or a Dremel®, trying to grind down to the copper but not going too far. I guess the methodology we talked about is worth trying but you may be chasing your tail on this.

Jim ›› Using a soldering iron though, I really question getting down to 1/10th of a percent with a dilution. I think you really have to grind it down to do that and still leave enough copper on there, not going to be fun. A real challenge one way or another. Good luck P.C.

Phil ›› Yeah, really because it may come down to scrapping or selling the board to some third world country, where they don't care about RoHS. In any event, somebody made a big whoops.

Issues With SMT Component Alignment

(component, defects, solder paste, printing, pick-and-place, DFM, reflow, apertures, stencil, area ratio, insufficients, ovens, maintenance, wetting)

Phil ›› Jim, there seems to be something in the air these days with regard to component shifting. We have three questions today on this topic. I think we will tackle all three of them.

The first one is from V.E. V.E. says: "We have a problem with chip component shifting that is detected during automatic optical inspection. The shifting is not limited to single components and changes daily, sometimes at one location and sometimes at the other location. What is likely causing it and how can we overcome this problem?"

The next question is from F.S. F.S. says: "We are losing large, two pin SMT inductor. During reflow it rotates almost 30 degrees. We have designed the footprint according to the manufacturer data sheet. Why is this component rotating during reflow?"

This is from M.M. who says: "What could be the root cause of SMT LED component shift during reflow?"

Jim ›› I would suggest we break it into two possibilities, Phil. Either it was misaligned before reflow or misalignment during reflow. Some of these people say during reflow, but we don't know.

Are they really inspecting the part post placement, just before they go into the oven, to make sure that the part is properly aligned or could it have been misaligned ahead of time? Anything is possible. I want to complement F.S. for identifying the importance of proper pad design. They said, we design the footprint according to the manufacturer's data sheet. And that is assuming that the manufacturer is giving them good data. If we are talking about alignment or misalignment during reflow, pad dimensions, pad size, shape and spacing is really important. If it is misaligning during reflow, it is because the surface tension forces formed as the solder starts to wet are out of balance and they are pulling the component out of alignment. The size and shape of the pads on the board are one of the most important thing affecting those surface tension forces. That is very important in all cases. To the other two, I would say have you designed your pads correctly? Although in the first one where it is moving around and not limited to one location, that would sort of negate that theory.

Phil ›› Assuming for the moment, that, along with F.S., the other folks have done their aperture design correctly. To F.S., are you possibly putting down too much solder paste? What is your solder paste height? Are you adhering to proper stencil guidelines with regard to the area ratio? And that applies to the other guys, too.

Jim ›› Particularly to V.E., where it isn't consistent. Is something in your printing process, your aperture shapes, your squeegee parameters causing a lot of variability so that you get inconsistent volumes of paste deposited that at certain extremes can cause misalignment?

Phil ›› So then, looking at the pick and place machine, never disregard the obvious. You may have something wrong with your program. That is one thing. Or your pick-up tooling.

Jim ›› Worn nozzles, incorrect nozzles.

Phil ›› Exactly, clogged nozzles.

Jim ›› They might not be gripping the component accurately. Bottom line the placement machine is not placing it in proper alignment every time.

Phil ›› And also, is your vision correction working correctly when you pick the component out of the tape pocket too? Certainly, among other things is what is your Z axis position when you place the part. Best Practices is to have the components sit between 1/3 and 2/3 into the solder paste deposit. If you are coming down too slight, it is going to float on top as the solder paste melts. I have seen this happen quite a bit. That would be another thing to check in your program with regard to the suspect components: What is your Z-axis positioning, and/or Z-axis downforce if your machine is equipped with such?

Jim ›› Finally, just maintenance of the reflow oven, the conveyor. Vibration in the conveyor is one of the most significant causes of misalignment.

They are sitting on those little pins on the edge conveyors, any vibration in the conveyor can cause those components to move particularly in the critical phase just as the solder is beginning to melt and the surface tension is starting to take over. They are very vulnerable to imbalances in the air flow, clogged nozzles, imbalanced fans, just basic maintenance problems with the oven.

Selective Solder Paste Printing for BGA Components

(solder paste, printing, BGA, aperture, stencil, reliability, via-in-pad)

Phil ›› Jim, today we have a question from A. J.: "We use common BGA packages on many of our low-end products. Could we print paste only on the pads that have functional requirements? Could we print all the perimeter pads at 120 pin BGA, but skip printing on 50 or more of the interior pads since they serve no function?"

Y'know Jim, the cost of solder paste is just so extreme. You just have to pinch pennies wherever you can....

Jim ›› I agree. When you think about all that paste being used in printing and cleaning the stencil and the losses and everything, that is a small amount of paste. It is hard to imagine it could be a significant cost. But if you are printing a high volume, consumer product where you are printing a lot of these, maybe it is. One technical thing that I want to raise to cite the example, we could print the perimeter pads on the 120 pin BGA and skip the 50 interior pads, are you sure they are non-functional? They may be non-functional electrically but they may be very functional thermally. It is very common to use pads and balls right under the center of the dye to conduct heat out of an active dye within the BGA package down into the board to keep the IC cool and happy and running with no flaws and at a temperature and speed you want and everything.

Phil ›› Before you write off those center balls, make sure they are not required for thermal dissipation of the package, in which case you definitely want to solder them down to the pads of the board.

You may even want to put through-holes in those pads to dissipate that heat down into a ground plane in the board. Your component manufacturer and/or design people should give you those instructions. So, the answer to your question A.I. is - yeah, you can. But that assumes that those balls don't indeed have a function - be sure of that. Beyond that, is it really worth it? That is for you to decide the economics of it.

Jim ›› There is another concern, which I don't think is applicable here. But in a high reliability situation you would be concerned about (by not soldering all of the balls) the long-term reliability of that part in thermal cycling, vibration and so forth. But with these cost considerations, I am assuming that this is a low-end product or that would not be a concern.

Phil ›› That is what he basically states, a low-end product so I have to wonder about the economics as well.

Should We Measure Solder Paste Thickness?

(SPI, solder paste, stencil, reliability, printing, area ratio, defects, lean six-sigma, BTC, BGA, micro-passives, inspection)

Phil ›› Jim, today we have a question from M.S. who asks,: "On average, how many locations should we measure our PCBs to confirm our solder paste thickness? Our PCBs are approximately 10" by 10". " I'll start off by saying that the answer is as many as you possibly can. But, let's qualify that, shall we Jim? First of all, if you're performing solder paste inspection (as well you should be), it depends on what vintage SPI system you're using and whether it's in-line or stand-alone. If it's an in-line system, again, what vintage is it? We're seeing more modern machines now that are capable of speeds where, depending on how many inspection sites you have in some cases pretty much being able to "digest" the entire board without being the bottleneck in your line. If you're doing SPI on an AQL basis, where you're sharing your machine, you're doing it offline. In either case, if you have to limit what you're inspection to avoid the bottleneck issue, I would recommend that you give priority to the most important areas of interest. Want to elaborate on that, Jim?

Jim ›› Sure, if you had to prioritize, I would pick the deposit which came from the aperture with the smallest area ratio. That would be the most likely to be non-repeatable and to give you problems. If you have a very big apertures, and you're worried about getting too much paste, you might want to look at those, too.

Phil ›› So that would mean your smallest component, like a .5 or .4mm BGA or CSP or an ultra-miniature chip component, like an 0201 or 01005. Those are the types of components that are typically more likely have very small apertures with restrictive area ratios - lower than .66 to use the traditional number. Beyond that, looking across the board, opposite corners and/or opposite sides, to make sure there's no variation, and so forth.

Jim ›› But as with any measurement, putting on my lead six sigma master black-belt hat, all inspection is non-value added and you don't want to do any more than you have to. Obviously, as Phil said, if you have a high speed in-line SPI system and it can look at all of them without slowing down your line, do it! If you don't, you want to focus on those points where you have a tendency to cause mistakes.

Phil ›› You should be correlating your defect data on each specific board and relating that to solder deposits at the locations of defects. If you're measuring a specific aperture, a pad on the board, as part of every board SPI strategy, and over time you find you never have any defects on that pad, do you need to measure it anymore? That would be the common strategy.

Jim ›› I'm disappointed in you, Phil. You didn't start off by saying, "M.S., we really applaud you for realizing the importance of measuring solder paste thickness".

Phil ›› Oh, I would think by now, that they heard our soapbox so often it's practically worn into the ground – or their heads, whichever is softer. But I do want to add one other thing (another area going back to soapboxes) - incorporating SPI to inspect other "areas of interest" would be the solder joints that you can't see, visually or with AOI, after they're soldered. In other words, get it right in the first place. Of course, we're talking about area arrays - BGA's, BTC's, and certainly chip-scale and flip chip, because now is the time to get it right. To me, that's one of the most mandatory and powerful applications for SPI. I think most of us have had the wonderful opportunity of having to repair an area array package. It isn't fun, and sometimes it makes things even worse. Getting it right in the first place certainly includes proper solder paste volume.

Jim ›› Taking it one step farther, my brother, once you get beyond the stencil printing stage the next stage is placement, and visual observation of those sites goes away. If you don't catch it at SPI, you're going to have to wait till you X-ray it.

Phil ›› Exactly. Assuming you do, indeed, do X-ray it. That's a bad time. It takes so much cost and so much labor to correct any problems. It increases exponentially.

Cure for the Grape Effect

(component, micro-passives, reflow, soldering, solder paste, defect, reliability, workmanship standards, profile, nitrogen, thermal considerations, flux, powder, oxidation, HoP)

Phil ›› Jim, today's subject is graping. I didn't say griping, I said graping. We have two questions. The first one is from AM (and no the second one isn't from FM). AM says: "We are processing lead-free boards with large components that require high heat temperatures and slow conveyor speeds in a reflow oven that does not use nitrogen. Our smaller parts are showing the grape effect. What is the best solution for this since we cannot increase the conveyor speed or lower temperatures?" We have a second question from RS, who says: "We have some PCB assemblies that show incomplete solder flow due to signs of flux exhaustion. Is incomplete reflow of solder paste as per 5.2.3 of IPC A610E a defect and would require rework, even If the fillet appears to meet IPC standards? "

Jim ›› The last question is very pertinent. The idea is how to evaluate, in this case the graping effect on the surfaces of solder joints. How is this reflected in IPC 610 standards? The issue here is these standards are released at a specific date. Although the IPC works really hard to keep them up to date. They simply can't keep them covering all of the new specific types of defects, such as graping. As we all know graping is a surface phenomenon due to, as RS identifies, flux exhaustion. Small deposits, as indicated in the first question, have a small deposit of solder on the joint. A classic one is a micro-passive - capacitor or resistor. The deposit of solder paste for those components is very small. Likewise, when you put those components on a board and run them in a reflow oven they heat up very quickly, much faster than your larger components, as pointed out again in the first question by A.M. So, what happens? You have this little bit of solder paste on a pad for a 0201 component. You come into a hot slow profile, as described by A.M., and you heat up very quickly. The flux gets active. It does its job. It cleans all of the oxides off of the three surfaces, the pad on the circuit board, the terminations on the chip component, and all of the little surfaces of the solder particles within the paste. That happens very quickly because it is a small joint. It heats up rapidly. The flux is activated so everything is clean and ready to go. But, because this is a long slow profile, that specific deposit may sit in this perfectly clean state for some time, until the entire board reaches reflow temperature and the solder actually melts and coalesces. As is indicated here, you are in an air environment. As soon as you clean all of those surfaces, the air in the reflow environment starts to try to re-oxidize it.

Phil ›› It is the job of the flux to try to prevent that. In these very small deposits, you don't have a very large volume of flux because the volume of the paste deposit is so small. It is not uncommon that flux can get exhausted and the surfaces, typically the solder particles within the paste on the outer surface of the deposit, becomes re-oxidized. When you reach reflow, all the solder particles melt, but the ones on the surface which have been re-oxidized can't flow together and coalesce to give you a uniform shiny smooth solder joint. You get these little bumps or "graping" effect on the surface of the solder joints. That's the effect. Is it acceptable?

Jim ›› My experience is that it is not well covered in the IPC spec and that it is a subjective decision. Most people feel it is only a surface phenomenon. That the solder particles in the interior of the joint which weren't re-oxidized have coalesced. You have a nice solder mass connecting the joint. So, everything but the surface is okay - good solid solder and it should give you good reliable solder joint Other people feel no - as long as I see that on the surface it is not acceptable. Reworking is highly questionable, particularly if you are down 01005. Doing rework on a 01005 is really highly questionable, at best.

Phil ›› Reworking it will expose it to at least another thermal excursion. The real question is whether it is a symptom or is it a defect? It should be determined whether it is a strictly cosmetic issue or not. This might be ascertained through shear and pull strength testing and cross-sectioning.

Jim ›› Phil, there are numerous pictures of actual destructive micro sectioning of solder joints exhibiting graping and they all show that the interior of the solder joint is a totally uniform, solid mass. There is little concern about reduced structural integrity of the joint.

Phil ›› There are some things that A.M. and R.S. and everyone else could try, or consider trying, if it is something that is bothering you. It is rare that you will ever hear Jim and I say this, but if you have a nitrogen capable oven you might try reflowing in nitrogen. As Jim said, discussing the way the oxygen mechanism and the lack of surfactants are going on there, reflowing in a nitrogen atmosphere might help counter the graping effect. But this is only practical if you have a nitrogen equipped oven. The other thing is the solder paste companies are all very competitive and they are all working on some very interesting formulations.

Jim ›› Many of the new formulations address graping by making the fluxes more robust, so that they don't get exhausted and they hang around longer and they prevent this re-oxidation. That is probably the best solution. But of course substituting a new solder paste into an operation requires qualifications that can be problematic and time consuming. I would use this as an opportunity to promote evaluations of new solder pastes. Graping is just one of a laundry list of issues. Head-on-Pillow (or Head-in-Pillow) is another one that is impacted by paste, voiding and so forth. The solder paste companies have been working really hard to come up with better formulations that reduce the tendencies for these defects.

Phil ›› If you are experiencing these defects, now would be an ideal time to do a solder paste evaluation including formulations that claim to alleviate them. Not to mention future syndromes. You are likely going to have to deal with these problems sooner or later, even if you are not seeing them right now. Keeping up with what is available from the paste manufacturers and having a system to evaluate and qualify a new improved solder paste are really important in today's world of ultra-miniaturization, which is driving a lot of these new defects. So, as we preach from our one of our favorite soap boxes, when was the last time you did a solder paste evaluation (if ever)? This just might be the excuse you need, along with all the other reasons. If it has been a while since you have evaluated solder paste, it is high time you did. We almost guarantee if you do a good, thorough, properly executed evaluation you are going to find something better than what you are currently using, and you just might find a formulation to solve that graping problem. Bring up, when you request samples, that you will be evaluating paste for a graping.

Jim ›› One more possible suggestion that was shown somewhat effective when the ultra-miniature chips started to appear and that is increasing the aperture size and actually overprinting the paste a little bit to give you a larger volume of paste. Therefore, with more flux in it to resist that flux exhaustion and the re-oxidation causing graping.

Phil ›› Yeah, definitely worth experimenting with.

No-Clean Residue Shorts

(cleaning, residue, flux, soldering, reflow, profile, contamination, BTC, QFN, reliability, SIR, entrapment, no-clean, water soluble)

Phil

Today we have an interesting question from T.Y.: "We have a PCBA with a QFN 44 using no-clean flux. We have encountered many test failures during testing. The test engineer claims that the failures are due to flux reside between terminations that affect the capacitance of the joints. Is this a valid claim?" Good question. And the answer is, yes, it could be. Of course, it could be something else, too – flux related or otherwise.

Jim ›› First off, let's say that the QFN is a type of bottom-terminated component, BTCs, to keep our terminology straight with the IPC specs. Yes, I agree that no-clean residues, under bottom-terminated components, QFNs, have been shown to have negative influences on certain assemblies. Years ago, when BTCs first appeared our friend Terry Munson of Foresite, one of the true cleaning gurus of our industry, pulled some QFNs off the board and started looking at the residues underneath and found that no-clean residues were not completely deactivated.

Phil ›› Of course, with a no-clean residue you are supposed to be able to leave the residue on the board because during the thermal cycle of the reflow the active flux materials are deactivated and the residues are benign and should not cause influence on the performance of the circuit, which would result in the test failures that are being seen here.

Jim ›› A number of other people have also advocated that this is what is happening although the flux material under the BTCs reaches the proper temperature(s), because they are confined under the chip, complete evaporation does not occur. Evaporation is one the mechanisms that no-clean materials use to deactivate the paste by evaporating the chemicals, chemically reacting them, and encapsulation. The feeling and the observation when people pull BTC components off is that the no-clean residues are not as hard as they should be, indicating the presence of non-evaporated solvent type materials.

Phil ›› We call this the "Gooey Syndrome". Also, there are consortiums, particularly those led by our friend Mike Bixenman of Kyzen, also evaluating and they are taking it a step farther to look at SIR values measured at the residues underneath. They are also showing, from a quantitative standpoint, that certain no-clean residues, even when completely reflowed at the proper temperatures still fail SIR test after reflow.

Jim ›› The answer is to clean, even if it is a no-clean. It may be necessary for your parts to actually do a cleaning. That means coming up with a cleaning methodology, a chemistry and a process that will remove those no-clean residues from under those parts.

Phil ›› Or attain a profile that allows for the proper activation of the flux and polymerization of the residue to encapsulate what remains behind. And I just want to add, I have read papers and encountered situations where no-clean residue, even when properly and thoroughly reflowed, can interfere with the functionality of the circuit within certain frequency ranges. You would have to research that and see if your application falls into these suspect frequencies. We are typically talking gigahertz range. Again, if that is the situation, as Jim is saying, you may have to go to a water soluble cleaning process. It's a process change, not just a material change. And if you have applications where certain parts can't go through a cleaning operation then we look at doing primary operations with a water soluble and a thorough cleaning and then doing a secondary op with a no-clean.

Jim

One more possibility and another plug for current solder paste formulations. This is an issue that is being addressed by solder paste manufacturers and some of them have flux formulations that perform better in terms of deactivating under BTC components. Something else you might want to investigate to solve this problem.

Phil ›› Be careful with any component that has a heatsink on the bottom-side of the package – not just BTCs, but DPAKs and others, too.

Is there a difference in process reliability between 5-zone and 8-zone ovens?

(ovens, reflow, SnPb, Pb-free, micro-passives, BGA, profiling, reliability, alloys, HoP, soldering, warpage)

Phil ›› Jim, we have a question from B.B. who says "We are a small electronic design company setting up an assembly line for small line production. We prefer to purchase a 5-zone oven, as cost is lower. But our concern is that five zones may not be enough to ensure a reliable reflow process compared to an 8-zone oven.

Our boards are 5x7", components on both sides, the largest thermal mask is an inductor which is 10 x 6mm. Most components are .5 mm pitch BGAs, .5 mm QFN and a .65 mm TQFP. Passives are 0603 or larger. With this board, would we see an actual difference in manufacturing process reliability between 5-zone and 8-zone ovens?"

I think I'll start by saying not from a reliability standpoint, although there is a caveat out there, please don't buy a cheap oven. There is some really suspect looking things out there, particularly if you start getting down to tabletop where they think a beanie propeller is an idea of convection. Better you buy a decent oven, even an older one, something that has been maintained and calibrated properly since there is no fixed tooling on it. But from my perspective 5-zone vs 8-zone, I do see a reliability issue but I also see a capability situation.

Jim ›› My feeling is that sooner or later that capability is going to affect your reliability. My general feeling is if you are going to do nothing but tin-lead, a 5-zone oven is okay. If you are going to process lead-free, it really helps to have an 8-zone oven. The reason is because with lead-free you are going to higher temperatures. Your process window at peak temperature is much smaller than it is with tin-lead. Reflowing lead-free alloys, most people prefer to use the last heating zone in their oven to control the initial cooling after peak temperature, that addresses principally warpage characteristics and grain formation within the solder alloys. To hit that tight process window between your 230, 235 minimum temperature and your 250 peak temperature, with one zone can be problematic. That, I think could challenge your reliability. Most people like to use two zones for the reflow section of their oven. A common set-up for profiling an oven with eight zones would be to use the first five zones for your preheat, maybe a soak, maybe a shoulder. Then to use zone 6 and 7 for reflow, usually with the first one a little hotter and the second one a little cooler to prevent overheating your small components. Then to use zone 8 at a lower temperature to control your initial cooling to manage warpage and grain formation in your SAC alloys. That is important because they mention that they mention they are doing 0.5 mm BGAs, so head and pillow issues due to warpage could be an issue. With a 5-zone oven with lead-free I think you could be strapped to really control the profile to get a reliable process.

Phil ›› Right. And that isn't to say that you can't do lead-free with a 5-zone, but this is one case where "more is better". We like the idea that the more vertical zones you have the more you can sculpture the profile and get everything where you want. An 8- zone, although it doesn't seem to be a concern in your operation, does allow for a faster processing speed. I totally agree with Jim. Go ahead, splurge for the 8-zone. As I said, even if it is a used one you'll never look back and regret.

Jim ›› Unless you're sure you are going to be using only tin-lead and then I feel that a 5-zone is good. I agree with Phil - you can reflow anything, anywhere, really. There are people who reflow boards in toaster ovens. But that doesn't mean that is a good choice as a reliable manufacturing process.

Phil ›› And make it easy on yourself. You have a lot of other stuff to worry about, especially in that printing process. I would go the "easy route". I hope you will consider the wisdom we have imparted here.

Afterword

The Wisdom of BoardTalk

- Never repair or touch-up for cosmetic reasons.

- Determine whether it is a defect or a symptom.

- There is, at present, no such thing as selective cleaning.

- One reflow recipe/profile DOES NOT reflow all PCBAs.

- All solder paste formulations are not created equal.

- You can't just attain the melting point of the solder alloy, you must bring it to full-liquidus.

- Never let the operator tweak the machine settings.

- Short term reactions to a problem rarely create long term optimization. BE PROACTIVE.

- Avoid people who take themselves much too seriously.

And, above all, *don't solder like my brother!*

- Phil and Jim

Index

About the Authors

Phil Zarrow

Phil Zarrow has been involved with PCB fabrication and PCB assembly since 1975. His experience includes extensive work in PC Fabrication and PCB Assembly as well as equipment and process development. Mr. Zarrow is recognized throughout the world for his expertise in surface mount technology processes, equipment, materials, components and methodologies.. Phil is a popular speaker and workshop instructor. He has chaired and instructed at numerous industry seminars and conferences world-wide. He has published many technical papers and magazine articles as well as contributed a number of chapters to industry books. Mr. Zarrow holds two US Patents concerning PCB fabrication and assembly processes and audit methodologies. Phil is a member of SMTA, IPC, SME, and IMAPS, a co-founder of ITM Incorporated, and is a past national level officer and national director of the Surface Mount Technology Association (SMTA). He was also Chairman of the Reflow Committee for SMEMA. He was the recipient of the SMTA's Member of Distinction Award (1995) and Founders' Award (2000) and ITM has been honored with the Corporate Award. Mr. Zarrow has served on the Editorial Advisory Board for Circuits Assembly Magazine and won awards for his writings "On the Forefront" and "Better Manufacturing" columns.

Jim Hall

Jim Hall is a Principal Consultant and resident Lean Six Sigma Master Black Belt with ITM Consulting. His area of responsibility includes working with OEM's, Contract Assemblers, and Equipment Manufacturers to solve design and assembly problems, optimize facility operations, as well as teaching basic and new technologies throughout the industry, world-wide.

Mr. Hall, one of the pioneers of reflow technology, has been actively involved in electronic assembly technology for over 40 years. Jim's expertise lies in process development and integration, fluid and thermodynamics, and computer control systems. As ITM's resident Lean Six Sigma Master Black Belt, Jim is a strong proponent of in-process data capture and analysis for all assembly and related operations and other continuous improvement techniques. Jim is one of the authors of the highly acclaimed SMTA Process Certification Course, along with Dr. Ron Lasky and Phil Zarrow. He has delivered numerous papers and workshops on surface mount technology at technical seminars around the world including those for APEX, NEPCON, IMAPS and SMTA.

About ITM Consulting

ITM helps companies of all sizes to set up, fix, improve, certify and enhance their electronics assembly processes, outsourcing, and equipment. In addition, our Process Failure Analysis and Process Root Cause Analysis expertise results in up -front solutions that help our clients avoid problems, streamline their assembly processes and improve their financial return.

Whether you are struggling with new technologies or a stubborn defect, lead-free or lead-inclusive, ITM's experienced consultants, with our proven diagnostic routines and resources can help you determine the source(s) of yield lowering defects as well as improve processes. ITM will help you resolve the problem expeditiously and economically. In-house or supplier related in materials, printing, placement, soldering (reflow, wave and selective), inspection, handling and/or through-hole – we get your problems resolved.

ITM's Process Troubleshooting Analysis and Corrective Action Report help our clients learn how to **avoid future problems and become self-sufficient** in diagnosing and troubleshooting. Each of our consultants have over 30 years experience in Surface Mount Technology – equipment, processes, materials and components. **In many cases, we not only know the process, we helped develop it.** With our extensive resources throughout the industry, we uncover the root cause of the defects and resolve them.

ITM keeps up on all the current materials, component, PCB, equipment and process technologies and methodologies. ITM has proven expertise and can help you resolve problems related to:
- Design for Manufacturability Issues
- Materials
- PCB Substrate issues
- Solder paste issues
- Stencil Printing
- Material Dispensing
- Automatic Component Placement
- SMT Soldering
    - Reflow
    - Vapor-Phase
    - Wave-soldering
    - Selective Soldering
- Inspection and Repair
    - AOI
    - Manual Inspection
    - X-Ray
- Conformal Coating
- Documentation
    - Workmanship Standards
    - DFMA Guidelines
    - Procedures

https://www.itmconsulting.com/

At ITM we prepare our electronics assembly clients for tomorrow's challenges by teaching and applying the principles that underlie the issues of today. We strive to earn trust and respect by providing innovative, effective and successful solutions to both technical and business challenges.